A Half of Two Lives

ALISON WALEY

A Half of Two Lives

McGRAW-HILL BOOK COMPANY
New York   St. Louis   San Francisco
Toronto   Hamburg   Mexico

© 1982 Introduction Hilary Spurling
© 1982 Alison Waley

First published in Great Britain by
George Weidenfeld & Nicolson Limited
91 Clapham High Street
London SW4 7TA

First U.S. publication in 1983 by
the McGraw-Hill Book Company

1234567890   FGRFGR   876543

ISBN 0-07-067807-3

LIBRARY OF CONGRESS CATALOGING IN PUBLICATION DATA

Waley, Alison.
A half of two lives.
1. Waley, Arthur—Biography.   2. Waley, Alison.
3. Authors, English—20th century—Biography.
4. Translators—England—Biography.   5. Sinologists—
England—Biography.   I. Title.
PR6045.A265Z93   1983   895.1'09 [B]   83-1160
ISBN 0-07-067807-3

'To be untrue to myself
could only lead to muddle.'

T'ao Ch'ien translated by Arthur Waley

'The one respect (apart from his genius as a writer) in which Yuan Mei seems to have been unique was his persistence, despite the advice of his friends, in publishing writings of a sort that other authors suppressed . . . in Yuan Mei's view it is the highest duty of a poet to preserve the truth (*ts'un ch'i chen*) to show all things, himself included, as they really are.'

Yuan Mei by Arthur Waley

Biography*

There will, of course, be books written about you;
by this one and that – reputable names
in academic circles:
old men now.   Or young.   Or yet unborn.

Ultimately,
stresses, mis-statements, lies
will resolve to conventional all-absolving shape;
irregularities
lopped here and there – the whole carefully pruned
to present '*A Life*': with tedious 'Introductions'.

Lesser minds and lesser intellects –
and lesser sensory equipments
– will strive to comprehend you:
as frigid stars revolve about the sun
and take its brilliance momentarily.

Telling the thus-and-thus, detached self-interest
will feed the machine precise appropriate cards.
You were a Scholar.   You were a 'private' man.
You were a Poet.   You had 'leftish leanings'.
You were a formidable foe.   A celibate.
A Saint.   A Sinner.   And a Genius.
You were a man divorced from human matters:

---

*Written in the library of Arthur's estate solicitors in 1966 while waiting for the AA to bring a new fanbelt for my car.

a man repelled by sentiment.   A blade;
ruthless.   As steel –
and sharpened to scalpel-edge.

The Machine will whir,
cough – whine
– lights flash to silence:
in time, less than your birth-cry
or your dying whisper,
the thing's resolved – the ticket is ejected.
There's your Biography . . .
My love . . . my love . . .

'To John and Antonia'

Contents

Illustrations

Introduction by
Hilary Spurling

When Arthur Waley died at the age of seventy-six in 1966, it came as something of a shock to many of his oldest friends to discover that he left a widow. Comparatively few people knew that he had had a companion in his house in Highgate for the past three years, fewer still that he had married Alison Grant Robinson a month before his death. Even so experienced an observer as Ivy Compton-Burnett (who had known Arthur, and seen him regularly, for nearly sixty years) never so much as suspected Alison's existence; and among those who had known her as a source of support and strength in Arthur's difficult last years, there can have been small inkling of the strange and eventually tragic story set down here.

Reminiscences of Arthur Waley commonly invoke the image of a mediaeval monk or hermit. In some ways the most sociable of men – he had 'perhaps the greatest range of friendship of any person I know,' wrote Osbert Sitwell[1] – he was also the most private in his reticence, austere devotion to learning and aloofness from mundane concerns. Part of Alison's appeal, when they first met in the spring of 1929, was perhaps that she had no connection with his world or anybody in it: her narrative makes it clear that their friendship involved from the start an almost Shakespearian delight in playing incognito. For weeks after the first meeting in Charlotte Street, so rapturously described in chapter 3, she knew Arthur only as the man with the green bicycle and the dirty plimsolls.

[1] *Noble Essences* (Macmillan, 1950) p. 3.

He was at this time in his prime: the publication of *A Hundred and Seventy Chinese Poems* in 1918 had brought him immediate recognition, and a steady stream of books appearing over the next decade consolidated his fame with both scholars and the poetry-reading public. By 1929 he was mid-way through publishing what proved probably his most startling and substantial single work, the six volumes of the mediaeval Japanese masterpiece, *The Tale of Genji*; this was also the year in which he finally retired from the British Museum to devote himself exclusively to scholarship and writing. He was already a distinguished and familiar Bloomsbury figure: Alison Grant, who had reached England from New Zealand less than three months earlier, must have been one of very few habitués of the Reading Room who had not asked, or been told, his name. No wonder she caused consternation, at a meeting of the Poetry Society that summer, by saying that the only English poet she would like to meet was the translator from the Chinese, Arthur Waley: 'They glance sharply at one another. What is this? A piece of play-acting? – and I am astonished to see on the ring of faces before me both puzzlement and irritation. Until one, speaking for all, exclaims: "Well! You *do* live in his pocket!"'

It was an understandably aggrieved reaction, and one can hear the voice of literary London taking the same line – vexed, proprietary, disapproving – over this affair from start to finish. Indeed one of the incidental pleasures of this book is its peculiar slantwise view of Bloomsbury seen by someone who was always, morally speaking, an outsider from that first afternoon in Charlotte Street, and afterwards in Gordon Square when Arthur's laughter so rudely dispersed the usual occupants of the square garden: 'There is a movement on the seats as gear of many kinds is collected . . . and presently the gate on the east side clicks as – one after another – the Stracheys go home.' It is not simply that the museum itself, Charlotte Street, Gower Street, the secluded grassy strip of Torrington Place, the rustic mounds and paths of Russell Square form a peaceful, unmolested habitat of pedestrians, cyclists, students, almost unimaginably different from the fumey, traffic-ridden concrete wilderness of Bloomsbury today. The landscape of this clandestine affair has the sort of heightened reality generally associated less with documentary accounts than with imaginative reconstruction: its streets and squares are framed and focused in much the same way as, say, Rebecca West's Kensington (in *Harriet Hume*), Elizabeth Bowen's Regent's Park, Iris Murdoch's dockland, Soho or Notting Hill. The story too takes on from time to time a mythical aspect in, for instance, the inexplicable, unexplained snow scene in chapter 25 of Part II, or the splendidly Murdochian seaside trip in chapter 14 when Arthur and Alison – bathing at Seaford in the 1950s – discover that a rising tide has appropriated their clothes so that the Sunday strollers on the parade find themselves confronted with the distinguished scholar (Arthur was by this time in his sixties) rising with his companion naked from the sea:

> 'One lady remained transfixed – leaning her large bosom outward over the rails – her parasol held high, her eyes screwed against the sun as though the immediate sea were a newspaper she was attempting to read without her glasses. It was obvious that we in particular were very small print. Pleasantly interested ... she had pointed us out to her middle-aged son; but now, peering incredulously, and perceiving her suspicion to be the horrible truth, she violently thrust her parasol before her son's face and – his arm in her stout grip – hurried him away. We continued to rise, brown as sea gods ... out of the green water.'

This incredulous, outraged, unknown citizen of Seaford may serve to represent the attitude of the outside world throughout this intensely personal narrative. The inhabitants of Bloomsbury impinge comparatively seldom, and then chiefly as adepts in the polite arts of exclusion and rejection at which the English have traditionally excelled. There can be few more authentic portraits of the cold, perfidious face of Albion, so familiar to aliens down the ages, than the sinister, even gothic tea party at John Hayward's in chapter 23 (Part II) when Alison is so expertly headed off from conversation with

T. S. Eliot. The same faint, unmistakable air of blight recurs
again and again in all its nuances, comical or cruel. It clouds
the trip to Kew when Arthur fails to introduce Alison to his
friends; it hangs over the mysterious Rembrandt private
view at the National Gallery where Alison blurts out her
opinion before the select Bloomsbury delegation – Vanessa
Bell, Duncan Grant, Eddie Marsh – and is hurriedly led away
by an exasperated Arthur ('"In England," he said, "one
doesn't always *say* what one thinks."'); and it looms with
special menace over Alison's encounters at the ballet and
concert hall with Beryl de Zoete.

Beryl herself, the third figure in the triangular pattern of
this book, was very much at home in Bloomsbury both in her
own right and for Arthur's sake. She had been his companion
since 1918, and was regarded by his family and friends as his
wife in all but name until her death in 1962. Theirs was a
flexible arrangement, allowing scope for separate living
quarters on occasion as well as for Arthur's solitary skiing
trips to Switzerland, and Beryl's constant adventuring
abroad with one or more appreciative male friends. Even
people baffled by the precise nature of their relationship
between the wars agreed that it seemed to suit both parties
admirably; and it was Beryl's ultimatum, despatched from
Fez in chapter 7 (Part I), that put a stop to the first phase of
Alison's affair with Arthur.

Ten years older than Arthur, Beryl had means of her own
and a pleasant flat in Russell Square. She had been one of the
early women at Oxford (she took a second in English at
Somerville in 1901), and a beauty in her youth according to
Bertrand Russell. 'She resembled an artificial flower made of
highly polished black and yellow plastic,' wrote David Garnett who knew her in later life.[1] Even in her fifties and sixties
her looks remained striking, her figure supple, and it was said
as late as the 1930s that her belly dance could still rival the
Moroccan girls' in the *quartier reservé* at Casablanca.[2] Like her
friend Marie Rambert, Beryl had been a pupil of the inventor

[1] *Great Friends* (Macmillan, 1979) p. 177.
[2] Harold Acton, *More Memoirs of an Aesthete* (Methuen, 1970) p. 27.

of eurhythmics, Emile Jacques-Dalcroze, during the brief flowering of his school at Hellerau before the First World War, and afterwards made her name as a teacher and writer on dance. She had won prizes at the Hammersmith Palais de Danse, and taught ballroom dancing to Hugh Gaitskell among others. She travelled widely in the Middle and Far East, spoke fluent French, German and Italian, was widely recognized as an excellent translator. It was Beryl who put Sacheverell Sitwell's *The Rio Grande* into German when Constant Lambert set it to music, and her English versions of Italo Svevo were said to read better than the originals.[1] She worked as dance critic for the *New Statesman*, *Daily Telegraph* and Richard Buckle's *Ballet*; but her strongest claim to fame, much talked of at the time, lay in her three pioneering books on the dance and drama of Bali, Ceylon and Southern India.[2]

A forceful and flamboyant personality, able, impetuous, demanding, Beryl was accustomed to getting what she wanted ('and like a child she often wanted things badly,' wrote Gerald Brenan who, for all his reservations, describes her with admiration and affection in his autobiography).[3] She had made up for a brief, unsuccessful marriage to Basil de Selincourt in 1902 by taking a string of lovers before she met Arthur, soon after the publication of *A Hundred and Seventy Chinese Poems*, and by all accounts fell for him at sight. Though the book's enthusiastic reception must have encouraged him, Arthur seems to have been otherwise in bad shape at this time. His energies had been depleted by the war itself, by the deaths of friends (Rupert Brooke and Ivy's brother, Noel Compton-Burnett, were only two of many casualties among Arthur's particular friends from King's College, Cambridge) and by his own equivocal position – as a handsome young man apparently reluctant to fight – with people who did not know that he had been incapacitated for active

[1] Anthony Powell, *Messengers of Day* (Heinemann, 1978) p. 163.

[2] With Walter Spies, *Dance and Drama in Bali* (Faber, 1938); *The Other Mind. A Study of Dance in South India* (Gollancz, 1953); *Dance and Magic Drama in Ceylon* (Faber, 1957).

[3] *Personal Record 1920–1972* (Cape, 1979) p. 99.

service by partial blindness in one eye. He had also been considerably knocked back, round about this time, by a hopeless passion for a woman whose affections were engaged elsewhere.

Highly susceptible all his life to what an old friend called 'the charm of girls', Arthur was famous for his lack of small talk which meant that his overtures to women were apt to be tentative and stiff. He found it hard to make the first move, and his friendliest advances could be disconcerting to anyone already daunted by his great erudition and long unnerving silences. One young student, later a close friend, recalled saying nervously at their first meeting that she found Japanese dreadfully ambiguous: '"Oh really," he replied in a high, level tone. "I have never come across a single case of ambiguity in my whole life."'[1] This, as she realized later, had been intended as an encouraging response. Peter Quennell describes how, when bored or irritated, Arthur would raise his already high voice to 'an almost supersonic level. By comparison, Strachey's voice was loud; Arthur's, dismissing a tedious subject or annihilating a stupid opponent, recalled the sound of a faraway autumn wind as it travels through a bed of reeds...'[2] It is scarcely surprising if even the most resourceful women found Arthur worrying: Ada Leverson was so flustered on being introduced to the great Japanese scholar that she could talk of nothing but Gilbert and Sullivan's *Mikado*.[3] Edith Sitwell said that talking to him on any given subject was like being asked at school to put down, in the fewest possible words, everything one knew.[4]

For someone so withdrawn and sensitive as Arthur, Beryl's lack of inhibition must have been a powerful attraction. She was not only older but far more experienced and not in the least deterred by his remoteness. Admiration was Beryl's forte ('Where the arts were concerned, she had the bump of

[1] *Madly Singing in the Mountains: An appreciation and anthology of Arthur Waley*, ed. Ivan Morris (Allen & Unwin, 1970) p. 21.

[2] *The Marble Foot* (Collins, 1976) p. 158.

[3] *Noble Essences*, op. cit., p. 134.

[4] *Madly Singing in the Mountains*, op. cit., p. 105.

veneration developed to excess,' wrote Brenan.[1]) She liked success, and found it stimulating. Arthur for his part seems to have responded readily enough to her drive, determination, unconditional self-confidence and furious appetite for life. For all his reserve, he liked company and gossip, and Beryl made both readily accessible: 'Beryl's cooing voice covered Arthur's silences like a cloak,'[2] wrote Harold Acton, who clearly found Arthur something of a strain without her.

Their backgrounds were in some ways similar: both came from large, clannish families, comfortably off and much intermarried. Arthur's paternal grandfather, Sigismund Schloss (the family took their mother's name of Waley in the First War), had come from Frankfurt to make his fortune as a cotton broker in Manchester. Beryl's grandfather, Herman de Zoete, who had made his money on the London Stock Exchange, was the son of a hatmaker from Holland. Both these patriarchs produced highly musical and intellectual descendants (Beryl's uncle, Reginald de Zoete, according to Arthur, kept a vase of fresh violets all year round in his room under a portrait of Bach, whose works he had inserted into the English repertoire by persuading many well-known organists to give up playing 'trash' which was 'the name he gave to almost everything that was not Bach'). Beryl read poetry well and she excelled, as Arthur said in the preface to her Collected Essays, at writing about dance, landscape, architecture and 'inspired vignettes of people'.[3] 'She was original, unconventional and unworldly ... often very amusing, and her gaiety and enthusiasm made her personality very attractive,' wrote Celia Goodman, who had known Beryl well for a quarter of a century.[4] 'Humour was certainly one of the strongest bonds between her and Arthur.' They also shared a certain frugality and indifference to material comforts.

[1] *Personal Record*, op. cit., p. 99.
[2] *More Memoirs of an Aesthete*, op. cit., p. 29.
[3] *The Thunder and the Freshness: The collected essays of Beryl de Zoete*, with a preface by Arthur Waley (Neville Spearman, 1963) p. 10.
[4] In a letter to Hilary Spurling.

They lived simply, seeming sometimes to exist on little more than Ovaltine and dry biscuits; or, if friends came to dine in the early days at Russell Square, they would heat up a tin of beans with apples and grapes for pudding.

At other people's tables Beryl (who was vegetarian) could be notoriously pernickety; and what Acton called 'her disarming and humorous caprices' – demanding insect hoppers filled with honey, or yak's milk at a cocktail party – seemed thoroughly tiresome to people who remained unmoved by Beryl's 'blend of sybilline agelessness with virginal amazement'.[1] 'She stepped like the Queen of Sheba through Gordon Square in spiritual communion with all singing birds and blossoming branches,' wrote Acton in *The Times* when she died, 'and I think she understood their language as Arthur Waley understands the most ancient of Chinese ideograms.'[2] This sort of estimate of Beryl's sensitivity seemed offensive nonsense – 'balls and bull-shit' in chapter 41 (Part II) – to Alison; and even Beryl's best friends freely acknowledged elements in her make-up of affectation, pretentiousness and self-importance. 'Arthur's extreme patience with her struck me as angelic, especially when she grew older and more quixotic. But theirs was a happy and lasting attachment,' wrote Acton;[3] and Brenan's summing-up suggests a similar spirit: 'Poor Beryl, she could in her bad moments be sillier and clumsier and more insensitive and selfish than most people I have known, yet I have good memories of her because she was generous and kind as well as loyal to her friends. She could irritate, but she could not hurt because there was no malice in her . . .'[4]

Other people – in particular ambitious and independent women to whom Beryl might in some sense be considered a rival – found it hard to be so tolerant. Edith Sitwell, who loved Arthur dearly but could never abide Beryl, put her in the same category of unwelcome appendages as Dylan

[1] *The Times* 21 March 1962.
[2] Ibid.
[3] *More Memoirs of an Aesthete* op. cit., p. 29.
[4] *Personal Record*, op. cit., p. 100.

Thomas's wife Caitlin. Margaret Mead, the anthropologist who had worked on ceremonial dance in Bali at the same time as Beryl in 1936, found that Beryl's 'acid tongue' and 'gift for destructive criticism' intensified the conflicts apt to arise among the members of any expedition:

> 'I identified her with the witch, a prevailing Balinese figure. And so, periodically, I would note moments of special felicity in my diary with the initials *r.p.*, which stood for *ranga padem* – the witch is dead – and conveyed my feeling that the influence of Beryl and the malign influences of Balinese culture, which emphasized nameless fear as a sanction, were temporarily in abeyance.'[1]

This was the aspect in which, some fifteen or so years later, Beryl appeared to Alison (who had left her husband during the Second War in order to resume her relationship with Arthur). The central section of this book deals with malign influences at work between these three protagonists in scenes like the extraordinary tea party in chapter 34 (Part II), when Alison makes the sign of the cross at the threshold of the darkened room where Beryl is waiting to receive her: 'The air is curiously electric, as before thunder. I fancy I can hear the faint crackle of my hair. A great silver witch-ball hangs from the ceiling . . . Gigantic masks mouth and leer from cupboards and corners . . .'

This confrontation took place at the flat Arthur shared with Beryl in Gordon Square some time in the 1950s, when Beryl was in her seventies and already ill. She had suffered what her friends thought of as a nervous breakdown a little earlier in Trieste, when she lost her memory, was found wandering and had to be brought home by Arthur who travelled out to fetch her. Though she seemed to recover over the next two or three years, she cannot have been reassured by his liaison with a mistress twenty years younger than herself. Alison describes how, at the time of the tea party, Beryl had already made successive attempts to prevent Arthur seeing her and to intercept her letters; at one point she apparently

[1] *Blackberry Winter* (Touchstone, 1972) p. 231.

planned to buy Alison a ticket to Mexico, at another to remove Arthur bodily to a cottage in the country. Alison's account of this struggle takes on gathering intensity and virulence over the next decade. Beryl herself seldom appears but macabre images emanate from her retreat in Gordon Square: one day Alison finds Beryl's jewellery emptied all over the butter and marmalade dishes on the breakfast table; another day the kitchen is scarred and blackened by fire. There are stories of Beryl setting the house alight and dancing in the flames. Cries and sinister noises are heard, strange events reported by the tenant of the flat below ('"I do not sleep," he mutters, "I do not know . . . which one of those two will come hurtling past the panes."'). Parts of this story read like the mad scenes in *Jane Eyre*, others like something out of Edgar Allan Poe: 'I looked up and saw him [Arthur] moving slowly, like a shadow . . . along the far wall. His face, white and staring, was towards me. His eyes were like hollows in a mask. He crept, came stealthily, as though I were a wraith . . .'

It is hard, at first reading, to know quite how to take these nightmarish descriptions of Beryl's malevolence, Arthur's exhaustion and despair. They seem to belong to a world of ghosts and goblins more than to the daylight reality of Bloomsbury and Gordon Square. But Beryl was already suffering from the disease that eventually killed her, Huntington's Chorea. It is a chronic degenerative disease of the nervous system, affecting both physical and mental function, causing involuntary tics or spasms and ending in decay, dementia and death. It is extremely rare and always fatal. It generally develops some time in middle age, lasts ten or fifteen years, and may first show itself as a mild fidgetiness, in bouts of depression or loss of memory: Beryl's 'breakdown' in Trieste seems to have been a fairly typical onset, with the physical symptoms – in her case, uncontrollable twitchings and facial grimaces – coming later. The illness is not always easy to recognize so that the 'brain tumour' reported in chapter 30 (Part II) may have been a false diagnosis, or it may have seemed to Beryl, if she knew or suspected what was happening, to offer a more acceptable, less unbearable explanation of her trouble.

For Huntington's Chorea is hereditary, which means that one or other parent of any victim must have had the disease, and died of it (unless he or she was killed by something else before the chorea had time to declare itself). It also means that someone who has inherited the gene runs a fifty per cent risk of passing it on to any offspring. In the preface to Beryl's collected essays, Arthur said that her family reminiscences would 'have read like a lost chapter from a novel by Ivy Compton-Burnett'[1]: he was referring to the de Zoetes' wicked butlers and tyrannical cooks but the remark would have applied as well to Beryl's pathological inheritance. There is, of course, no means of telling how far the family themselves were aware of the disease, or its implications. Beryl's parents were assumed by her friends to have died before she met Arthur in 1918; she had three sisters, two of whom married though only one produced a child (a son killed in the 1914–18 war). She herself was said to have turned Arthur down, though he begged her to marry him, and she told Gerald Brenan that she had married de Selincourt on the strict understanding that, since sex was coarse, the marriage should not be consummated (which it never was). She also said that her first love affair had involved herself and the young man taking off all their clothes and swinging about in adjacent poplar trees till they made the branches touch ('They themselves never did so.') She had had an equally chaste liaison with John Hope-Johnstone, and possibly even with Arthur: 'There was something so ascetic about him and so erotically equivocal about her that many people believed that there was no physical link between them,' wrote Brenan.[2]

At all events Beryl's illness accounts for much that might otherwise seem barely credible in Alison's narrative. It explains, for instance, what happened at the ill-fated tea party so ominously described in chapter 34 (Part II) – the rattling cups, Beryl's trembling, her precipitate retreat, Arthur's

[1] *The Thunder and the Freshness*, op. cit., p. 10.
[2] *Personal Record*, op. cit., p. 94.

agitation and distress. It throws new light on what seemed to Alison at the time grotesque and cruel play-acting on Beryl's part: convulsive grimacing, moroseness, suspicion, anxiety, anger and a craving for attention are all described in the medical literature as classic symptoms of the disease. People who knew that Beryl was ill – who had seen Arthur supporting her at parties and gatherings with a patience and devotion that struck his friends as heroic – had no more idea than Alison of exactly what was wrong. Beryl was able to write brief letters and take short walks at least until the winter of 1960–1. Arthur had promised her that she should never go to hospital; but without his help she could hardly have concealed the drastic nature of her illness so successfully and for so long.

There is no treatment for Huntington's Chorea, save for sedatives to calm the jerking; it is recognized as imposing an intolerable burden on relatives and friends; most patients spend the last part of their lives in geriatric or psychiatric wards. The strain on Arthur must have been almost insupportable. Doctors' flat clinical accounts of emotionally disturbed patients unable to speak or feed themselves or swallow, weakened and emaciated by years of 'constant uncontrollable writhing'[1], find their counterpart in Alison's horrific imagery: her dream of Arthur sinking step by step into a swamp of slime, her descriptions of him torn, ravaged, haunted, possessed, bound by invisible manacles. Madge Garland, and other friends of Arthur's, remember him sitting drained and silent, or moving like a sleepwalker on the comparatively few occasions that he left the house in the final phase of Beryl's illness. David Garnett describes coming to visit Arthur at this time, hearing bloodcurdling screams from above and assuming that someone was being murdered until assured by a nurse that 'Miss de Zoete was having one of her bad attacks'.[2] Arthur's family and friends were astonished at

---

[1] Dick Bates, Director of the Association to Combat Huntington's Chorea, in *Phoenix* Vol. 3, August 1981, 'The Quarterly Journal of the Association for Independent Disabled Self Sufficiency'.
[2] *Great Friends*, op. cit., p. 178.

his unsuspected gentleness and tenderness. The few who saw Beryl – 'the frothing jaws, the blackening and writhing spider's-body' described in chapter 49 (Part II) – were appalled. She had become shrunken, wasted, withered, toothless; her limbs jerked ceaselessly; Arthur himself told one visitor that only drugs prevented her from being violent, perhaps even homicidal[1]. After she died, he told another friend that he had read his Chinese poems to Beryl, night after night, when only her eyes showed that she understood[2]: it is the scene Alison describes in chapter 49 (Part II): 'Seated beside her, Arthur offers the only magic he knows – to soothe, beguile, that lost and lashing spirit . . .'

The heightened language and fraught atmosphere of large stretches of this narrative belong to an inner landscape of the emotions rather than to the biographer's world of documentation, scientific accuracy and 'tedious introductions', so feelingly evoked in Alison's prefatory verses. Some of the stranger episodes – the demonic emanations at Plaw Hatch, for instance, or the mysterious burglary in Great James Street – do not tally with other people's recollections any more than the anguished and tormented Arthur of this book matches previously published reminiscences of the great sinologist. For a more objective picture, readers will still have to go to the many striking literary portraits left by friends like the Sitwells, Peter Quennell, Gerald Brenan and David Garnett.

But the one point on which all accounts agree is that, in spite or perhaps because of his shyness and constraint, Arthur possessed a formidable presence. Junior colleagues were commonly terrified of him (and it was often those who admired him most, who found him the most alarming); he was capable of dominating any gathering, if only by his silences; he could not enter a room or cycle across Russell Square without turning heads. It is scarcely surprising that such a powerful personality should arouse correspondingly strong feelings in the two women with whom he chose to share his life: if Alison

---

[1] *Madly Singing in the Mountains*, op. cit., pp. 24–5 and p. 61.
[2] Ibid, p. 113.

saw Beryl as a witch or vampire, Beryl in return is reported (in Chapter 32, Part II) as having seen Alison as 'Quint', the evil demon contending for the children's souls in Henry James' *The Turn of the Screw.*

Alison's narrative is itself in some ways strangely reminiscent of those tragedies of dispossessed or thwarted lovers in the Japanese Nō, several of which Arthur included in *The Nō Plays of Japan*:

> 'We are brittle as the leaves of the *bashō*;
> As fleeting as foam upon the sea.
> Yesterday's flower, today's dream.
> From such a dream were it not wiser to wake?'[1]

The dream in question is a tangle of jealousy, anger, cruelty and malice, retold by the baleful Lady Rokujō who loved Prince Genji, murdered his lover Yūgao, and now returns to take revenge on his unlucky wife. As in so many Nō plays, the formality and lyric freshness of the words belie the horrors they describe; and it is perhaps not entirely fanciful to see in Alison's extraordinary story something of the perturbation, the feverish, fragmented intensity and nightmare conviction of Lady Rokujō's dream.

---

[1] From '*Aoi Nō Uye*', in *The Nō Plays of Japan* by Arthur Waley (Allen & Unwin 1921) p. 182.

Author's Note

The following record covers a period in my life and that of
Arthur Waley – between 1929 and 1966: a period which in
the latter years was one demanding almost superhuman courage and endurance – both of which he had – and it is a record,
scrupulously exact, of events and circumstances, both auto-
biographical and biographical, for which I make no apology.

After the interval of so many years I have been unable to
identify the isolated verses which I use to preface the three
parts of the book. In each case they were copied out by
Arthur from his own translations and slipped through my
Bloomsbury letterbox as oblique communication. I too came
to use this method. Often we wrote the first line only, as
allusion to the whole. While searching for the originals I came
across two more examples from his *Japanese Poetry, The
'Uta'* – a classical form used traditionally for the same
purpose:

> My love
> Is like the grasses
> Hidden in the deep mountains;
> Though its abundance increases,
> There is none that knows.
> > Ono No Yoshiki (d. 902 AD)

> Love which is greater than oneself is like
> The glow-worm,
> A thing which is impossible to hide
> Even though you wrap it up.
> > Akahito

Chronology

1879 Birth of Beryl de Zoete.

1889 Birth of Arthur Waley.

1901 Birth of Alison Grant.

1918 First meeting between AW and B de Z.

1929 First meeting between AW and AG.

1930 Marriage of AG and Hugh Ferguson Robinson.

1932 Birth of John Grant Robinson.

1939 Alison Grant Robinson travels to Australia and New Zealand with her husband and son; they return in 1942.

1943 Alison GR and AW meet again in London; AGR separates from her husband.

1945 AW elected Honorary Fellow of King's College, Cambridge.

1948 AW appointed Honorary Lecturer in Chinese Poetry at the School of Oriental and African Studies, London.

1952 AW created Companion of the British Empire.

1953 AW receives Queen's Medal for Poetry.

1956 AW created Companion of Honour.

1959 AW awarded the Order of Merit of the Second Treasure by the Japanese Government.

1962 Death of B de Z.

1963 AW and AGR move to Highgate.

1966 February: Car accident in which AW breaks his spine; May: Marriage of AW and AGR; June: Death of AW.

PART I

Quest

1929-1943

If only — a seed shall fall,
Even among the waterless stones
A tree will grow.
If you love and I love
Can it be we shall never meet?

10th century.

[1]

The Wind Blows High

The wind, the wind, the wind blows high,
The snow is falling from the sky.
Maisie Drummond says she'll die
For want of the Golden City.

Children's Game

The last day of February 1929.

At Bayswater when I enter the Underground the sky is dull as canvas and still – the shadowed ceiling of a marquee without so much as a flap. Here, at Charing Cross, I step into this white and whirling dance of snow. I stand on the kerb-edge beside this huge policeman. His black cape flaps out like a crazed or injured bird while his broad red hand directs those who wish to cross the Strand. I do not wish to cross. I stand there, the palms of my ungloved hands upturned, face flung back, eyes closed, mouth open to catch the dancing flakes. It is no use, they melt before one can taste them; they do not make enough moisture even to swallow. But they touch my eye-lids with infant's fingers. And my dark hair is full of a scatter of white flowers. 'You want to cross?' the police-man's voice is very loud and close; I open my eyes with a jerk.

'Isn't it marvellous,' I say.

'Marvellous? Ugh!' He guides a child by the arm and crosses between the stationary traffic: then, ponderously, taking his time, he returns to my side.

Now he looks me over. My face, my throat and the backs of my hands are brown as an Indian's.

'You a Londoner?' he asks.

I laugh at his perplexity. 'Yesterday – not. Today ... perhaps,' and find myself perplexed.

'You staying long?'

'Forever.'

And then ... Is that true, I think ... am I staying forever? London. This city to which I've travelled twelve thousand miles – whose streets my guided fingers traced at the age of four – nostalgic since infancy? Not the land of the Maori – but this so-strangely-known city, birthplace of my father ... is it to be my city also? – the goal, the end of seeking? This 'Here and Now' ... at last my home?

I fling my arms wide – 'For all my life,' I add.

The Who, The Where and The Why

So . . . it's England. Not the Highlands, land of my fathers. But yet, London, city of my father's birth: its streets, its buildings, its squares, its parks mapped ineradicably in my childhood's mind by his storied memories.

London, 1929. A London still war-bereaved, demoralized; stripped to the bone by victory; neurotic: in flux: yet with a surge of upward-straining life that charges the air like an electric current.

I have shed my life's garment as surely as a serpent sloughs its skin. I stand stripped, patient to await what now shall come. For somewhere, most surely, the fates are at work which shall hand me another. The discarded garment – warp and woof of tragedy, pain and joy – lies twelve thousand miles behind me; is mine no longer. Naked I am, as the warriors of my family crest: as they, so shall I 'Stand Fast'. Here in London I owe allegiance to none but myself and – as did my forefathers confronted with a new and untried world – I exult.

I shuffle my letters of introduction, proffered for my safety. Each holds within it a new life; a new door which, should I choose to but tap on it, will open wide to security of other, and satellite, worlds. All are here: the 'confines' – of churchmen, of scholars, of politicians; of actors, musicians, poets; even of marriage. But no. Not yet must I enter. I am as a creature from another planet. New born. And . . . 'Time must have a stop'.

I kneel before my fire-grate. Slowly I read each through: with gratitude, but also with resolution. I know my need. It is not security. It is freedom. Slowly I crumple each, thrusting each, page by page, into the embers. I hear only my father's words . . . alone, dying, in my six-year-old arms – 'Remember. No Cults . . . isms . . . osophies. These are traps. You belong only to yourself. And life . . . is wonderful.'

So, alone – yet not lonely – I move from my Bayswater luxury to a bare office room at the gates of the British Museum: and find my freedom. A Reading Room ticket is the only Open Sesame needed. My new world closes about me. Minds, living and dead, companion me. Old, young, male, female, anonymous as I, nod in passing, squat on the broad steps in argument, stroll off each in his separate way to solitary or to esoteric or to convivial rendez-vous.

As always, I write; I type; I free-lance.

Quickly I sell my return ticket to New Zealand; and, since funds are running low, investigate curious advertisements, attaching myself at last only to the one task which offers the most personal liberty – the writing of 'Crits' as reader to the madman, 'Mac' the publisher.

The pattern of my days becomes richly variegated; I am seated between Lance Sieveking and Val Gielgud at the dinner table of John Reith. I am at family tea with J. B. S. Haldane, his young nieces and his beautiful sister whose paralysed left arm is concealed by a black mantilla. Now I am at a roof party to cheer the Boat Race at the home of Naomi Mitchison. Now at a salon for the French guests of a Canadian writer somewhere behind Piccadilly. At a country house party near Reading, where one rides to hounds and inspects the herbacious borders before breakfast. At a gathering of prelates somewhere near Guildford. At a riotous opening night of Paul Robeson's Unity Theatre. At studio parties, pub parties, poetry readings, fringe-Bloomsbury gatherings. But always I am careful to disappear, vanish discreetly, to my bare-boards-and-pigeons retreat . . .

When, across the landing, night comes, piano music issues forth from a nameless musician and is accompanied by the frying of bacon by his nameless mistress. My travelling rug spread, islanded, for carpet; my fur coat tucked about me; my typewriter mounted on my travelling trunk, I work through the night hours at the 'crits' that earn my rent. Dawn brings the rustling of pigeons stationed along my window sill, and I glance up to note the slant of light on the eight pillars of the museum's façade. They are my clock; as accurate for my purpose as a toll of bells. Now it is time to collect my writing. Now to make my coffee at the open fire. Now to dress and arm myself with toilet things for the moment when the great gates swing back and I am first through them to the Wash Room. Presently I shall emerge immaculate, cross the labyrinthine hubbub of Covent Garden to collect my mail from the High Commissioner's Office in the Strand ... and the day – a whole new London day – is mine.

In all this tapestry of events and non-events I am careful to stand, as it were, in the wings. For no one play can persuade me to join the cast. No one actor is lure enough. No one score absorbs. The fascination of the scene lies in its vastness and its variety. I tread my way as cautiously as one treads the thermal crusts of my discarded land.

And I am happy as never before.

So, February. So, March. And into April – my month – the month of my birth ...

[3]

But Now it is Spring

Now it is spring.

May days. Hot, shining days such as only England, under enchantment, can do.

And with the first of them comes a parcel from Honolulu. The Belgian vaudeville tumbler who houses and rehearses his troupe in the larger of the second-floor rooms brings it up to me and waits, fascinated as a child, in the doorway of my attic while I tear open the many wrappings and shake out the lovely contents.

It is a dress – a belated birthday present from Sir Truby and Mary.[1] There are no sleeves. The neck is wide and low: the bodice fitted closely. Oh, such a dress! Of white organza . . . the skirt springing full and crisp with a feeling of ballet from the clipped-in waist: the hem wide-scalloped and finely-bound in tangerine to match the sparse and tiny embroidered sprigs that fall irrelevantly here and there, like a casual scatter of petals. 'Alison Wonderland' pockets at the waist for my few coins . . . an out-of-this-world dress for an out-of-this-world day.

I put it on – over the sheerest of crêpe de chine slips, slide into my slender ballet shoes and step forth into the sun-crazed streets.

To what? To whom?

To my life.

Who, today, remembers Antoine's as it was then, on the

[1] Edinburgh-born world-famous paediatrician, Head of Child Welfare in New Zealand and later, Director-General of Mental Health; Mary – his adopted daughter.

Part I: Quest, 1929-43

Charlotte Street of 1929 . . . where – at one or another moment of the twenty-four hours – everyone passed? Surely – divided by Oxford Street from Soho – it was the Latin Quarter of the time. Here, names that were known or were to be known were bandied in Kleinfeldt's Bar. Here, faces that were known or to be known appeared above the restaurant tables . . . Bertorelli's, the White Tower, Schmidt's. Here, under gay summer awnings, figures that were known or to be known lolled and sprawled on small metal chairs – folios propped against them, books piled beside them – in gay esoteric gossip. Here strode or lolled in snow or yellow sunlight Havelock Ellis, always willing to talk – Axel Munthe, with his insomnia – James Joyce, his eyes obscured always behind his heavy black glasses, bitter against his inherited blindness – little James Stephens, shy as a fawn – W. B. Yeats, the lyric poet turned Sinn Feiner; top hat no less astounding than morning-coat and spats – Harold Monro of the Poetry Bookshop – Epstein, Sickert, Augustus John, Duncan Grant, Vanessa Bell, Clive, Virginia Woolf, Leonard, Roger Fry, Tom Eliot . . . One shared one's bread with Bill Coldstream in Constable's studio . . . or one's beer with Nina Hamnett and her pugilist in Thackeray's . . . or swam in the Serpentine with 'the Dicker', his beard floating out on the water.

And I – a stranger from twelve thousand miles, whose childhood feet, on the underside of the world, had scaled volcano walls: whose body, whipped by icy winds of snow-clad Ruapehu, had plunged for respite into the hot pools on its slope without guide or chart . . .

Certainly the hot springs were active on this spring day – no geyser could have been more surprising, more effective, more fateful.

An ancestral caution to avoid a foe's descending dirk in my shoulderblade has always seen to it that I seat myself with my back to a wall. Also, all is in one's view: no detail of the human show is missed. And so, now, I place myself and my new elegance carefully, choosing a small table thrust against the Antoine façade and twist the one chair outward.

[9]

A waiter, napkin neatly folded under arm, menu proffered, appears instantly from inside. And panic seizes me. Antoine's! How *can* the handful of silver – even though it is my whole day's budget – buy one single course at such a place? What will happen? Oh, crazy, crazy! ... This resplendent waiter will view me, and my lovely organza, with just contempt. Can I feign sudden illness? Can one eat à la carte? I snatch Mary's letter from my pocket, shuffle its pages, swing a pre-occupied glance at the card held so obsequiously before me.

'For the moment ... melon.' Desperately I repeat it, with the slightest hint of impatience. Yes – that is it! Be deaf. Stone deaf perhaps. Mad, if necessary.

I peruse my pages. The waiter loiters – but for a fraction of time – thrusting out his lower lip, tapping the swart upper one with his pencil. 'Yes, Madame. Certainly, Madame,' he murmurs very low, and departs. Did he guess? Did he *know*? Did he know I'd used all my money? Did he know I was a 'nobody'? Did he know I'd burnt all my excellent letters of introduction? Did he know I bathe daily in the basins of the British Museum Reading Room – first in last out? And still refuse to take a job because each hour of every day is too good to squander on work?

Suddenly an explosion seems to happen under my table ... under my chair ... under me! A geyser of scalding steam gushes through the open pavement gratings and envelops me in a white but food-reeking cloud. I spring to my feet but it is too late – I am instantly saturated. It might have been the Russian Room at a Turkish Bath: my garments hang, cling, are all but invisible.

'Christ! You can't sit there! Share my table.'

A voice? Where? Oh, humiliation. But I am being snatched away and re-seated by a young man ... Is he young? I do not know ... I am appalled and near to tears: I cannot lift my eyes. And presently gazing down my front I see that it is covered by no more than a film of wet gossamer.

I cannot speak.

And now the voice ... very low now, very gentle ... is saying, 'I think if you sit quite still in the sun you'll become opaque again.'

But is there just a hint of amusement – is he daring to enjoy my dilemma? I feel my nostrils dilate as they always do when I am angry. I raise my eyes. And meet his. He smiles. But gravely, slowly ... and as a man who proposes to step on to very thin ice.

The waiter – now discretion itself – had placed my melon before me. Again, 'Ahem ... What will Madame have to follow?' I shake my head. My heart is leaping to the skies. It is like a balloon at a fair. It has broken loose. The string is out of my keeping. It soars ... soars ... makes straight for the sun. It was always a sun worshipper – and now is one with that dazzle of light. I think, 'I shall never get it back. Where will it land? ... where land? ...'

'I ... feel ... ill,' I murmur.

'The melon goes on my bill, Waiter. The lady is not feeling well.'

Long afterwards – many years away – he is to whisper: 'Do you remember Antoine's? The sight of me made you sick.'

He has all but finished.

Presently he calls for the bill, tucks my few coins back into my pocket and helps me to my feet. I have dried out. I am 'opaque'. My skirt hangs like a rag, but can at least conceal.

Now I look obliquely. He is of medium height. He seems to be clad with an air of great carelessness: an open shirt, cotton trousers of some grey striped material and extremely grimy plimsolls. He reaches across and takes possession of a battered green bicycle across which is slung a light alpaca jacket, its pockets torn from their moorings with the weight of books and pipes and beret crammed into them. He disposes of the waiter and, moving leisuredly, he pushes the bicycle with jacket still swung across its handle-bars into position. Then he turns to me. 'Shall we go?'

*   *   *

Now I see his face is lean and brown; his hair with lights of gold and of bronze in its brownness is carelessly thrust to one side. The muscles about the mouth are strongly carved, the nostrils narrow and chiselled: jaw narrow, the cheekbone high above an almost sunken cheek. Behind the.brow's unusual width retreats an unusual depth of skull. The 'seeing' games I'd played as a child with my father on our day-long walks had not been for nothing: for a glance gave me all this . . . even to the pale gold tangle of hairs that filled the ears like nesting birds.

Where are we going?

His movements are slow. Pushing his bicycle with an un-hurried grace and leaning slightly to the task as against a stiff tide and a strong North Wind. We walk in the curious silence of two who now have little need, and certainly no urgency, to speak. But I see that everything pleases him exceedingly – colours, shapes, sounds and passers-by; all are part of a décor of mysterious perfection. And as for me, an enchantment seems to have descended. Time stands still.

The heat blazes down. The asphalt of the pavements all but melts. Yet . . . for us the groves of Georgian houses blossom. Grass springs beneath our feet.

As we walk we steal glances. We look at one another ob-liquely – in what each hopes is secret – scarcely daring. We laugh. Both know – with a bubble of joy – that nothing need be 'secret' any more – so long as we both shall live.

Incredulous. Yet certain. And again incredulous of this very certainty.

The Here and Now.

Is it not enough that we exist? Here we are – the one for the other. For as long as time.

Does either suspect – not I, not I – that more than thirty years of shadow . . . in despair, in direst doubt . . . lie before us?

[4]

A Ring of Keys

As we walk we talk.

'Have you no family here?'

'Yes. An aunt[1] in Park Lane. Tall and narrow. With rounded balconies. The house, I mean. She considers me eccentric – Bohemian – because I arrive at her door on foot.'

'Is your family at home satisfied that you are alone in London?'

'Not at all. They want me to go to Italy. To Florence. To paint. They think I'm an artist.'

'And why do you not go?'

'Oh . . . awful things could happen!' I laugh, looking at him sideways, 'Henry James would make me marry an American or a travelling English peer! And also, Florence would be too wonderful – too loaded: I'd never paint.'

'You might.'

'No. Not there. To paint I'd have to be poor. And find Bill Coldstream.'

He glances quickly up in comical amazement. '*Bill Coldstream?*'

'Yes. Do you know him too? It was his friend, Alan Temple, you see – with his tales of Lundy and Tintagel – who, as it were, played Perseus to my Andromeda.'

'Perseus . . .?'

'Well, yes. I was chained to a rock, you see – a social and colonial one. Don't you think something has sometimes to happen – something quite unforeseen – to make our decisions *for* us: when we can't make them for ourselves, I mean?'

[1] Mrs Usmar, my father's eldest sister Agnes.

He looks at me curiously.

'I mean, when it's a matter of vision – or even courage perhaps – and one just hasn't got it.'

'I see. And so . . . it has to be London. Why London?'

'Ah, why? I don't know that. That's what makes it interesting. Yet I think now I have always known it was to be London. My father died when I was six. Before I was four he had taught me to draw maps of it: its parks, its squares, the river. Strangers in the street ask me the way to places and I can tell them.'

'Did you come with letters of introduction to people here?'

'Yes. I burned them in the open grate: to boil my kettle.'

'Who were they to?'

'Oh, odd people. Sir Evelyn Wrench[1]. . . the MacDonalds.'

'What MacDonalds?'

'Ramsay. Malcolm. And Lloyd George's daughter, Megan. It wouldn't have done at all. No, no. One must be free. And the jungle's full of traps.'

He looks at me queerly.

'Yes . . .' he says and is suddenly grave.

We are moving through a square: a wonder of plane trees in a space well hedged, high-railed and guarded lest one should see what is beyond.

Suddenly he pauses, takes from a pocket a heavy ring of keys, fits one in the lock of a small gate between the tall iron railings and we enter.

It is, after all, but one of the lesser magics of this spring day.

He props his bicycle against a gardeners' shed and we move together over the lawns to a grassy un-cut knoll beneath small branching trees. Lying now on our faces between clumps of daffodils we make a curious exchange of earliest memories.

His first sound? 'The tick of my mother's French travelling clock.'

And sight? 'My mother's cut-jet brooch – the flash from light to dark of its many-faceted surface as she moved.'

[1] The then head of the English-speaking Union.

[14]

(Proustian, I think.)

'And yours?'

'Sound? The organ music of Erewhon as the winds from the Antarctic thread the needle-peaks of our Southern Alps. I lived there.'

'And touch?'

'The feel of platypus fur on my naked palms.'

I say, 'I nearly married a dean.'

'A *dean*.'

'Yes. Brilliant. But scholars are so boring, aren't they. I mean, they can't bear not to complicate simple matters.'

'What matters?'

'Oh ... like the Holy Trinity.'

'The Holy Trinity!'

'Yes. You know. Father, Son and Holy Ghost ... Body, Mind and Spirit ... the whole man. Like a three-legged stool. Take one away and the thing topples.'

He laughs; and rolls on to an elbow: 'You and Blake!'

'Blake? Oh well, but he wasn't a scholar – he was a poet. And wasn't he supposed to be a bit mad? ... which is always an advantage when it comes to knowing things.'

He is silent. Then, 'Where did you live when you first arrived?'

'Well, the first week in Bayswater. My luggage got instantly "lost" at Southampton and the London taximan took me to where I would, he assured me, be "acceptable" without any. A street of splendid but identical drawing-rooms, where identical ladies discussed identical servant-problems, bandied county names, systematically robbed one another at bridge and knitted mufflers for the church. I had my hair shampooed from its brine where Edith Sitwell had her nails gilded ... no, it was silver ... and they were an inch long, like a mandarin. It was a "right" milieu. All very expensive. All, in fact, that I had fled from. I stayed a week, to sleep off the voyage. I had two proposals of marriage: one from a Member of Parliament, one from a widowed barrister. I hadn't come twelve thousand miles for that. As soon as my trunks turned up I broke free.'

'And then?'

'I walked the length of Fleet Street and thought it would be rather nice to live in Ludgate Circus. While I was buying a Theodore Dreiser in a basement bookshop, I asked the Cockney girl my chances. She was almost incoherent with sinus. She said: "Wher d'yer live naow?"

'I said, "Bayswater."

'Then she gazed at me with sisterly compassion and made a speech of classic comment I shan't forget: "*Byswater!* Ooo, I say! It's all very well fer girls as likes it but fer nice girls wots bin brung up praaper like you an' me ... Ooo I say! ... Don'cher *know*? ALL THEM WIMMINS KEP' BY MEN!"

'I had a vision of the specimens gathered about *my* marble mantel: "There's no accounting for tastes," I told her.'

My companion's eyes glimmered appreciatively. 'So then?' he asked.

'Oh, then. You mean now? A bare room opposite the gates of the British Museum.'

'You sleep in it?'

'Yes. Though this was not permitted. It is an office only. Rather by an accident (but that's quite a story) I gave a lecture at Reading for a Madame Montezambert[1] of Apple Tree Yard. She wore a lace bed-cap and sat up in a four-poster entirely covered in typescript while secretaries fussed. In the end she forgot to mention the subject of the lecture. It turned out to be "Old London".'

'But you'd only just arrived!'

'Oh, that was all right. You forget – my mind was "conditioned" at four: they said it was easy to see that I'd lived all my life here. In return, Madame Montezambert – she was a French Canadian – gave me a chair ...'

'A chair! You mean you sleep in that?'

'Well, no. I prefer the floor; my travelling rug; and my fur coat for cover.'

'Do your friends come there?'

'I know no-one. Assorted pigeons live on my window-sill.'

---

[1] French-Canadian historian of London.

'Are there other people in the building?'

'I think, only the "composer" and his French mistress. They live across the landing. He has a grand piano. She fries bacon on it. The fat spatters the keys and the backs of his hands. Then they fight.'

'Is there a bathroom? A lavatory?'

'Oh, no.'

'How do you ... manage?'

'One gears one's habits to the opening and shutting of the British Museum.'

'Do you work?'

'To live? Yes. The minimum. I read – but in my own hours – for "White Trash", the publisher.'

'*White Trash?*'

'That is what he calls himself. He was reared in the Alleghenny Mountains. I read manuscripts. For every three pages of criticism I get three shillings and he gets three guineas. It is a perfectly acceptable arrangement. I like doing it and I only want enough for food and rent. And time, of course.'

'Time?'

'Freedom. That's the expensive thing. That's the luxury. The more criticism I do, of course, the more of it I can buy. White Trash understands. And he's tried to teach me to do crits without reading. But I'm not good at it. I get involved with the minds of the writers. Young miners in Wales. Old ladies in Menton. But at least I can do them through the night – which leaves my days free.'

'But ... what do you *want* to do?'

'Write short stories.'

'So do I. Do you write poetry?'

'Of course. Everybody does, surely?'

'Perhaps not everybody. What sort of poetry do you like?'

'Well ... it used to be all, or nearly. But now it's spoilt a bit.'

'What *do* you mean?'

'Well, I got hold of a book – scarcely even that – called *Poems from the Chinese*. Translations. Part of a series. Published by Benn. I got not only it but all the poets – Binyon, de la Mare, Blunden, Davies, Yeats, everybody – but *The Chinese* is the only one I brought twelve thousand miles. It's somehow made other *kinds* of poetry just ... dull.'

'Who's the translator?'

'Waley, I think. Yes, Arthur Waley. Do you know him?'

'Yes.'

'Oh, how lucky you are – you know everyone!'

'I ... don't know him very well.'

I pluck a grass stem, peel it and suck its sweetness. His eyes are upon me, and presently he does the same. I ask, 'And do *you* work?'

'Yes.'

'Where?'

'At the British Museum.'

'I haven't seen you in the Reading Room.'

'No. I work in the Prints Department.'

'You mean you've got a *job* there? A nine-to-five *job*?' I am shocked: and a little disillusioned. Certainly saddened.

'Is that bad?'

'Bad? It's immoral. You must leave at once.'

I am deadly serious. But he lets out a roar of laughter that surprises me. The heads jerk up from books and papers. There is a movement on the garden seats as gear of many kinds is collected ... and presently the gate on the east side clicks as – one after another – the Stracheys go home. We have the garden to ourselves ... till fading light and longer. Adventuring in and out of one another's minds, we do not notice we have the garden to ourselves any more than we had noticed we had not.

He is silent.

But I find myself glancing back, detachedly, over my shoulder, down the years ...

'Mine was a Diocesan school, "more English than England" – its staff hand-picked, personally, by our headmistress and almost annually, from Oxford – brilliant, mildly Lesbian ... like Tennyson's *Princess*. A sort of paradise; remembering it now. It must have been quite a bit Victorian too: I mean, it was considered vulgar to sit for "outside" examinations.

Curious! but my feeling never ran to Oxford: always to Cambridge. It was the colour of the word, of course.'

'The *colour*?'

'Yes. "OXFORD" ... it's so indigo ... and leaden – like an Arctic sea. But "CAMBRIDGE" ... Ah, *there's* a word – the colour of a peach! Do you think I'm mad?'

'No.'

'I'm glad. My mother did.'

'Because of this "colours" business?'

'Yes. Mixing them up with sound. Orchestral music "blinded" me. A gallery of paintings could be "too deafening" or "too shrill". I suppose I could never quite get my senses separate. I can't still. The National Gallery is like a thunderstorm. The Tate – especially the French Impressionists – like cicadas in the tropics. Oh, perhaps it *is* mad.'

'A Frenchman has written about it.'

'Written about it! Then ... you mean it's *not* mad? Or not awfully?'

'Not mad at all. Not the least in the world.'

'Oh! It *was* useful, in lots of "memory" ways. When I was seven my mother would say, "I've forgotten that lady's name: can you remember it?" and I'd answer, "It was cobalt," and rush to my paint-box. I'd paint a streak of cobalt and mutter to myself all the "cobalt" sounds ... and after a bit hand her the name!'

'Fantastic!'

'But you've just said, *not* fantastic. Was it? Or wasn't it? My father would have understood perfectly: but my mother ... well, I rather think she just considered me "difficult" ... almost beyond endurance. I was sorry: I mean, I was sorry for my "difficultness" but no-one can *change* what he *is*, can he?'

'No.'

'Oh, Oh, Oh – I'm so happy!'

'Why?'

'I feel ... absolved. You're the first person – ever – who's understood. But there were other things: worse, I suppose, for her.'

'What other things?'

'Oh, like thinking the sky was radiant when it was grey and deluging with rain ... or believing I was ten feet high.'

He smiles, twisting his head sideways to look into my face. 'That *might* have been a little disconcerting for her,' he says.

'I know. I know. But what could I *do*? In the end I could only come away ... here ...'

But my voice peters strangely out and I bury my head in the daffodils. Their petals are colourless now, but still warm with the day-long sun.

I think of the policeman in Charing Cross with his "You staying long?" and my answer "Forever!"

For an instant time stands deadly still – not daring to move.

But ... Yes. I am 'home' at last.

'Come,' he presently says, and takes my hand. In the all-but-dark we follow round the little path that winds between the tall close bushes of the perimeter. We turn a corner and he pulls me to a halt. Before us – rising from the grass – stands a young tree. A white-flowering cherry. It is not more than a head high; its blossom-laden arms spread like a benediction. Parting them carefully, he draws me in and we stand together. We are walled and canopied; our faces turned to one another dim-lit by petals.

It is a ritual.

And suddenly my heart takes fright. Fright.

[5]

Of Nothing and No-one

It is summer 1929.

Miss FitzGerald – daughter by his first wife of Gerald FitzGerald, Irish Gent, Irish eccentric, whose dawn-light dance we had so often in childhood watched from our high windows that looked over and into his garden of rare roses: the secret and frenzied dance atop his mountainous and fly-infested manure heap – Miss FitzGerald, Hostess and Unofficial Chaperone at the London, Strand, offices of the High Commissioner for New Zealand, takes me aside: 'My dear, you will forgive me, but – for the sake of your family – I must warn you. One should be very careful indeed in London in one's choice of acquaintances.'

Who are these? Whom do I know? My Park Lane cousins – Madame Montezambert – Dorothea Vincent – Havelock Ellis – Harold Monro – J.B.S. Haldane and his sister – Naomi Mitchison – the young Count Potocki[1]– the charming Lane boys – 'the Dicker' – the art student, Bill Coldstream ... Where does my indiscretion lie?

No – with none of these. But – 'My Dear ... the gentleman with the green bicycle ...'

'... and the dirty plimsolls?'

'... *and* the pipe. Yes, Dear. One *can't* be too careful. Who is he?'

'No-one.'

Her face is kind and puckered with concern. 'What is his name?'

[1] New Zealand pretender to the throne of Poland; poet, publisher and well-known London character.

'I don't know.'

'You *don't know*!'

'But no! He's ... wonderful. There's no *need* to know.'

'Oh, my dear ... my *dear* ...'

Miss FitzGerald's small apple-features wrinkle in dismay: but she is at a loss. 'Your Aunt Forrest ... would be *very* disturbed. Sir Thomas[1] asked me to speak. For the sake of your grandfather ...' Her voice tails off in real distress. How nice she is! I grin, squeeze her hand an instant – and am back in the Strand again.

'Perhaps you'd better leave your bicycle outside,' I say to my companion, who is preparing to hoist it in as usual. 'They don't seem to like it here. *Or* your plimsolls.'

'Am I to leave them outside too? It's not a mosque!' he exclaims.

'Oh, I don't know – in a way, it *is*, you see. And Sir Thomas Wilford is disturbed because I don't know your name.'

'Do you *want* to know it?'

'Not in the least! There are holes in your socks. Come. Let's buy some more at Woolworth's.'

He grins delightedly, settles his pipe between his strong teeth, ties the arms of his pullover about his waist, removes his trouser-clips and lifts the offending bicycle into the roadway.

'We'll drop this in the square and then row on the lake, shall we? And eat under the mallows ...?'

Their broad shade leans above us. And beyond ... *How blue the sky, how golden is the sun* ... *Oh never, never let our love have done.*

'What's that you're scribbling?' My companion stretches a lazy arm; but the fragment is already in my pocket.

'Nothing.'

It is some weeks yet before I find myself at a rather special function of the Poetry Society in Fitzroy Square, surrounded

[1] Sir Thomas Wilford, family friend and later High Commissioner for New Zealand in London (1930–3).

by women members and interrogated with what is, surely, unusual interest. I am standing beside Housman. I lean against the wall. I am bored. But the women are kindly, and cluster about me: after all, I too am a guest.

'And are there any English poets you would particularly like to meet? That is, apart from your Poetry Bookshop friends?'

'Ah – I wonder. Disillusion is so ... uncomfortable. But yes – perhaps there is one. That is, if you think of him as a true poet. The translator from the Chinese: Arthur Waley.'

They glance sharply at one another. What is this? A piece of play-acting? – and I am astonished to see on the ring of faces before me both puzzlement and irritation. Until one, speaking for all, exclaims: '*Well!* You *do* live in his pocket!'

[6]

A Shadow of Leaves

September 1929.

It is past midnight and I am exhausted with the long journey from Holyhead but Arthur has said: 'Ring me the moment you get back.'

His voice is instantly alert, and wonderful; 'Darling! Where *are* you?'

'Near you. At the Endsleigh. The train was full of pilgrims going to Lourdes. I feel I've caught all their diseases. I long only for a bath.'

'But you can bath here!'

'I've booked in here – and *must* sleep – tomorrow I must find a new home.'

'Book out again. I long for you. I cannot wait till morning. Come.'

I am waking beside the stored apples in the attic of No. 36.[1] The smell of coffee rises. Yet another bath is running. Arthur is playing his klavier. Under the slope of rafters I lie in bliss. I am home.

Presently he calls up the stair; 'If you come now you can watch Paul[2] dressing. He's putting on a dark blue shirt. Very handsome ...'

I tumble down the attic ladder and together we stand and watch the tall dark-haired figure at the window across the way arranging its white tie.

Arthur brings our coffee on a tray that floats: then sits side-saddle on the edge of the bath.

[1] The address was Endsleigh Street although the house overlooked Gordon Square.
[2] Paul Hyslop, architect.

'Tell me all that happened,' he says, 'from the beginning.'

'Oh but it's so much and so much. Surely that will bore you.'

'You could *never* bore me!'

And so – as I bath, as I dress – I tell him. Of Dublin's Horse Show ('Did you know all the Irish are Americans?') – of Lady Gregory, of the Abbey Theatre, of the lank Lennox Robinson, of Yeats and A.E., with his portrait of the young James Stephens, of Juggling Jerry of County Kerry, of Hugh and the jaunting-car, of the Mother Superior and the pole-axed bull ... 'And it turned out that "Australia's" trouble was that she'd always been in love with her cousin whom the family had made into a priest ... but we need think no more of her for I've deposited her on the imposing steps of her family's grand house and we are free of her forever!'

By which time Paul has arranged his tie in a manner that, it is evident, strikes him as becoming ... and Arthur, snatching my hand, hurtles me down four flights of stairs and out into the sun.

Alone I find my perfect room – vast, empty, balconied, silent – in the frayed anonymity of Regent Square. Ragged and derelict with its Georgian slums, it is – by a few yards – east of Bloomsbury's un-mapped border and, to that extent, enchantingly non-existent. From tall windows, a pattern of plane trees is cast, by night and by day, on the white-washed walls. It is a timeless room.

Its barrenness is what best pleases me. But soon the Count Potocki has made me a bed – no more than a palliasse and but a foot from the floor, but which I place now centrally on my travelling-rug. Michael Cardew has brought me beautiful 'failures' from his pottery. Rex Fairburn[1] has placed low shelves of boards and bricks to fill the shallow alcoves on either side of my Adam fireplace. Allen Lane has filled them with my books and many more. There are no chairs, but on my fur-strewn couch many cushions. Between the windows is a single narrow table on which stands my typewriter. Here,

[1] New Zealand poet.

at last in solitude, I can work. Indeed it is a room I cannot easily leave even for an hour, for joy in it. But I will not permit Arthur to see it until all is in place.

I wake, listening. The sun casting its oblique rays across the ceiling tells me it is very early. Birds in the great branches of the Square are but murmuring drowsily as yet. What, then, has wakened me?

Tap. Tap, tap.

I rise, move to an open window and step on to a balcony.

Arthur is on the pavement below. He is laughing and eating cherries: the stones land at my feet. From the room I fetch the key and fling it down to him. I return to my couch which is spread with fur and on which I have slept in my Japanese house robe brought from New Zealand. It is very beautiful, of softest cashmere, in colour a muted pink and embroidered closely with silver thread in a pattern of chrysanthemums.

Arthur closes the door softly and springs to my side. 'I have been walking about for hours. I could not sleep. I could not sleep.'

I am silent. And suddenly, sinking on one knee, he takes up the long dark strands of my hair and holds them to his lips. 'You are beautiful ... beautiful,' he murmurs.

But still I cannot speak.

And surely indeed he knows the reason why – for what ear could not have heard the tumult in my heart. A hundred horsemen charge and gallop there.

Yes; he too. For 'Yugao[1]...' he cries, starting up, 'Yugao ...'

Wildly he stands, looking about him at the high bare walls with their shadows of leaves.

Wildly he stands – and is fled down the stairs.

I turn on my face, crushing it into the pillow. And it seems as though all the loneliness of the world bears down upon me and will never lift.

---

[1] Character in chapter 2 of the tenth-century Japanese novel, *The Tale of Genji*, by the Lady Muraski, who dies in Prince Genji's embrace. Arthur was working on his six-volume translation at the time (George Allen & Unwin, 1925–33).

[7]

A Lady in Fez

It is midnight.

We are walking down the stairs of No. 36. We have nearly reached the bottom of the last flight.

'There is a lady in Fez ...'

'Yes?'

'You must never come here again.'

'A lady in Fez' ... The words are without meaning.

'She's ... coming back.'

I stop. I am motionless.

Then we are standing, facing one another – I, a step below him, in the half dark feel him catch at a strand of my hair to kiss it as so often. I try to see his face. There is a look on it that I have never seen there before: a look of tenderness, yes ... but also of, can it be loss? Loss, my Darling? ... my love? – when all is so surely found?

But his face now is working, is reflecting an agony, a knowledge, that I cannot share ... but that is real. That I cannot understand. And therefore is *not* real. What did he say? Already I have forgotten. Because, of course, the words were nonsense.

But now he repeats them. They are quite clear. 'You must never come here again. There is a lady in Fez.'

Both are rigid. Cold with fear. With loss.

And now words burst from him. 'I've *tried* to explain. I've sent her cables – she's there with three lovers – assuring her I am not lonely – that there is no *need* for her to come. *Not* to come. *Not* to come back.'

I look at him, unbelieving. There is no reality in all this. It is a moment from which we presently shall wake. I put up my hand and touch his cheek. It is wet. I touch his mouth. It is trembling.

So. It is over. I am over, for him. As he must now be, for me. Yet the instinct for life is strong.

I say: 'But . . . you love me.' And at the same time my mind is noting *'neither has used that word before.'* And then, *'neither has needed to.'*

'Yes. I love you. Every sort of way. Even physically.'

(Long afterwards, that last is to strike me as strange – significant. And – so much later indeed – as wonderfully true.)

I know blindly that what is happening to me now is happening to him also: and equally. We are like two parachutists about to jump. Someone – who? – has pulled the ejection cord. An uprush of black and icy air lashes my face. I am dropping . . . dropping . . . The sightless earth is very far below.

There is a lady in Fez.

I grope for the door, open it and slide out into the night.

Part I: Quest, 1929–43

In the four years between 'A Lady in Fez' and 'Hotel Russell' I marry Hugh Ferguson Robinson; live a year in Spain; return to England and settle in Suffolk where our son, John, is born – subsequently coming to London to work with publishers.

[8]

Hotel Russell

1933.

The Russell Square of that day was an unsophisticated affair, a piece of park land – a snippet from the Duke of Bedford's one-time town seat – hedged by Georgian houses of great beauty – but unplanned, much perhaps as Becky Sharp had known it, and but casually tended; the trees grouping themselves rather more thickly along its south side about the statue of the ninth duke, leaving a space of irregularly-cut lawn on the north where children and nurse-maids were free to disport themselves. Here, too, were a green painted coffee-stall, a verandahed shelter and, for one or two seasons at least, a canvas-covered stage set up by the imaginative Holborn Council of the day for the entertainment of the public. A delightful square – half country, half town – lacking all the formality of the West End; a pleasance and a rendez-vous for students and for the haunters of the British Museum. Its planning was of the simplest, evolved solely from the requirements of Bloomsbury's pedestrians. Thus, straight paths crossed from corner to corner while another circled it a yard or two within the tall iron railings. These, too, on its south side with its close groupings of laurel, veronica and rhododendron offered seats and sheltering-places for lovers.

At each of the square's four corners was a little humped and rounded hill, a knoll. In the case of three of these, young impatient students' feet had worn tracks for short cuts to the corner gates, though they in turn wound perforce irregularly between flowering shrubs. These tumuli had, each, its difference. The knoll to the north-west of the square was known to all as 'the mound' – grassy and open to the sun and carpeted with prone human bodies, their coats, their sandwiches, their books, their hastily-scrawled love-letters strewn about them – a rendez-vous from which at least one eager figure seemed always to be collecting himself in haste at the glimpse of another, afar off, magnetically approaching down the long straight paths.

The south knoll at the corner of Kingsway was not easily frequented. It had been hollowed out to make a hidden space for the rough work of the garden: half a dozen stacked barrows, a small shed for garden machinery, a regiment of primitive besoms were all secreted within this roofless igloo hidden by the thickness of bushes that grew on its grassy rough sides and by the pungent smoke that rose and hung volcano-like above it, from its never quite extinguished garden fires.

Hurrying up Kingsway, entering the garden at this point and turning sharply left into the perimeter path that would take me to the Montague Street corner, I stand suddenly still.

I am alone and I am in haste. Yet I stop as though a lassoo had jerked me to stillness.

I turn on my heel.

Seated in a small patch of sunlight high among the bushes, the white smoke curling up behind him as from his own funeral pyre, is Arthur. His face as he gazes down at me is grave, gentle, apprehensive and glad, all in one long look.

Years fall away. What years? Have there been years?

In silence he puts out a hand. In silence I bound up and am seated at his side. We do not speak or touch. Perhaps we feel nothing in that moment but gratitude to be caught again, even for an instant, in the slip-stream of the inevitable – against which possibly, at some too-deep-to-fathom level, we both had set ourselves to pit our strength.

Respite.

I sink down in the longish grass until my heart shall settle back into something like its normal routine. The long slant of the sun, setting soon now behind the battlemented chimneys of Gower Street ... where, in a tall house my husband waits and a child lies naked on a bed, wrestling happily with his own ten-month-old limbs, until such time as his mother shall come to bath him.

But his mother rises and, gathering up the strew of books, handing the flutter of papers to another, she turns and moves in the direction of the Hotel Russell.

The two mount the steps. The liveried doorman nods. The vestibule opens out into the wide spaces of the staircase, padded fields of carpet, mirrored distances – crimson and gilt reflected again and yet again.

She asks: 'Why are we here?'

He answers: 'I live here.'

She is incredulous.

For a creature so simple in his tastes – so private a creature – what a setting! If the gods had devised a punishment for such a one, could it be greater? What ... has happened?

As he leads her to the lift her face is grave with concern. 'How ... terrible,' she says.

He flashes her a look – 'You so *delight* me!' (there is a four years' echo in her heart) and now, in his splutter of laughter – a glad, un-terrible laughter – they are ascending.

His room is on the fourth floor. It is vast and long, terminating in a great crescent of window. The ceiling-high panes give back the tops of trees, a foam of green, and the last shafts of the sun from a colouring sky. An immense table fills the window-space and this is strewn with the books and business of work. But it is Genji he takes from a shelf; sinks into the deep shadow of a chair with, 'Shall we read?'

At the words she has, from an old habit, kicked off her shoes and placed them by the fire. He leans forward and, again from an old habit, lights it. The evening is warm. Though it has rained in the night the spring wind has long since whipped the world to dryness. Yet now – from an old habit? – he picks up her shoes and places them carefully at its side. In a voice that at first is inaudible but strengthens as it goes on he opens the book and begins to read: 'Yugao ... Yugao ... have pity on them – these two, caught in the snares of timelessness.'

And perhaps she indeed had pity. For a loud rapping at the door brings each springing to his feet. A porter stands there – his buttons gleaming urbanely in contradiction of his words: 'The management does not allow ladies in gentlemen's rooms, Sir.'

I dare not glance at Arthur.

Unbelievably the creature stands, one arm holding wide the door, while I slip my feet into my shoes, snatch up my things and leapt past him.

I am in the street – across the traffic – across the grass, running, running ... before Arthur catches up with me and we stand bewildered. I am at a loss. I can collect neither time nor space. All is broken about me. All is broken. And suddenly tears stream down my cheeks and Arthur is saying in a voice far, far sadder than I can bear to hear – 'Oh my Darling ... my Darling.'

Then I know where, who, I am ... and swing round on him: 'No.' I say vehemently, 'No. No. No!' Then dashing my tears into my hair I say loudly, 'Would you care to walk with me to my house? I believe it is the one the Vicar of Stiffkey cherished his whores in ... before he sat about naked in a barrel, you know ... for money ... at the seaside.'

His eyes flicker with pain. With pain and bewilderment. For it is *his* turn to wonder what has happened.

And still in a voice I cannot recognise I hear myself saying, 'Also, I'd like you to meet my husband. And my son. He's nearly a year old. Rather nice. You might like one another. It would be amusing to see. Though I swear he'll out-stare you. He's a very superior person.'

Christ – hold my tongue from babbling on – babbling on ...

I am leading the way briskly now and already we are at Gower Street. I march up the flights of dark stairs and enter our attic room. Hugh has laid out the towels, is filling the hand-basin and wondering why I am so late.

'Hugh – this is Arthur Waley.'

'Oh ... hullo. I am so glad to meet you. My wife tells me you translate Chinese ...' He is drying a hand and stretching it forth ... smiling with pleasure.

On the bed John sprawls naked, one foot gripped high above his head, eyes alert and watching. And now brown eyes meet brown eyes and hold – in steady gaze.

With no word spoken, with no glance towards us, the onlookers – Arthur turns and dives down the dark and squalid stair.

Hugh murmurs, 'Funny chap.'

I cross to the window, thinking to hear the door slam, but see instead Arthur's fleeing figure – running – running – across the road and round the corner – to shelter ... to safety ... to the vulgarity of the Hotel Russell.

[9]

Here and Now

1938.

Well, it was a Tuesday, I think.

In the revolving doors of the British Museum I find myself face to face with Arthur. Five years have gone. And with an equatorial line between us.

Without a word he turns to the great corridor where stand the stone busts, the stone figures, of the long dead. We sit on a stone bench and look with a sort of detached interest yet again at the stone faces. They look back at us. There is tyranny. And tenderness. There is cruelty. Brutality. Intelligence. Innocence. Two or three thousand years of it.

Behind our awareness, Hitler's voice reiterates his broadcast promise – '. . . at four o'clock this afternoon . . . London will be bombed.'

We stare ahead of us, moveless, unseeing.

Arthur says quietly, 'There is no yesterday. And no tomorrow. There is only Here and Now.'

Here. And Now.

'I must get back to John,' I say, rising with a jerk.

And – inseparable – we separate.

In the streets, loud-speakers blare.

'Wardens will direct you to your nearest centre for distribution of gas-masks. School children will assemble, with their teachers, at Euston, Marylebone, Paddington and Victoria Stations for evacuation. Will you please proceed immediately to . . .'

The roads to the west are jammed with stationary cars: a sitting target.

Petrol is £4 per gallon.

That afternoon, bony, aristocratic and bravely beringed fingers in a local Church Hall hand me three gas-masks.

Mine – for my face is thin – falls off. John's – for he is a child – falls off. There is only one size. Chiquita's – for she is but a hound ...

Nevertheless, I take them home. Hugh's fits. I say, with a rueful smile, 'You're going to be the sole survivor of the family.'

Our Staffordshire Bull Terrier rolls a liquid brown eye and wags a tawny tail.

We go and picnic in the park ... where the unemployed of six years are lethargically digging shallow trenches with borrowed spades for one shilling an hour.

Four o'clock chimes. All is serene.

My mind says over, out of the past ... 'Quartro horas y el cielo es tranquilo' ... and I smile: remembering Old Valencia.

We sit and wait in the yellow sunshine. The squirrels flash in the boughs above us; rustle the long grass.

We are still there when the customary sun sinks into the customary lake.

Now, all trail back to their homes: those with empty dog leads, cages and cat collars (for they have chosen that their pets should be destroyed without terror) in tears.

The frenzied – and sadly futile – digging stops. The unemployed are again unemployed. There is a whole year before us ... After all – a tomorrow.

[10]

Akropolis

1943. Begin with the future . . . Begin with pain . . .

I have returned again to London,[1] England – an empty-seeming London of holes and fine dust – and all Hell falls from the sky.

As I enter the studio door with a rush, my cloak flying behind me, flinging my parcels onto the elegant Sheraton-chair, Mrs Gilman[2] rises from the reception-desk, one hand pushing through her wild coarse hair, the other replacing the telephone receiver.

'A message for you,' she says, gathering up her papers for the day and thrusting them into a drawer; 'Mrs Waley hopes you will dine with her tonight. The Akropolis in Percy Street at 7.30.'

I think . . . six months, since a volume – *Monkey*[3] – had mysteriously found me: direct from the publishers. Six months of silence . . .

'Mrs Waley hopes you will dine with her tonight. Mrs Waley . . .?'

What does one feel when an adjustment such as this has to be faced?

And why 'adjustment'? Is it not – this new married state for such a man – the most logical, the most likely thing in the world? But, 'Ha!' says Fate with a demoniac chuckle, 'You didn't think of that, did you? You didn't think of that one!'

I put up a hand, almost as in defence, and it touches my

---

[1] In the five years since the preceding chapter, I had travelled to New Zealand, with my husband and son, to visit my mother who was ill.

[2] Widow of Harold Gilman, the painter.

[3] Allen & Unwin, 1942.

face, which is ice-cold. But Mrs Gilman is sweeping towards the street door. 'Thank you,' I hear my voice, infinitely remote and foreign to me, 'Thank you, Mrs Gilman. Good-night.' I lower myself slowly, deliberately, among my strewn parcels on the Sheraton chair. Time ... must have a stop. 'Begin with the future,' I think. And then, 'Begin with pain.'

Suddenly, under the small disc of the restaurant table, his two feet draw me towards him – his knees seek and encompass mine. I feel my cheeks burn. I think, 'How vulgar! How wonderfully and deliciously vulgar.'

I think, 'If he should stretch out his open hand across the table I would pluck out my heart and place it in the palm.'

I think, 'I would fold the fingers over it – gently – firmly – so that he might hold it secure forever.'

I think, 'We have had no wine, yet my wits are melting away. I am surely crazed.'

I think, 'He is married. To whom? How? How *could* that be? Mrs Waley has asked you to dine ... Mrs Waley ...'

I say, 'A man seated at another table is watching us. Do you know him?'

He glances up. 'Yes,' he says, 'it is Peter Quennell.' He is quite without embarrassment.

Instantly I am disturbed, shamed – my joy fades. Under the brief table-cloth my knees disentangle themselves. I withdraw my hands. I feel the blood drain again from my face and I feel slightly sick.

'Shall we go?' he asks.

'Please,' I murmur.

Outside, Percy Street gleams gay in the china-blue light. We turn abruptly and I find myself confronted by the delightful paved way of Colville Place. I fling out a hand and laugh. 'I had a room there once ... for a whole week,' I say. 'A back room, very poor. I received a letter from Count Cedric Potocki who asked if he might visit me. When he came I led him to my room. We'd not met before. There was only the bed to sit on. He had come, he said, to explain to me that it was he and not his brother who was King of Poland. As I listened, puzzled and astonished, the door of my room flew open and my landlady stood there like a flurried bird. She burst out, 'If you want *that*-sort-of-thing you'd better go to the other side of Tottenham Court Road!'

Arthur flings back his head and laughs delightedly. 'What *did* she mean?' he asks.

'I can't imagine! She said it was called "Bloomsbury". Is it?'

'Yes! Yes!' he cries, taking my hand, running me into Goodge Street and, at full tilt, across a main route of traffic. 'Yes!'

And suddenly we have stopped. We are out of breath. He takes my other hand and we stand there laughing together. I may be being taken to meet Mrs Waley ... Mrs Waley ... but somehow it just cannot matter: it has no importance at all: my heart bubbles up and will not be suppressed. Joy ... I find to my dismay ... cannot be quenched.

No. 50, Gordon Square,[1] the tall façade all but screened by the summer trees of the garden. The impressive stone stair-case with its cushioned carpet that dwindles in grandeur as we climb; that becomes, indeed, hair-cord as we near the top.

Arthur pushes the door which opens at his touch. Inside, we stand – while I listen to the silence.

I listen to the silence. Another stair climbs higher. I glance up. Arthur has moved into a sitting-room. The panes of its windows, night-blue like the wings of African butterflies, are all we can see. I stand still while he moves to a fire which he switches on. At once the night recedes before the red glow. Couches and chairs spring into view. Cushions piled. Books piled. Sliding a couch into the direct gaze of the fire, he flings himself down and stretches a hand over its curved back to beckon me.

It is now all too painfully familiar. The years ... the so strongly-built barricade of the years in which I trusted ...

---

[1] Arthur was now living on the top two floors (the former Clive Bell flat) with Beryl de Zoete ('the lady in Fez').

have dropped away. Be careful ... my family's crest flashes up before my inner eye like a red light, a warning light – '*Prenez Garde*' ... Take care, be careful now. Slowly I move across and seat myself primly on the edge of a chair. I feel his amusement ... yet, oddly, know his discomfiture is as mine.

'Shall we read?' he asks now ... he asks down the years.

And the voice is a voice in an alpine valley ... the three words ring round the peaks, repeat themselves, fade, drift ... back into the past whence they came.

But I resist that magic. I say, 'When will your wife come?'

'My *wife*!' he cries, amazed. 'My *wife*? I *have* no wife!'

I slide to the floor, without comment. He reaches for his book and, my face against his knee – in the old way, the old way – he reads.

At ten o'clock sharp he closes the book and I rise to go.

I have heard, indeed, not one word.

'I will come with you as far as the Tube,' he says.

On the brief journey back an air-raid has been in progress: at Bond Street station travellers are not permitted to emerge into the streets. Across the way, a corner of Selfridges flares gold against a crimson cloud. The Hyde Park anti-aircraft guns boom shatteringly. Fingers of light gouge the sky, slice it into segments, converge to hold quivering a raider trapped like a moth. Horror, too, has its beauty. London ... blooms like a rose.

The warden presses us back.

'Not goin' out in this lot, yer not, Miss ...' pressing me back among the passengers assembled now and glad to be in shelter.

Under his armpit and under the crackle of guns, I whisper, 'I live just round the corner. Please let me go.'

For answer, he looks the other way and gives me a violent shove with his elbow ... I am out ... and running.

South Molton Street is a scatter of flak. Small pits and gashes are torn in walls and roadway. At a sudden bend I pause and stare up into the bruised peony sky. An arm from behind is flung across my chest and I am jerked backward as a crash of concrete coping scatters where I stood. The street warden – an old fellow who, accompanied always by a huge imperturbable tom-cat, patrols the area – grins.

'So it's you. Sorry, girl – no night ter be out wivout yer hat.'

'Where is the raid? Where has it been?' I ask him.

'Came sudden. Over Euston way,' he answers.

Over Euston way . . . over Euston way. Goodge Street. The square. 'I will come . . . as far as the Tube.' Oh, keep him safe: safe. To whom, to what, does one pray?

Sliding into the silent house in Brook Street, I climb to the top but stand a moment at Hugh's open door. He is awake. 'Raid,' he calls.

'Nothing much,' I answer, and enter the glass-roofed attic-studio where, on a table and ranged in white boot-boxes, are John's hawk-moths. I fling myself down on the red blankets of his narrow bed. How long, how long? And at last all dwindles, falls to silence. The all-clear sounds, piercing the night like a blade. The quake of war has passed on.

But deep, deep, in the silence that follows it – in some no-place of the spirit – I feel the continent of my marriage split and sever. In strong tides the land-masses are drifting apart. 'It is over . . .' I whisper into my pillow, weeping: and, still weeping . . . 'It has begun.'

Then I go below to the telephone.

A familiar voice crackles over the wire. 'Hemel Hempstead Police Station. Yes. Ah, M'am it's you. No, your boy's quite safe – Gadebridge School is still standing. 'Twas the Brush Factory got it tonight. Quite busy, they were – *quite* busy. Well, good morning to you, M'am.'

Does he guess, this police sergeant, that he is speaking with a new entity: an entity but lately born?

And all but consumed by joy?

'Good morning to you . . . M'am . . .'

I switch off the light and, crossing the room, draw back the black-out curtains. Small glowing tomatoes in our window-boxes, like crimson lanterns, are getting the first horizontal rays of the sun.

[11]

A Course is Set

The sirens are wailing and fingers of light are probing the sky for the solitary raider: now trapped, pinned like a silvered moth; now lost – now trapped again.

But ... I have no cigarettes. It is 9.30 p.m. And, in war, cigarettes are more important than food.

In the dimness of the blacked streets I make my way over the pock-marked paving-stones to the South Molton Arms and, pushing aside the door curtains of heavy leather and, beyond, the inner one of heavy velvet, I am in a dazzle of light. Cheerful light. Calculated light – to light the memory of other times. The bar is tight-packed with it. It falls in chunks on counter and floor – on men's faces (there are no women) and on glitter of glasses raised ...

'Well – here's to it, old chap! See you give 'em hell!'

The head of the young man *in brand new air force uniform* jerks proudly up. I am appalled to find myself noting it in finest detail, feature by feature: its beauty, its glowing and terrifying faith ... And suddenly it is *all youth* – spiralling down an indifferent night sky.

Quickly I move to the far interior, where fewer bodies press and beyond the crackle of words ... that are suddenly criminal in their utterance.

Here, two men face, close, to the counter.

The shorter, to gain height, has flung a leg up on to a high mahogany stool: the other, tall, stands nearer and, lifting his glass while at the same time inclining his head sideways, says in a low voice:

'Yes: but what can she *do*? This "lady from Fez" – what can Beryl de Zoete *do*?'

The response is not immediate. When it comes it is enunciated with exact care and the words are spoken so low that the tall companion (I have observed him, and my decision is that he is a foreigner, a stranger to our shores, a Dutchman: as is the shorter of the two, for he is a familiar figure to me in the stripped and depleted world of wartime W1) has now to lean still further to catch them.

'She can do ... what few *English* women ... can do. She can *destroy* a man. She can render him *unfit* for love or marriage.'

Cigarettes are forgotten. Swiftly I move between the standing customers, pass through the heavy curtains, am out in the street.

I lean against the South Molton Arms. Head lifted, the better to breathe. And words drift down upon me ... assail ... more sharp than flak ... out of the past: out of my youth's inconsequent years. Words woven of lies and of truths; of malice and treachery, but also of horror, of pain past enduring ... adrift but stinging in the smoke-heavy air of that rendez-vous, the English pub – 'cannibals ... sex and blackmail ... jungle play ... superior techniques' ... the lady from Fez ...?

Even, yes, of human despair that seeks – and finds – an end. Recounted tales. Myth?

Nerveless now, and mindless, I lean against the South Molton Arms.

And now another voice is moving out of the past. Merciless. Accurate. Directly aimed. Yet hesitant. Decisive. And ... broken.

'*There is a lady in Fez. You must never come here again. She's there with three lovers. I've entreated her not ... not ...*'

I am standing at the foot of the dark staircase of No. 36. I put up a hand to touch a mouth. It is quivering. I touch eyes, cheeks. They are wet.

'*But ... you love me.*'

'*Yes. I love you. Every sort of way ... every sort of way ... even physically.*'

Even physically.

[43]

Every sort of way.

Suddenly, from Hyde Park Corner, the guns boom forth against the enemy – *a boy in brand new Luftwaffe uniform* – in-the-sky ... and I hear my voice lift with them: 'NO! NO! NO!' I shout – *but at neither war nor raider* – 'NO!' – and it seems to me that, high above the ear-pounding clamour as of bronze gongs, far beyond in the upper air, the single syllable so fills it that the guns are as squibs and sink to silence.

And again in the dark street – and in my heart – all is still.

I lean against the walls of the South Molton Arms. 'No.' I whisper now. And have nothing in my consciousness of doubt that the word – so caught, so held – speaks only truth. And I hear my own voice strange to me, quiet still, yet alien in its strength, adding, clear and firm, strange words ... for to whom, to what, are they spoken? *'I will not permit it.'*

Standing there, in the deep of silence now and as in trance, I stare down the endless-seeming and darkened corridors of the future – to where it shines, a single word; a syllable; more glowing, more steadfast, than a star. 'No.'

A course is set.

PART II

Journeys in Parallel

1943–1962

As flogged by tempests
A wave I have seen
Dash itself against the rocks
So in these bitter hours myself only
Am by my thoughts destroyed.

10th century

[I]

Stone Owl

A note said simply, 'Shall we meet in the Stone Owl's Garden?'

Many weeks, months, had gone by. During which, time had floated, indifferent to itself. Where all was urgent, with me was no urgency. For I woke to happiness of certainty. As I went about my business in the deserted village of wartime W1 joy leapt at me from every corner; but yet could not take me by surprise for I felt I was joy's self. I took to using the back streets, to avoid encounters with those I knew or even with strangers, for the mask of my face was an embarrassment to me: their glances, intercepted, showed their astonishment; 'Good Lord! Look at that woman's face ... she's in love.' In love. In love. I had, myself, turned to my companion with those or similar words, seeing two lovers – tall, beautiful, ageless; she, elegant as a princess; he, a prince inadequately disguised in front line battledress – lift their eyes unwarily from afar off in the crowded noonday street and come together, come together as magnet and metal. So that they stood, moveless and isolated; roped off, as it were; ringed about by their own enchantment. So that the scurrying midday pedestrians paused, fell away; and 'Cor!' murmured a Cockney voice at my side. 'Ain't arf got a crush on one anuvver, them two ...' And the Oxford Street sun shone brighter again by just that half.

Arthur, of course, was adept at the oriental mask and was discretion's self when he remembered to use it.

'But you're hopeless at it,' I said to him later. 'As with me, seeing your face people stop in their stride. Try the back streets.'

We became lurkers in alleys, in doorways: there was no blitz-hole aflame with fire-weed we did not make our own, no low-tide strand of Thames to which we failed to gain access. Ah, but how uselessly.

But now – and strangely – I felt no curiosity about Arthur: nor alarm. His life. His days. My own were difficult. And wonderful. Time . . . could afford to loiter. And though bombs continued to rain from the skies, death – I knew – would not find us so.

'Shall we meet in the Stone Owl's Garden?'

What, now, is Torrington Square? . . . that rendez-vous behind the School of Oriental Studies . . . that narrow sylvan strip to which only the professors had access and few, I feel, used for romantic meetings. The Stone Owl on his war-neglected grass beside the narrow twisting path, who now remembers him? The great branches of the plane tree beneath which Arthur now sat awaiting me.

I said no word, knowing well there was no word to say. Yet . . . presently . . . he found four: It was a statement. Simple. And certain.

'You still love me,' and added, 'From the first glance?'

I nodded.

'Me too,' he murmured. 'Me too. It's always fatal.'

Twenty and more years on, when, seated, paralysed from the breast down, Arthur slid the thin octagonal ring of Victorian silver on to my finger and, in accordance with the laws of the land, question was put and answer given, nothing was said which could further validate our union – on a spring day; under a plane tree; with but a Stone Owl for witness.

And now, half turning, I met with a radiance I had not bargained for: a face so ardent as to burn my gaze. I whirled my head away again to make escape from the inescapable, forced my eyes to give attention to matters of tree and sky, of bird and branch and gently loitering cloud.

But – like the onlookers in Oxford Street – these laughed gently back at me.

'Cor! Ain't arf got a crush on one anuvver . . .'

All had been said. And time . . . was forever.

I rolled slowly over on to my face, and kissed the English earth.

[2]

Miss Leverett

Days, nights, bombs, the Studio, Dee's friends – all are exhausting, suddenly an alien world in which I cannot live. And live I must.

Rounding the corner of Tavistock Place, I all but collide with Arthur who at once falls into step with me.

'Where are you going?'

'Home.'

'In the wrong direction? You live at No. 20 Brook Street.'

But he has swung round on his heel and we are moving rapidly back towards his square.

'Ah – not now! Solitude is the precious thing; the luxury. I shall *stay* at 20 Brook Street, but I shall *live* with Miss Leverett. Or rather, her baggage. In her flat.'

'Where is it?'

'Handel's house; an attic. Against St George's Garden. The bomb that demolished the Scottish Synod blew part of the roof away and the back wall: the war damage people are mending it for me. It's wonderful. There's a Sumac tree that blooms every four years – I think Handel must have planted it – and you can look out over the rubble of the houses behind to the "open country" of Brunswick Square where sheep are grazing. Miss Leverett's gone, of course.'

'Where?'

'To India. Her brother, Basil, came on leave and persuaded her to return with him. She hated leaving her things, but she knows I'll take care of them. I've poked them all into the box-room until the roof's put back. She'll be worried about the bomb; but now . . . the men will have packed up and gone. Would you like to come . . . back with me?'

'Yes.'

We climb the stair of the deserted house. There is no need of keys: doors are down; and one interior wall. A tarpaulin is spread over what remains of the roof tiles. Workers' tools litter the landing. Stepping carefully over these, we stand in a doorway and gaze, suddenly enraptured.

I had that morning brought my first items of furniture – a naked divan and a wrought-iron basket fire-grate. The workmen had placed the divan against a wall: and now, stood firmly on its stone plinth in the dim aperture across the room and abloom with a rubble wood fire, the little grate glows a welcome.

'Magical . . .' murmurs Arthur over my shoulder, 'magical.'

Seated close on the divan, fingers linked, heads together, our backs against the broken plaster, with the quiet of a Saturday afternoon in the streets, the curious intimacy of the scarlet embers, an odd peace holds us silent. All is yet to come. But, here and now, already the room – life – is furnished.

Presently I whisper: 'I see'd the little lamp.'

It is a single line of a Katherine Mansfield short story.[1] At once he recognizes it, nods, and asks: 'Did you know her?'

'Well . . . I was too young. We went to the same Diocesan school . . . which then was merely a large house in a garden clinging to the lip of a sixty-foot-deep earthquake crack. The front looked on to a terrace of dark, stunted trees. Their thick interlocking branches roofed over the asphalt paths. They were out of bounds; but once set free among them we were like squirrels, moving out of sight from one to the other, dropping to the ground, one by one at surprising distances. "Ole Underwood" used to press his face against their rough bark, muttering endearments. Then we would whisper replies, until – over the years – he told any passer-by who would listen to his nonsense that the trees talked back to him.'

[1] 'The Dollshouse'.

'Wasn't that rather unkind?'

'No. It made him happy. It's true, as Katherine said, he wore a sailor's peaked cap. And bright blue sailor's eyes, and high scarlet cheekbones, and tufts of beard. To read K's stories now is to live my childhood. We had the same music-master, played to the same metronome, tunnelled up through the same giant fennel on the same steep zig-zag track, slipping back on its hard, dried earth, every nerve aquiver and frayed out to the monotony of the same neurotic wind. She must have left for England when I entered the kindergarten ranks; but even so, "Katherine" was a name that could lay an interesting hush on the conversation of our elders. And I knew her houses: I've spent nights in that Karori one: deep-gabled, netted with creeper in a garden alive with insects – yet in some way more English than this England. Tell me, why was she so unhappy here?'

'Was she?'

'You knew her?'

'Of course.'

'Then you knew she was. At least, at the end. All that being away – alone, and so ill – in Menton ... and dying like that in that wretched humbug place at Fontainebleau – it all seemed so idiotic. Did no one of all her friends love her? Love her enough to be with her? To care?'

'They ... admired her.'

'How beastly. How ... grim.'

I am angry. There is a savagery worse than war, I am thinking: there is the human jungle.

Suddenly tears begin to stream down my face – and Arthur, alarmed, snatches me to him. He takes out a handkerchief and clumsily smudges them over my cheeks. Tenderly he kisses the smudges but, idiotically, the tears cannot stop.

'What is it?' he cries now.

'I don't know. I don't know. Oh, I feel so humble! And I just can't bear to think of all the other women!'

'Other women! What other women?'

'Why, all the other women in the world! Their poverty,

while I'm so rich! The other women who don't love you, don't even know you – from birth to death *never* know – and have to make do with other men: other men like Middleton Murry. It frightens me.'

He is astonished; bewildered. He says, 'I expect they know . . . other things.'

But not at once am I comforted. 'That's just it. That's what's so horrible. They search the world . . . and never find you. Oh, I could drown in tears for them – I'm so happy!'

He laughs now uproariously, pulls me to him by my hair, pushes me away, holds me at arm's length. 'You . . . invented me!'

I wriggle free and am out of the door. I fling back over my shoulder: 'Well, if that's so . . . D'you know something about inventions? There are no such things. I mean, they're always *there*. It's only that nobody's noticed . . .'

But we are rattling down the stairs.

Re-entering Gordon Square, at his corner we stop. I say: 'About Miss Leverett. Shall I tell you something about Miss Leverett?'

'Yes?'

'She's not true.'

'Not *true*!'

'Not one word of her. *Nor* Basil. It's none of it true.'

'You mean . . .? But I can *see* her!'

'I know. So can I. She wears that dreary crumpled water-proof.'

'Yes.'

'Too long for her. And that faded felt hat.'

'Yes.'

'She's got that habit of walking with her hands in her pockets – I've always thought it so odd; she's awfully well-born – and staring at the ground.'

'Yes.'

'There's not a Leverett left now, you know. I mean, she and Basil are the last of them. She'll be happier in India.'

'Much.'

'I don't suppose she'll ever come back, do you think? Though of course she'll always mean to.'

He gives a quick nod of agreement. 'She'll stay,' he says with finality.

'And I – I shall take great care of her baggage . . . Forever!'

'We shall *both* take great care of her baggage!'

And he adds: 'Do you think she would mind very much if you were to take care, also, of my mother's little desk? It's real: I mean, it's "true". But you'll want somewhere to write, won't you . . . and it struck me it could stand nicely between the front windows.'

[3]

Monkey and All

The war . . . is over.

The deserted village is beginning again to be inhabited.

The Area Warden, companioned by his huge bull-dozing tom-cat, appears no longer with his warning admonishments.

And oddly, now, I wear a hat.

The tramp, never absent – that ancient, bearded and gentle-voiced individualist who should surely rank among Edith's *English Eccentrics* – sits, still grimed but even more resplendent, on his favoured doorsteps. He has, over the noisy, demented and derelict years, shed none of his four embroidered waistcoats, his three surmounting 'toppers', his medals of shining milk-bottle tops.

And again, in South Molton Street – that one-time nineteenth-century Bond Street – miraculously emerged from the rubble, is my friend the organ-grinder, monkey and all.

[4]

Renaissance

It is the winter of the long freeze: and the deadly electricity cut.

In the hour that it has taken Old Hassall[1] to die – recalcitrant, resisting: her buccaneer's voice, her defiant shout ringing in my ears; 'There's nothing the matter with me, m'Darling, except that I'm dying: God damn this dying!' – a new world, an almost forgotten world, has been born: exposed by the long-despaired-of thaw. Many weeks of ice and snow now take upon themselves to turn to lake and river. The great white limitless-seeming landscape of Hyde Park, as we have come to know it, cascades and trills, glitters, slips, slides until lawns, paths, flower-beds are exposed and awash like the decks of a dreadnought. My feet, ill-prepared, ignore their dilemma and wade gaily homeward; my mind, my whole consciousness, launched forth with the intrepid Hassall. Black earth appears. Minute, astonished blades thrust, as with a shout, into the light. Last year's rosebuds hang, ice-preserved, as fresh and sweetly-seeming as those of a season yet to come. Everywhere the past is the present, the present is the future. In a solitary hour, of a whole world a rebirth: Genesis. Time becomes confused.

I shudder – laugh and shudder, shudder and burn, in alternate ice and fire – and in strange elation that has nothing to do with the miracle of seasons – or with Old Hassall – but a great deal to do with double pneumonia.

Less than a week later I am lying, too weak to sit, on the

[1] Painter of Spanish landscapes.

foot- and baggage-crowded floor of the Golden Arrow and bound for Pontresina. I have a battered card in my pocket with an address: Fetan.

With the Engadine, life – years – creep back: with great gulps of ice-air from my attic window, with sudden pools of sunlight on the thirty-foot deep of snow, with the new and crystal-clear certainty of lying once more in arms that hold me precious.

At length I am recovered enough to telephone: at once to hear (for which hearing I would travel again as far, as precariously) the incredulous, joyful, 'Darling! Come!'

In ski clothes and sheepskin too heavy almost in my weakness to bear, I make my slow and careful way down the icy slopes to the little railway station. There the young porter who had thought, his eyes had told me gravely, I had come to die, greets me with surprised gladness. 'No!' my heart answers gaily, 'To live!'

Fetan.

On the diminutive empty platform I stand alone, uncertain, while the toy train draws away to the Austrian border. Here the moutain rises sheer, it seems, and gleaming to the sky. There is nothing to break the whiteness and the cold: no human spark. I alone can move; but in what direction? The bones of my skull burn white-hot: my mind blurs. Surely I have travelled the world to arrive at this spot: but why, and whither am I bound? Worlds. And lives. And at the end only myself, no other life acknowledging me: this, then, is to die, to be dead.

But, as I stare up the mountain-face, my eyes focus on a speck of movement; a speck that grows; a bird surely; far distant but descending with speed; swooping now with man-sized wings enveloping me, wrapping me about, wordlessly lifting me, placing me with ineffable tenderness among the great skins of a fur-lined celestial taxi, wordlessly draws me close, covers my face with a thousand kisses – with especial tenderness loitering long in the hollows gouged by illness ... until 'Ah,' I think, 'I must be ill indeed, since Heaven itself has taken me in its keeping': and faint away.

With an especial tenderness Katalina half-lifts me on a strong respectful arm across the sleigh-gouged route to the snow-bound Hotel Garden where two chaise-longues stand parallel in the sun. Arthur is cancelling his skiing arrangements and coming towards us, his arms laden with fur covers which he spreads across the light cane couches. Lightly he picks me up and as lightly lays me down again in the soft snow nest. How strong the mountains have made him, I think; forgetting that I have shrunk to a wand. Now he lies beside me, stretched full-length in the depth of fur, turns that bronzed face towards me ... and, glancing up, I see on Katalina's comely peasant features yet another tenderness that has nothing to do with me: and love her for it.

At the end of my return journey the young porter leaps forward, incredulous, to receive me, to help me alight. What, I wonder, does he know? For, *'Alles ist gut?'* he questions urgently.

'Alles ist sehr gut,' I reply.

If his face is a mirror held to mine, I think, then I am radiant indeed. But at his next words it is I who am amazed.

'Where angels go,' he says softly, 'heaven is sure to follow.'

'Where,' I demand, amazed, 'did you learn your English?'

'Where, Miss?' he laughs. 'Why ... in Tunbridge Wells!'

Is it chance, I muse, as I ascend the hill, that he names, of all England, Arthur's birthplace?

A month later we are seated in the enfolding dark of a concert audience. But even a programme of mediaeval French music cannot tether our quivering senses – I, mad with gladness to be alive and breathing, crushed against the wall of the Wigmore Hall; conscious only of a hand that slides quickly to where my own hangs to receive it, of fingers intertwined in silent eloquence, of a head that leans sideways until it touches my own and, breathed against my ear, the single word – 'Fetan'.

Sun glints on icy peaks and, far below, the little Schloss Tarasp floats on a cloud. Sudden tears spring from my eyes and splash on to the programme in my lap: tears, a little of nostalgia; but tears, also, of sheer weakness – and sheer joy.

But, in the darkness, Arthur – with raised eyebrows and a quick sideways grin – whispers in mock admonishment: 'Now, now! I can't take you out if you're going to be a cry-baby!'

[5]

Careless Rapture

Now, under my feet is again London – a London exhausted, quiescent as an invalid – as are the many other cities – in its strew of rubble.

John and I have moved from 20 Brook Street to 88 Sloane Street.[1] The tall house is a shell: cracked, shored up, open to any and every weather, it is yet a home: a sanctuary of space in which to live – not quite as ever before.

And such a spring as this is must somewhere be recorded – perhaps with that other millennium of 1929 – as among the springs of all time. Christmas snows are no sooner done with than impatient leaves burst with a shout from the bare boughs and, from the brown earth, impatient flowers spring overnight.

Alone in the empty house, on the ramparts beneath the eaves, the low coping broken with Blitz, I watch for Arthur's approaches – his phantasy sight espying me from afar off. He is running, running in the crowded street below, his rucksack bobbing loose on his shoulders, to reach the door before I wrench it open and we stand breathless in one another's arms for all the world to see.

Yes: it is *our* spring again. After twenty years another for us.

And ... all the world sees.

Climbing the broken stairway to the top, stepping at last carefully on the gaping floor-boards of my room, seated at

[1] I kept Handel Street as my secret Bloomsbury address until after Arthur's death.

last on the same narrow Yugao-couch of long ago which is
yet the room's only furniture, he lowers his rucksack in which
he has stuffed – as might a boy at school – pyjamas, tooth-
brush and the first clumsily-folded but enthralling galleys of
Li-Po, stretches with urgent arms to draw me down between
his knees and says: 'I want to show you Venice.'

'Venice! You mean we'll go there?'

'I shall take you there.'

'Oh! Oh! While the men are mending the house? It's a good
time. I *could* get away. They know exactly what to do. But
. . . at *last* with you! You know why I've never been – through
all the years, dodged it – don't you? Because I've not wanted
to see it at all unless it could be through your eyes – with you.
When do we go? Now? Oh, now this minute?'

I babble on. His smile, lit with love, pauses.

'Well, perhaps not *just* now. But soon.'

'We shouldn't wait till it gets madly hot, should we? Tell
me when we go in time for me to fix things. I made sixty
pounds yesterday in a single hour, photographing a White
Russian princess. Better than the four-and-eightpence I
made selling matches at Liverpool Street Station to know
what it felt like to be poor. I'll start saving from this
minute!'

Well, but why not? Much of the business of life has been
dealt with. I no longer live with Hugh. John is in his last year
at Marlborough and thinking of the Sorbonne. Surely we are,
both, now, free as air!

Ten days later we are seated behind the same high roof-
coping. Below in Cadogan Square the fine net of the trees is
blurred with tenderest green. I point – and then to the
clear-climbing blue of the sky.

'Look!' I cry. 'The leaves are positively jostling. We'll have
to hurry. I never knew such urgency! This spring is out to
challenge – to race us! But I'm ready when you are, darling.
And I've bought some clothes in the Kings Road. I long to
show you. A suit of that fine creamy stuff that huntsmen's
trousers are made of. The jacket is tight-fitting as a bull-

fighter's. Over a moss-green chiffon blouse. Over just me. The skirt – Oh, but the skirt is wonderful! Spanish dancer length. And laid flat on the floor it is a single disc with a hole in the middle. I pirouetted in it so that it swung out at shoulder level. The shop girls were delighted. Then I flung it up into the air like a toreador's cloak, dived under and came up with it on and hanging perfectly. I've paid for these. And other things. But I brought away only the chiffon blouse. The others I said I would come back for only on the eve of our departure. They think I'm crazy, of course. But no – not crazy. Just – in love. Are you, too, crazy?'

'Crazy.'

'And in love? Oh Honey, Hun, not – *still* – in love?'

He says quietly: 'I don't change.'

While spring, hilarious, rampages on in heavenly uncontrol, the gang of post-war Irish – as uncontrolled but thinly disguised as 'builders', which a war-torn London has imported to mend the holes in its tattered houses – sets about replacing the floor-boards of my upper room. All else continues to offer exercise in expertise for a cat-burglar – the stairs negotiable only to experienced mountaineers. From the heights of these can be viewed far below the deep subterranean pool of the kitchen premises. On its dark shining surface floats in ghostly fashion the white form of an un-moored bath. Cats sit motionless on narrow beams. There are no rats.

The house – 'Prohibited' as it is and served with a 'Danger Notice' – presents a strong fascination for Arthur, and that I choose to lodge in secret and alone under its broken eaves delights him. So, through the spring nights carrying our glimmering candle-ends to this corner and that, spreading soft luxurious furs on the bare boards for cover, we take pleasure in views which are of the time only; to be walled and closed from us even on the morrow. Only behind the two-foot roof-coping can we be sure of permanency: and from its giddy height, nested on cushions, hour upon hour we look down – unseen, unsuspected – on the movement of Sloane Street as watchers from another planet might view an alien life. I think

'If there were chimney-pots it would be *The Stranger on the Stair*[1] – and know he is thinking the same.

But now again I speak of the future – and of Venice.

'Darling . . . we ought to go soon. If we leave it much longer, you see, John will be home for the holidays.'

No answer comes, and I lean a little to see the shadowed face so close to my own. Even in the muted starlight – for the street lights are far below – I think I see that it looks sad and am puzzled.

Then, before I am aware, I am saying a thing I am to remember: 'Sweetheart . . . Don't let's wait till we're old. That would be unfair to Venice as well as to ourselves. Don't let's wait until . . . until . . . all we have strength for is to spread our hands on a counterpane . . .'

But never did I tease him for answers.

And now, at my words, even in the darkness the sadness on the loved face deepens, deepens, so that I cry out: 'Oh forgive me – forgive me, Pitten! It's *nothing, nothing* – it doesn't *matter*! What has Venice that is better – or more – than our Here and Now?'

It is to be fifteen years before we are in Venice. A half-masochistic, fate-defying, self-promise-kept Venice. A Venice . . . too sad for tears.

I am never to go back for my clothes. But I am to see Venice. And through his eyes.

[1] A novel by Chapman Mortimer (Rupert Hart-Davis, 1950).

[63]

[6]

Sesame Opens. And Shuts

'Will you come to meet Edith?'

'But I have met her! No, no – I don't mean that. But at least, I've seen her long ago. Where do we meet?'

'A tea-party at the Sesame Club. Rather a big one. I'll call for you; tomorrow at four.'

Edith is enthroned on a dais to the right as we enter the Sesame's long drawing-room. It is abuzz with guests, and Arthur leads me quickly past her to a large, round window-table, wedges me in with my back to the light, and departs. Quickly the chairs on either side fill with ladies who are strangers to me. They converse with the ill-suppressed social excitement of overseas visitors who, by some miracle of a benign fate, find themselves dropped into a holy of holies. I am amused. And a little bit charmed. Americans. Children at a party. And, on my right, a woman I immediately like for her frankness, for her fresh elegance, her total lack of English ennui – and the defiant gaiety of her wide, white picture hat. 'Pure Henry James,' I think.

Suddenly she lays down her beautiful French gloves on the table and presses a strong, yet delicate, hand on mine. She whispers: 'Oh my dear, I *am* so excited: If my daughter could only *see* me here! She just won't *believe* me when I tell her I've taken tea with Edith Sitwell!'

The table is emptied. And Arthur has not returned. I begin to feel a little like a piece of deposited luggage. Perhaps he has lost the ticket. I extricate myself from the chairs and make my way to where a group of young people, men as well as women, are seated with refreshing informality in a circle on the floor. Instantly they make room for me and I sink down among them – delighted with their ease and consoling friendliness.

Soon I'm telling them much: of my three-month wartime voyage; of the small, condemned merchant ship with its eight passengers, its mutinous crew, and its cargo of cheese; of submarines in the Pacific, of splitting liberty ships, of the breaking-up of our Atlantic convoy, of the coasts of Iceland – and of the ultimate miracle-green of England's grass.

They are delighted.

'But who *are* you?' they cry. 'Why haven't we *met* you? Why don't we know you? We all live in Chelsea – where do you live?'

'In Sloane Street. No. 88.'

'Round the corner! Why, you *must* come to see us – You *must* come!'

But quickly a hand is on my shoulder ... and Arthur is saying: 'Edith would like to meet you.'

Edith is still enthroned, surrounded by henchmen and going through the somewhat theatrical ceremony of speeding her party guests. She beckons me up to the chair on her left, and Arthur to the one on her right: We, also, are to be henchmen. Now the guests file slowly past to touch the beautiful, heavily-jewelled, extended hand and move to the door. My little American woman approaches. Frank amazement in her eyes to see me seated so, among the mighty, she makes her awed adieu. She is the last to go and Edith relaxes among her intimates.

'Oh my dears!' she cries after the receding figure with its gay, courageous hat, 'The cartwheel, the cartwheel! Oh, but *what* a bore – what a *deadly* bore these people are!'

But my eyes are following the cultural pilgrim. Do I imagine that unadulterated pleasure which I had found so charming is a little quenched; or that the white flower on the wide white hat now nods with something less than assurance?

And Edith is turning to me: 'Arthur tells me you write

poems; *and* draw portraits! Have you any you could show me?'

'Yes. I've one at the moment of Violet Vanbrugh[1] that I made for the *Sydney Morning Herald* – and, why yes, always plenty of poems.'

'Then you must bring them to me here. If I like your portrait, I may let you draw me. In any case you must have my new book. I'll send it to you; Arthur will give me your address ... Yes, I'll be in town again on Wednesday of next week; could you lunch with me on that day? Alone? I'll let you know ...'

I bring the poems – and the portrait – as promised, to the Sesame Club. 'Miss Sitwell has guests.' But I wait while the porter delivers my package into her hand.

I do not see its contents again. Nor hear from her. That day. Or any day.

It is nearly fifteen years later that I fall into the habit of driving Arthur, from our house at Highgate to Saturday tea with Edith; now established in the large block of mansion flats at Hampstead. Bedside parties now; but gay with her friends and her cats. I drop him at the door, returning for him an hour later. He tells me of these visits in detail; and I know they are important to him.

Quite suddenly, and for no apparent reason, they cease. I hear rumours that Edith has moved, with her secretary, to an adjacent cottage. But no note, now, drops through the letterbox; no summons to her bedside. And Arthur says no word.

One day I enter our high room, a newspaper drooping in my hand. Arthur is seated, working at his desk between the windows. I pause. 'Darling ...' I say, 'Edith ...'

His back is to me, but he turns quickly, his face aglow with pleasure, '... has asked me to tea?' he cries.

'Is ... dead.'

It is as though a light had gone out.

[1] The actress.

[7]

'No Buggers – No Party'

The summer of that year was hot and wonderful and apart from our morning coffee our meals were taken in the grassy, tree-shaded spaces of the Cadogan Gardens opposite our windows. There seemed no longer reason why we should not have a party.

John at school, Arthur used his small attic room as a study: and now was seated at the improvised desk – a huge drawing-board supported at either end by fragile open 'pigeon-holes' filched from a wrecked aircraft. For an hour he had worked silently and busily, the window light falling athwart his intent countenance, his pen moving rapidly down the margins of the galley proofs which lay across his knees and strewed the floor. I flung myself flat on the goat-skin rug and proceeded with my guest list. Presently I came to a ruminative pause and Arthur, intuitive always and no doubt hearing the silence of my pen, said without lifting his head;

'What is troubling you?'

'It's the men. I've managed the women, I think. But I can't get the men sexually balanced.'

'Sexually balanced.' He repeated the phrase with an undertone of interest while I rose, but only to my knees, to come to his side.

'Yes,' I said, 'You see how it is.' – and I held up the block-pad on which I had written: 'PARTY GUESTS. MEN.' Below that, heading two columns: 'NORM.' 'QUEER.' Under the first were three names, the last followed by a question mark. Those of the second extended the length of the page and, in smaller and smaller script, proceeded along its margin.

Arthur scrutinised this for but the fraction of an instant with his microscopic eye. Then he made his comment – terse as always and to the point: 'No buggers – no party.' . . . and dropped again to the business of inscribing rapid and jagged marginal marks on the galleys of *Li-Po*.

[8]

The Party

No. 88 Sloane Street is a blaze of light – from the nursery kitchen at the top to the large Dutch one at the bottom, still half-blasted by the Blitz, ceiling looped with temporary flexes from which innumerable bulbs droop and swing like lanterns at a fair.

It is our house-warming. And Arthur, arriving early, and begging the job of doorkeeper, is soon bounding up and down the broken stair like a chamois.

Though the tall French windows are open to the balconies and the spring night, at both ends of the long wall of the L-shaped drawing-room fires are aglow ... the walls are close-hung with the originals of Gettli's[1] illustrations of *Monkey* ... and soon the warm murmur of guests is rising to hubbub. Arthur is ensconced at last, knees drawn up in under-graduate attitude on one of the divans; young faces leaning, eager and lit, to catch the concise and rapid fire of his words. Glancing again with delight to see it so, I think how cold and creaking a word is 'animated' to say the visible beauty of the human come-and-go of like spirits: as variant as Canetti and Rose Barrington; as universally linked as scholarship and youth. Everywhere, it seems, there is a bewildering felicity. Clement[2] has brought her eldest daughter, Natalie. The child stands alone, looking on with grave preoccupation at the adult antics and manoeuvres of an assembled company – tall, motionless,

---

[1] Dr Georgette Boner, Swiss writer, artist and producer.
[2] Head of the Paint Room at Covent Garden; wife of Sir William Bloch, musician. Natalie, her daughter by her former husband, John Davenport, the reviewer.

lovely; aloof as youth is, always, at the brink of such a world.
A voice somewhere is saying 'Are you Naomi?'[1] another
replies 'No. I'm Ruth'[2] . . . and a splutter of laughter ripples
towards me. Arthur has leapt to his feet and is standing close
to the marble of a mantelpiece. Level with his eyes is a gourd
from which flash out the pink nose and the twitching white
whiskers of John's pet mouse . . . and his voice carries the
high excitement of a child as he calls to me, incredulous, *'Is
this a traditional mouse's house!'*

Now the party has spilled over with rugs and cushions on to
the lawns of the square: Canneti must leave early and Clem
must return to her children.

'Let's share their taxi and vanish with them up to Hampstead for an hour or so, Pitten! The party's running itself . . .
and you and Canetti can be locked in an intellectual clinch
all the way!'

At Well Walk, Clare and Oriel are awake in flannel
dressing-gowns and whooping with joy as we, all seven, close
round the huge kitchen table with its mugs of steaming cocoa.
Each fact and incident of the party must be related hilariously, while Arthur and Canetti cling at the table's edge as
to the rim of a crevasse in the promised intellectual combat
and never look up.

But, it seems now, it is Clement's birthday; and, suddenly,
loud above the babel of voices, she is announcing in theatre-
filling tones: 'God has given me the great gift of youth!'

This irrelevance has all the authentic declamatory ring of
her grandfather, Sir Johnston Forbes-Robertson:[3] and the
two scholars, deep in eye-to-eye argument, glance up startled
as though a bomb had been dropped: then instantly resume.

The children, crowded round the table, shriek hysterically
. . . and suddenly I am alarmed to observe a strangeness
descending on Clem. She stands at her full height; magnificent; her gold cropped boyish head flung up above the green

[1] Naomi Lewis, writer and reviewer.
[2] Ruth Tenney, American poet-reviewer.
[3] The actor.

velvet of her 'bandsman's' tunic: 'Will *no-one* listen to *me?*'
she cries now in savagely strident tones, *'Me! Me! Me!'*

This goes, surely, a disturbing step or two beyond a mere
plea for attention. But yes, I think, we *are* in her house – and
the two guests that matter to her are in a huddle of isolation:
as securely shut away as under lock and key from such matters of high moment. It is a state of things to be broken up:
and on the instant.

I am seated at the far end of the table, where is a drawer of
its width and with handles; and this I am inspired to pull out.
It is full to brimming of a scatter of silver, a good square yard
of flung knives, forks, spoons, into which I now dive my two
hands and rattle with such a din as to bring all to amazed
silence. Then I leap to my feet.

'Goodnight, dear Clem, and many happy, happy days!' I
cry, snatching Arthur by the hand, 'Come. It's back to Sloane
Street for us. We're hosts, and missing. We'll go by Tube; it's
quicker than looking for a taxi.'

Standing close and swaying in the tight-packed compartment, inches only dividing face and face, observing ever anew
the sensitive beauty of the mouth so close to my own, I think
with gratitude how nature has fashioned us in stature of such
happy similarity – and raise my eyes to his. They are waiting
for mine and shining in a way that makes me drop my gaze
and I think; 'The Tube's no place for lovers.'

But, 'El Greco ...' he murmurs with seeming irrelevance,
'Pure El Greco.'

As we bound up the stairs we are aware that the party,
though missing us not at all, has considerably dwindled.

But ... entering the drawing-room together we are confronted by three strangers. Seated stiffly as spinsters on the
Sheraton between the tall windows – the central figure teed-
up, as it were, by two dubious-looking henchmen – glum-
faced and unfestive – they are being served a special brew of
'institution' tea on individual salvers.

'Good God ...' murmurs Arthur, riveted; all joy undone.

'Gate-crashers?' say I.

[71]

'Gang,' he mutters. 'It's *Gang*.[1] With Ackerley-Joe,'[2] and I see that, for him, the party is indeed over.

[1] A group of homosexual friends who kept one another informed of what was going on socially.
[2] J.D. Ackerley, editor of the *Listener*.

[9]

Kurt

'Will you take Kurt Joos[1] to be your lodger in your Sloane Street house?'

'A lodger! Well! The back of the house has fallen into the garden and it has to be shored up – the danger notice has been served – there's not a safe square yard to lodge a pigeon!'

'His family would stay in Cambridge: but he badly needs a place in London.'

'But – he's Kurt Joos. Choreographer. Ballet master. Famous. And he could fall through; from top to bottom! Why, even the stairs have yawning gaps so that you have to cling on to posts and rails like a Gibbon ape. You *know* that! No, no – he'd have to be a cat burglar.'

'He *is* very careful on his feet,' murmured Arthur.

I laughed.

'Oh, very well then. I suppose he can have what space he can find for himself on the first floor and the second. The thirty-foot drawing-room is still seven-eighths there and would certainly be perfect to rehearse in.'

'Darling – I've seen Beryl.'[2]

'You *have?*'

'Yes. In the audience at the Shivaram recital. She was pointed out to me.'

'And what did you think of her?'

I pause a moment. But Kurt had said and repeated:

[1] German-born dancer and choreographer.
[2] 'The lady in Fez', who had recently returned (alerted by Kurt Joos) from a year in India.

'Arthur and Beryl share the same flat but they go quite different ways. They have quite different friends. They live their own separate lives, she and Arthur.' So now I answered cheerfully enough: 'Well actually it was in the dark – from the back – and in silhouette. Pitten, she seemed to have red hair, has she? Two tight wire curls – like a rabbi – on either side? I thought she looked rather ... snakey.'

He laughed. But said, swinging away from the subject: 'How is Kurt? Is he settling in?'

'Oh yes. He's borrowed a piano and put up a practice-bar in the thirty-foot drawing-room – which the Cadogan Estate is incensed about, and baffled: they're convinced it's for 'hanging wet towels'! But, tell me, why is Kurt – well not quite *all* the time but nearly – almost dead with sadness?'

We were seated on the grass at the base of the Achilles statue. The Serpentine gleamed through the trees.

'Shall we walk?' he said, and rose to his feet.

Now Kurt had taken me to the Steiner Hall. I leaned forward to look along our row.

'Kurt ... there's the strangest creature, some way along on the left: a sort of effigy of Pocahontas. The thin-beaked profile of a bird of prey: an eagle perhaps. Jet black Egyptian straight-cut fringe and hair. But, Kurt ... this is so odd ... feathers, no, I mean fine down, on the cheeks. Lean very discreetly.'

I sat back so that he might do this. But almost at once he had jerked upright into position; and was collecting his things.

'Do you mind if we change our seats?'

'*Change our seats!* Kurt, the lights are going down. Why must we? Why?'

'It's Beryl de Zoete. I don't wish her to see me.'

'What is? Who is? Not the Pocahontas Bird Woman? It can't be. She's not *like* that. I've seen her. She had red wire curls like a rabbi. That's *not* Beryl de Zoete.'

But Kurt had risen to his great height and was gone. I

followed. He stood at the back of the hall in the dark. I whispered: 'Kurt, what *is* the matter: are you ill? You know her well: you have known her well for years – yet truly, that is *not* Beryl de Zoete.'

'There are *many* Beryl de Zoetes,' he, in his turn, whispered ... as the curtain rose on *Les Sylphides*.

[10]

'Everything Quite All Right'

The airlift is on.

I decide to go into Berlin on a York bomber. Arthur is amazed. And ... can it be ... a little envious? There is also, he warns me, the danger. 'But why, *why* must you go?' he asks.

'I don't *have* to go,' I laugh, 'I just want to. To see if the headlines are true or false. All that flak and shooting up business ...'

On the day before I leave he is waiting, as always now at the foot of Achilles' statue. We run towards one another; then wander off into the 'open country' of the park. Soon we are at the Serpentine and sit at some distance on our tier of green to feast our eyes on the grey silk of the water.

Presently he says, 'Beryl wishes me to ask you if you will take some letters to her friends in Berlin. Will you?'

I had never met Beryl. I had hardly seen her. I did not know, or greatly care, about her place in his life. Our happiness together left no space for curiosity. Now I answer lightly, 'Oh, no. I think she'd better post them in the ordinary way. You see, I'm flying blind: I've no plans: the whole thing will be – is – quite *verboten*. I don't know even if I'll get there. Besides,' I add, 'it might be dangerous.'

He flashes a swift sideways glance at me: 'Quite right,' he says, 'I'm glad you refuse.'

'That sounds a bit rude,' I laugh. 'Do tell Beryl I'm sorry I can't: but that I think it better ...'

'Of course.'

The park is a dream of loveliness.

When we part he says, 'You'll telephone me before you go in the morning, won't you. What time do you leave?'

'Liverpool Street, 11.20. I'm not taking much more than my camera – and I expect that will be stolen at the border. I'll be in a tremendous rush, my darling; but yes, I'll ring you.'

I dial and wait.

Arthur's voice: 'Hullo ...' high, strange and somehow stringent.

I pause. 'Did you think ...'

Then a woman's voice. Beryl's? 'Damn her! Damn her! Damn, damn, damn!'

An uproar of sounds, of savagery. Then Arthur's voice again, shouting above it, shouting ... 'I *didn't* think! I DON'T think! I DON'T think of you. I don't think of YOU!'

Silently – fastidiously – as one closing a door, as one tip-toeing away from a scene of obscenity – I hang up the receiver. I sink down on the stair. The effect is that of a swinging blow. Thought refuses to flow. I can understand nothing. I feel sick. I feel ice-cold. Yet some part of my mind tells me I am alone in an empty house; I must not faint. I slide down to the landing and lie there on my face, very still.

But I must have lain a long time – perhaps an hour – for when I turn on my side and look at my watch I see that it is time to go. Time to leave the house. To leave England. Arthur. Love. Perhaps life. I feel nothing.

Slowly and carefully I mount the stair. I hold my wrists in hot water. I fling some over my face. I pick up my camera, my shoulder satchel, my keys.

Outside from the steps of the house I put up a hand to a taxi on the Pont Street rank: at once it answers my signal and rounds the corner.

As it pulls up at the kerb, a Post Office special messenger approaches. He asks my name and hands me a telegram. I tear it open. It reads: EVERYTHING QUITE ALL RIGHT.

My heart doesn't lift. I *have* no heart. I stuff the message, crumpled, into my pocket.

And there – were it possible to find a coat after so many years – it may well still be.

[11]

A Pain called Failure

When pain is done with; or grief; or joy – when these extremes
have been suffered – it is not wise to turn again; to burrow
the dark and desperate warren, to climb again the crucifix, or
to soar beyond the eagle-heights to the sun's self. For there
are human limits; beyond which it is unwise, willingly, to
trespass. When poets juggle words of dazzling splendour one
knows it is, for them, already over – backward-glance, a
memory-daring they can ill afford: that they speak a state of
being where is no articulation. For at the core of dark is the
impenetrable dark: at the core of colour is no colour but the
white light that strips of sight: at the core of clamour is
silence. And these three are not for human encounter. At
these approaches it is wise to let that sixth most merciful and
saving sense take over: turn and reel an exhausted way back
to the things we can, in safety, know.

Of that time . . . what, then, did I know?

'Beryl wishes me to go with her to Rome' – and so, without
address, Arthur goes.

Kurt returning, triumphant and again with heart, from his
Chilean venture, concentrates with desperate hope to collect
and assemble the fallen sticks of his life. I write of him in
Ballet Today. Working daily at the studio, all goes with the
felicity and ease that is inevitably success.

John comes home on vacation and together we move in
cloudless days.

Nothing is difficult. Nothing is tedious. And I become

aware that I walk in puzzling bliss, a rightness of being, that sets me, even visibly, apart.

Only one face is clouded, darkened. And this, as the weeks pass, I grow to fear. A strange fear, a fear that pursues like a deepening shadow.

For suddenly, as a woman does, I know the reason for my heart's elation: am beset no longer with doubts and questions but with joys and terrors. What is now to happen – what is life's instruction – what, now, is demanded? Can I bear anger? Or the worse agony of distrust ... never to be dispelled? Or – must there be parting ... this time, forever? And what of John? Are we two once more to vanish? For from John I can never part.

The future lifts and gathers, gathers and lifts, like a mighty wave above me: its curled crest gleams in the sun – but, it is about to fall.

I long for Arthur's return. No word comes.

A telegram at my door: with only a date, an hour, a flight number.

And Arthur is pushing through the crowding passengers, arms outstretched: 'Ah ... How *wonderful* it is to be met!'

In our taxi's shrouding gloom I crouch in the enfolding arms, mad with joy and fear; and fear; and joy. I cannot speak.

But Arthur's hands are twined in mine: he says in tones of immeasurable gentleness: 'Your fingers are very eloquent. What is it they would wish to say?'

I hear my voice make what must have been indeed a strange utterance: 'I am afraid. I am afraid of Dee. I think she is insane. Mad.'

'Insane! Mad! My Darling ... *I* am back. *I* am with you now.'

I crouch deeper. 'Why,' I murmur, 'did you come?'

'On ... because I hated Beryl's friends ... because I wanted to be with you ... because ... *I could not stay.*'

Is, my heart wonders, is – after all – everything going to be 'quite all right'? For never was one fact more sure; his love is at last of the stuff love is made of; profound; and forever.

I think: so. He came ... because he *knew* my need of him. How wonderful a thing is life.

I lift my face to his kisses. But am silent.

I am at the telephone. It is Dee – demanding, in her high dictatorial tones. I say: 'But ... however urgent it is, the ladder to the attic is vertical: How *can* I get the box down through the trap door?'

There is silence. I say at last, 'I *beg* you do not ask me to do this thing. Send someone. Send someone. It is not just a matter of strength – of lifting and carrying ... or any of the difficulties. It is something more and different. I cannot. I dare not.'

Again there is that silence; and this time it chills my heart. The words that at length are spoken are quiet and measured: 'I see. Well – but you will *have* to, won't you.'

The receiver has clicked silent: and, already, the doorbell from four flights down is ringing madly. I climb the ladder and thrust back the ceiling door. I drag the box to the opening's lip, descend a few rungs, and stretch my arms up to receive it. I pray for strength. But more than strength. More ... than strength.

It is evening; and Dee stands at the foot of my bed.

She says in tones that fall like chips of glass, 'What is the matter with you?'

'I ... am ill.'

Again the measured tones: 'I see.'

There are silences more loaded, more horrible, than any weight of words.

And there are times when fear takes on an especial quality; becomes primitive; is foreboding. I hear myself cry out, struggling to extenuate: 'Oh, but how *could* you *know* what was at stake ... all in two lives ... three!'

The face, as at the door it turns, is round, flat, and hard as a pebble. The voice comes, dredged from some primaeval deep: clipped, and sharpened to incise. 'But of *course* I knew. Of *course* I knew that you were bearing Arthur Waley's child.'

The door shuts.

And in my body I feel life stir . . . and die.

It is late evening now, and Arthur has come, and he holds me close. His smile is bent above me, serene, radiant. 'Why, then . . . we must just set about bringing it up.'

Bewildered, I cry, rocking back and forth in his arms: 'Oh, oh . . . but you don't understand. I have lost it – lost it. In this thing of all things I have failed you. *You* can forgive me because you most wonderfully love me . . . but perhaps life . . . life will not forgive; either of us. Don't you see, we weren't . . . to be trusted?'

I draw away from him, crush my face into the pillow, staring behind closed lids at something I sense rather than know – for it is, as yet, in the future – and torn with present pain; the pain called failure.

I feel Arthur's arms go strongly round me. Lifting me close he holds me still. In silence, his lips descending from time to time to touch my head, with an infinity of compassion, a heaven of tenderness, he holds me . . . till I sleep.

I open my eyes to the click of the door. Arthur is gone. I close them again, imploring sleep, imploring release from consciousness. But again the door clicks: and John stands there, tall and motionless. His eyes are glittering, large with sorrow; tears fall slowly one by one down his darling face. He says in a voice scarcely lifted to reach me: 'Don't you know . . . don't you understand . . . that I too am brokenhearted?' and is gone again from the room.

Poetry Ho!

One day he came: picked his way carefully over the gaps in the blitzed stairway and, pausing, at the top, announced quietly: 'I have asked my friend, Herbert Read, to arrange a poetry recital for you and me.'

'I don't understand,' I answered, 'I don't think I want to hear Herbert Read read his poetry.'

'No,' he answered now with an especial gentleness. 'It is we – you and I – who are going to read *my* poetry.'

I looked at him, unbelieving. Never had he done this. Never before. Never had any person been able to persuade him to do this thing. 'You . . . will read your own?'

He nodded. 'And you. If you will consent to help me. I think it's rather dull for an audience to have only one reader, don't you?'

I could not speak. I knew of course why he was doing this thing. I knew too that he, for me, was overcoming, was breaking, his set rule; that it was far from easy. And – as it proved later – far from wise.

'Herbert Read is arranging it through the ICA but, since it must be soon, they are having difficulty in finding a hall: it seems now that it will be in Cowdray Hall.'

We spent a happy afternoon or two selecting what we would like to read and timing one another's reading. We thought it a good idea to break up the spoken word with music.

'Shall I ask Kyla Greenbaum to play the piano again? She did at my Manchester recital, you remember, and all was a great success. She plays with such splendid authority: wonderfully: strong: like a man.'

He smiled. 'I think that an excellent idea. I shall leave that to you.'

'Tell me, Darling . . . Is Beryl happy at the idea of your recital?'

A shadow fell across his face. 'She naturally feels some . . . *unlust*,' he said, low.

'You mean . . . she doesn't *want* it?'

'She doesn't want it.' He repeated my words flatly.

'Then . . .?'

'No. It is going to happen. And she must get used to the idea.' I could see his mind was quite made up.

For an instant, however, my heart had sunk very low – and, even with the so-wonderful prospect – it took all his gentle charm to lift its wings.

'Will she come?'

'No.'

'Have you asked Edith?'

'No. I think it better not.'

'But wouldn't *she* be glad about it? You've always gone to hers. Wouldn't Osbert? Wouldn't Sachie?'

'I think it better that they should not be invited.'

'To whom, then, shall we read?'

'Oh I expect there will be one or two who will drift in, you know . . .'

Whatever lay behind this talk, I knew it could quench neither my interest nor my ability in the task ahead. Poetry for me wove its own spell to secure me against all 'unlusts' – all criticisms – even against joylessness: I was set apart; in safety; as secure – in this way – as he.

Who was in that audience, I wonder now? That all was success is certain. Yet, if any recalls that unique recital at this long distance of time, he will recall the facts that enjoyment of the poetry, as from both readers, was made manifest in no uncertain terms of applause and murmured appreciation; that Dr Waley descended to receive those who afterwards crowded forward to express this; but that, strangely, any who made approach to the other reader were dexterously diverted; none was introduced. She stood alone and at a loss, uncertainly returning those friendly and congratulatory smiles of Arthur's friends that succeeded in reaching her over his obscuring shoulders.

At last, however, I managed to whisper, 'Kyla has had to go early . . . but I have prepared a wonderful small supper for us at home.'

Arthur did not turn his head. He said, with raised voice and coldly impersonal: 'I shall be going to Hampstead with Clement Bloch.'

I made my way home, climbed the long stair, lay watching the movement of Sloane Street's late night traffic trail swiftly in light and shadow across the ceiling of my high room: my heart, puzzled and unhappy, asking continually: 'Darling, what has happened . . . what . . . has happened? Why . . . did you have to do that?'

Two questions which – though ever unput – were, over the years, to become 'familiars' in my mind: the answers – to this day – elusive, obscure, uncertain.

[13]

The Forest

Once, returning from the sea, he directed me off the road to a large house standing on its slope of lawns that face the western sky, its garden hedged about with forest, and pointed to a central window immediately above the elaborate entrance.

'That was my room,' he said.

I looked in astonishment: this front of the house had all the disadvantages of cold, dark viewlessness. 'But it is not a room,' I exclaimed, 'It is a cell.'

'I always had the smallest room!' he said.

Would it be for preference, I wondered? For safety? For security? The feeling of being held close. But, no. No-one likes to be cramped up unnecessarily: and here was one who needed space for books: who, moreover, took a quite unusual pleasure in beauty and light: whose very need was air. No – it would be a diffidence, I thought – a diffidence that was to turn to masochism. That, with the inordinate love the mother had for this 'second' child who followed so swiftly on the death of the true second that made her, from very guilt, give him, her darling, always the least. How complex his inheritance indeed. I looked at him.

'Were you a monk?' I asked, smiling.

'Perhaps,' he answered with seriousness. 'I did not mix easily with my brothers' friends.'

'So that you were always missing, or with excuses, or sliding off by yourself . . . being "unsatisfactory".'

'Yes.'

'I know it. Escaping. Being "strange", "ungrateful",

"odd" – with me they called it "dour" ... escaping to the freedom of one's own world, a world of wonder, and passion. The passionate monk.'

He looked at me quickly from under a flutter of lids, then down. 'How do you know it?' he asked.

'Because I've been it too – so far as a small girl can – a "middle" child, a second who was really a third: pushed back unduly because of a parent's love, and guilt of that love.' I added, 'And as for how I know it of you, it all came into the dream.'

'The dream?' he asked, as we turned away, making for the main road where the car had been abandoned, crushed against the bracken. 'Have I heard it? Have you told me?'

'No. Not this one.'

'Why not?'

'Because it disturbs me strangely. Even now. I don't think I want to tell it.'

We came on a patch of turf enamelled gold by the late afternoon sun and urgently he pulled me down beside him.

'Tell it.'

'I was your sister. That was strange. Your sister. Older than you. About fourteen perhaps; fifteen. You were about eight. We loved each other. Too much. In the dream we'd wandered for hours – all day, it seemed – as we loved beyond all else to do, in the forest. Together: and alone. Which both knew for perfection. We'd peopled the forest with every imagined thing. Your energy was extraordinary. I felt mine ebb – but still you danced and darted at fantastic foes, tilted with troupe upon troupe of unseen creatures. I sank down to rest, on the edge of a clearing. Like this one – but that it was shut in by trees and blackest shadow. Here the light fell slanting. It was getting late and we had far to go. I called to you, "No more. No more, my darling. Come. Rest awhile. No more jousting with enemies. No more make-believe."

'You did not pause. And then I became aware that you did not – *could* not – hear me. I leaned up on one elbow and looked at you intently. Your face was flushed as with fever.

Your eyes glittered with a strange excitement, an unnatural light. Furiously you whirled and tilted; furiously you charged and turned again. Alarm beat like a drum in my throat. "Darling ... Darling! Stop! Stop, I beg you!"

'But I could see you were no longer with me – nor in your own control. I did not exist. Fear leapt now. What was it? What had happened? Phantasy had taken over. You were enchanted. Enchanted – and in direst danger. I leapt forward to arrest your mad whirl. You flung me off with fierce, unseeing gaze – and with more than a child's strength. Suddenly I was terrified. I fell back and sank down in the shadows to watch. And all my love, all my heart, all my energy, all my thought – my very blood, it seemed, and every nerve – implored you.

'Your arms dropped. You reeled to me. You sank with your head in my lap. You looked up at me and your beauty made me catch my breath. I thought my heart must break with love. Slowly – almost imperceptibly – you closed your eyes. You lay inert.'

We were silent – and I saw that he was strangely moved. And I saw more. I saw the man – but also I saw the child of eight. Flushed. Wild.

But then, on a long breath, he drew me to him: crushed kisses upon me, murmured 'Love me. Love me *now. Now.*'

We lay a long time.

The sun sank low into the forest.

[14]

The Krakens

On one of those blazing days of summer that happen so rarely one remembers them forever, we went to Seaford – to our 'Stallion Rock' that, when the tide is withdrawn, juts suddenly and magnificently from the sand of finest gold – and put the car as near as was possible to the unfrequented cliffs. Here, at the eastern end of the esplanade, an iron ladder drops vertically to a miniature bay cut deep into the chalky base and wearing as its sole and central ornament this massive, almost bison-shaped stone, hung with its green weed. Though, as I see it now, this might have suggested by far more fitting a name, perhaps because of its armoured look and its strips of flowing drapes that evoked the battle-charger of mediaeval days, we had long since named it The Stallion.

Few – on any morning – had the temerity to descend the rungs of rusted and broken iron fixed into the face of concrete at this farthest end of the parade. The descent involved an eight-foot drop on to rocks, and once within the closed circle of sand one's time was short for the tide swept back to all but submerge this twenty feet of granite and crash against the white chalk of the sheer cliffs. There was, in fact, no other escape from disaster than this narrow inadequate ladder. For these reasons the place was deserted and there were times of the day when, with noon immediately overhead, one could strip naked and sunbathe in complete privacy.

On such a day, then, we lay beside The Stallion, caparisoned in its silken jade ribbons, and watched the gulls wheeling high on the cliff face far above us.

There is always a breeze on an English coast and always at

the foot of cliffs at least an up-shaft of air; but where we lay the embrace of the great stone body gave us complete shelter and soon, baked through and through, to swim, and to swim naked, seemed irresistible. We folded our few garments and, placing them in The Stallion's care, ran down the fine and steeply-shelving sand and plunged in.

We swam strongly and were soon far out, afloat and lazy in what seemed a tideless sea, swimming and resting alternately in the placid silken waters. I was very proud of a trick I'd developed. We would float on our backs in parallel ... when without warning I would twist and dive deep, coming up on Arthur's other side to float again. 'Like a seal ...' he said; 'I should throw you a fish to catch!' and I told him how Samoan girls seated on rocks would break off conversation to dive, catch and eat a passing fish – biting off the heads and tails with as little ceremony as we might pluck and peel a banana.

But time to return: figures began to show on the parade for the ritual after-Sunday-service stroll.

We turned lazily, lay a little on the noon-warm breast of the sea before we struck out for the shore.

As we neared our bay we looked in sudden alarm for the Stallion Rock. Its grey, diminished surface alone lay on the water, its green weed covered: the tide had imperceptibly turned too and was lapping the foot of the cliff. As we looked, our few odd garments rounded the corner of the groin and came, drifting in welcoming array, to meet us. The sea here was silken-smooth and Arthur's pink shirt, cotton trousers, my dark-green linen dress, my brief bits of underwear – all made such pleasing patches of gently-moving colour that, looking along the surface of the water, they could be colonies of jelly-fish in some sub-tropic clime.

'Jelly-fish!' I called to Arthur who was viewing them with dismay, 'but not the stinging kind! Let's collect and make for the groin – it's the only way out now.'

Arthur made a lunge at his passing shirt and called, 'But there are people there!'

'Yes. And only our starkness will make them go!' – I

snatched at my drifting slip of a dress – 'Follow close behind me and do exactly as I do ... We're going to walk up the groin towards them.'

Over the rails now small groups watched fascinated as we collected our few garments and turned again to the shore. As our feet felt the groin beneath us and we began to rise little by little out of the water, it became evident that, but for the strange dripping bundles with which our heads were draped, we were – we were going to be – naked.

The onlookers paused unbelieving: then dispersed slowly, discreetly – reluctant, discouraged. One lady remained transfixed – leaning her large bosom outward over the rails – her parasol held high, her eyes screwed against the sun as though the immediate sea were a newspaper she was attempting to read without her glasses. It was obvious that we in particular were very small print. Pleasantly interested, though not a little alarmed, at our emergence but a moment before, she had pointed us out to her middle-aged son; but now, peering incredulously, and perceiving her suspicion to be the horrible truth, she violently thrust her parasol before her son's face and – his arm in her stout grip – hurried him away. We continued to rise, brown as sea gods, our heads seemingly crowned with coloured weed, out of the green water.

'We must make straight for the car, Pitten – she's gone to fetch the mayor and corporation.'

And this we did – slipping on the extra jackets we kept strewn on the back seat for just such tricks of weather or Fate, and were gliding quietly along, pointing out to one another faint outlines of ships aflutter on the summer sea when the 'protest' – headed by that outraged lady still dragging her bewildered middle-aged son – turned the corner from the town and moved rapidly past us to the point where the groin emerges on the shingle.

[15]

'Keep the Dog . . .'

Seated together one evening in more than content and gazing into the glow of the little 'magical' fire, Arthur suddenly puts a question: 'What did you mean,' he asks, 'when you cabled from New Zealand, *Keep the dog until I come?*'

I glance at him in fright; incredulous.

'Keep the ... Oh, Lord! You? ... *You* received a cable ... that message?'

'Certainly,' he answers calmly, and adds, 'I thought it a trifle bizarre.'

'Oh, no, no, no ... Oh, don't you see? Then I mixed you up. I mean, you and the dog. My temperature was 103°.'

'You mean there was *another* message? That it was not the *right* message? That it was not meant for me? Where did the *right* message go?'

War casts no shadow.

It is summer, 1939. I see again the docks at Tilbury. The great hull looming high above us of the ship that is to take the family – Hugh, John and the tawny Staffordshire bull-terrier bitch Chiquita – even yet again, to New Zealand. The dog leaps from the taxi, tail high with excitement, her heavy chain – in the wrenched hand of a BBC friend – stretched taut. We are at the gangway. An official is perusing our papers. The dog's, in some detail, is incomplete and the man is adamant. She cannot travel with us – and we are obliged to leave her in the stranger's care. He will await our instructions. He calls to us a final word as we ascend, disconsolate. The tawny tail beside him but a moment before held high as a banner droops low; is still. Surely, argue the toffee-brown eyes, there is some dreadful mistake? But no – Chiquita's world, her whole world, is moving from her. There is water between; green, ever-widening depths of water.

Then it is the New Zealand scene.

War has broken out even while we were still at sea. Nightly, on the news programme from London, Big Ben booms out over the globe's twelve thousand miles like a call to arms . . . or is it a knell to mark an end?

Entering from the bright sun into the dark of a cinema, I am assaulted by the gigantic screen on which is depicted the curve of a London Street ablaze in sheets of flame; its girders showing stark against the London sky. My heart all but stops. Is Arthur, too, perched in his Ministry of Information, ablaze against a London sky? I return home numb with fear to find a message – a wisp of paper on which is written in his jagged hand: 'Thank God you at least are safe . . .'

Next day I rise from my bed in the grip of some strange-seeming illness and make my miasmic way down the hill to the city and the GPO. Filed away at the back of my mind there has been for long a telegram of importance to be sent. But now there is another: and since, I think in my delirium, the world is quite evidently coming to an end, one of infinitely more vital urgency.

'Where,' Arthur repeats now – and I fancy I detect a certain relish in the insistence, 'did the *right* message go?'

His eyes are warm with interest. But I am gazing at him aghast.

'To a Director at the BBC.'

'And what did it say?'

'It said . . . it said . . .' I can scarcely articulate: – 'Oh Honey! It said . . . *Darling I love you forever.*'

As Arthur explodes with a shout I break into gales of laughter and we rock together in ridiculous delight.

A Fountain Pen

It is mid-morning; and Arthur stands at the top of my stair. 'I want to buy you a fountain pen,' he says, 'in New Bond Street. And afterwards I thought we might go to see Janey's[1] pictures.'

I rise and come to him.

'Janey's pictures – yes,' I say, smiling, but wondering a little at this unpremeditated expedition and the oddness of the sudden gift. 'But the fountain pen . . . You do know what will happen? I shall lose it almost at once. I'm no good at pens, Honey. They just disappear . . . like all the conventional things. Umbrellas: they vanish. And wrist-watches . . . that, in any case, stop as soon as they are on my wrist.' He makes no comment: and I see he is not listening to me: his mind is somewhere else. 'But it's a gorgeous morning . . . Yes, let's go!'

As we sally forth into the little street I say, 'How is Beryl?'

His voice is lofty; remote: 'She wishes to spend the day in bed.'

Ah. I am a bit puzzled. But I know no question is to be put: and, as usual on these spontaneous jaunts, joy bubbles.

We take the Tube to Green Park, saunter leisuredly along Piccadilly, turn up Old Bond Street. The street, the shops, the happy surge of pedestrians – all is perfect. I am saying to myself: 'It is not Christmas. It is not my birthday. But . . . I am going to be given a fountain pen . . .' and wonder vaguely, idiotically, if such things are ever worn like Victorian lorgnettes, on a chain about the neck.

[1] Artist daughter of Dorothy and Simon Bussey.

Part II: Journeys in Parallel, 1943–62

We are approaching the corner of Burlington Street. Suddenly I place a hand on Arthur's arm. I say, cheerfully surprised and without stress of any kind: 'Look darling, there's Beryl!'

She is standing just behind the corner, at the kerb-edge. She has seen us and I move forward to greet her. But – a wrench on my arm and I turn quickly. Arthur has fled. My eyes search the traffic. Bent almost double, he is diving through and all but under it. For an instant I am frozen with fright. I glance quickly at Beryl; across the few yards that separate us. To the astonishment of passers-by, she is laughing shrilly, her 'Mexican' head thrown back, her finger pointing in triumphant derision.

I have no room in my mind for question, for anything but alarm for Arthur's safety: but I see him now on the opposite pavement, running. I make the same death-inviting dash and, always fleeter than he, am soon at his side. He does not speak or glance at me. A little breathless, I fall into step demurely beside him: and soon we have covered the length of the Bond Streets, crossed the Brook Street intersection, and are apparently at the pen shop.

'What pen do you wish to see?' The servitor is spreading his wares on the counter. 'What pen did you wish to see, Sir?' he now repeats. 'Had you any particular make in mind? Any particular price?'

But Arthur's gaze might now be on the most remote of the Tibetan peaks for all the awareness he is displaying. I choose the cheapest of the range of pens. Arthur returns from Tibet momentarily to place a fiver on the counter. I slide the change into his pocket and we depart.

Janey's pictures, I observe, are showing at the gallery opposite.

Poor Janey. In the silent and deserted rooms we move before her oils, her water-colours, almost without pause . . . wordless . . . and are out on the street again.

On the corner of Lower Brook Street Arthur comes to a quiet halt. He turns, faces me, and, lifting both hands, places them on my shoulders. I do not wish to leave him here, so, but as always I take my orders from his silences and know that it is his wish. With like gesture, I, too, lift my hands to his shoulders and, isolated, protected in the human stream, we stand looking each into the other's face. He bends forward to kiss me, and in the instant of the kiss my eyes flicker up, as though drawn, to a group of persons who, on the opposite corner, stand regarding us. Their regard is smiling, amused a little, and they stand close-grouped; three men, two women. They are young. They are Ballet. The watchers. They meet my gaze. Their lips move.

Arthur's kiss is brief, tender. He moves from me, is lost towards Oxford Street. I continue to stand; now, with lifted head, meet those communal eyes. Each head nods towards me. Each face is smiling ... with a curious interest, even understanding: not at all unfriendly ... 'An odd exchange,' I think.

But, though he must by now be several blocks away, Arthur's voice is in my ears, distinct as though we still stood, so, together:

'Thinking ... will do you no good,' it says.

Where -- and at what point of time ... a week? ... a day? did my fountain pen vanish from me?

And did I see, fluttering, high in the air above Brook Street – even Brook Street – a straw in the wind?

[17]

'Trouble'

We are at Kew. It is midday – 'lunch-time'. This means that
most morning visitors will have returned to their homes, the
afternoon ones will not yet have sallied forth. I am aware
that this time of the day has been 'chosen': and that the all
but empty garden has effected the choice. I have learnt to
accept both choice and reason. And I ask no questions: for I
know, intuitively, the 'reason' is a good one. It is to avoid
'trouble'.

Yes: the walks are deserted.

A cold wind blows. We enter one of the smaller heated
houses. The hot pipes run along either wall. In the centre is
jungle: a planting of towering tropic things. Trees, ferns,
vines, lush-fleshed and exotically twining, drip monotonously
into water below. This swampy habitat is arranged in three
bays: the limpid shallows are pebbled and starred with ex-
quisite leafed and flowering things. On the hot pipes facing
the central bay we sit and open up our sandwiches. We are
alone. And we are in another world.

Presently the door to our far left opens and a group of three
women enters. Arthur, I see, is aware, and in every nerve: but
he does not turn his head to examine them and they settle
themselves at once in the first of the bays. I notice that they
glance at us with some curiosity, well-concealed, and confer
inaudibly before they ensconce themselves.

Who are they and whence did they spring? Are they Ballet? Certain they are what the army calls a 'task force':
efficient, and amused. Now, quite suddenly, their voices are

lifted clear in conversation. Arthur sits frozen. Presently one calls to him, 'Oh, Arthur, is that you? What an unexpected place to find you! And how is dear Beryl? Do come across and tell us your news . . .'

I – my presence – is, as usual, ignored. I do not exist. Not to embarrass him, I rise quickly and cross to the pool. I bare my arm and, crouching down, thrust in my fingers, lifting the pebbles in apparent fascination. Arthur – I am aware – without one word of rejoinder, but with unhesitating compliance, has gone to their 'bay' and is seated among them.

Their conversation is now not audible to me.

It seems a long time. And I am hungry.

After a while I return to our hot pipes and pack up our sandwiches, for I know quite well none will be eaten here.

At last it is observed that I am ready – with rucksack, coats and rug – to go: and though no reference is made to the fact, Arthur is, at length, courteously liberated. Like a sleep-walker now he follows me to the far exit doors. We have not enjoyed one moment of the beauty or interest of the place, but he seems content to move again out into the rather bitter wind. I help him on with his coat, put on my own, hand him the re-packed rucksack which he takes automatically and we proceed at slow pace across the lawns.

So far as I can discern, glancing behind, we are not being followed but, bending through screens of hanging boughs I direct our steps to the 'wilderness' where I know there is a shallow grassy trench: shallow but yet deep enough for us to lie invisible to distant peering eyes. Here – in its hollow and out of the wind – I spread our car-rug and soon, lying in its comfortable curve, our eyes fixed on the moving afternoon sky, we are at last munching our sandwiches: in silence.

We have brought books to read to one another. But it is obvious there will be no reading today.

After a longish while I glance at him and see that he has 'thought of something': his eyes are lit again and his mouth curves a little in a bemused smile. At once – and as always – I am intrigued to know what it is he is mentally savouring, what it is he is about to say, what odd 'way out' he has found.

And I have not long to wait. He turns to me: 'Strange ...' he says slowly, looking at me with affection, 'Do you know ... my friends thought you were a child.'

For an instant – envisaging the coils of my hair done up in a 'bun' on the crown of my head, the thin but nevertheless unchild-like silhouette my body must have made as I leaned out over the clear surfaces of the water, my closely-gathered and rather long skirt flowered out about me – just for an instant, I am taken by surprise. 'Darling,' I think, 'this is not one of your best "tries".' But I say, quietly and without astonishment: 'A child? You're not generally known for taking out children: they must have thought it a bit odd, did they?'

'Apparently not. They made no remark.'

He is looking far away from me now, back into the shifting pattern that is building up within the kaleidoscope of his mind.

'Didn't they wonder why you didn't introduce me?'

He considers this, and settling it to his own satisfaction answers with finality and a certain primness: 'One doesn't introduce a child.'

I smile. I think of the meticulous social conventions of Victorian parents parading their off-spring. I say: 'My father, as you know, died when I was six. He always introduced me.'

'Ah!' he exclaims – as if to say, 'I can hardly be held responsible for the idiosyncrasies of your father!' And I know the 'case' – as it were – is dismissed.

Suddenly the clouds part, the sun breaks through, quite hot. I put up a hand. The wind has dropped. I take off my jacket, unbutton the neck of my dress, remove the few pins from my hair, thrusting them deep into the long grass and the soft earth beside us and, parting his coat, creep into his armpit. Still staring at the sky he puts his right hand across, touching the flat plane of my cheek with the tips of his fingers, lightly and tenderly – as a blind man might – moving over every feature.

Suddenly, swiftly, he turns to me, grasping the ropes of my

hair, and kisses me wildly. He is laughing with pleasure and so am I. 'You so *delight* me!' he cries.

'Hush,' I whisper, struggling up a little, 'it's only not *seen* we are. We can still be *heard*.'

In close embrace we wriggle down to await the sunset pageant.

I am nearly asleep when I murmur, 'If I can't find my hairpins when we go, how shall I pin up my hair?'

'Will a pencil do?' he asks.

'Two pencils might . . .' I answer, and we are asleep.

[18]

The Ring

It is Christmas Eve, 1951.

At Handel Street, at the top of the tall house, although (or because) it is snowing, I have flung open the wide casements and secured them from sight against the outer walls. Framed, then, in the great uncurtained space is the beauty of the Sumac Tree, a nerve-net decked with snow-buds gleaming in the only light, which is the one flung up from our fire. Between it and the sill, a frail backdrop of straightly-falling flakes: the whole, a theatre-set: enchantment.

'What can I give you?' I ask, twisting on the hearth-rug to see Arthur's face. 'You are a great nuisance to me – because you have everything.'

He leans to kiss the top of my head. 'If I have "everything" it is because you give it me.'

'Darling idiot – I mean something concrete.'

'Oh, not *concrete!*' he demurs, his face comic.

I laugh happily. 'All the same, I've something "concrete" for Beryl.'

Among my New Zealand treasures I have found a ring of limpid greenstone, a beautiful piece, translucent as jade. I reach up and take it from where I have laid it ready. I hold it out to him: 'Will you give it to her for me?'

He is utterly silent. He stares at the thing as though baffled, repelled, and he withdraws, and will not take it in his hands.

Now he picks his words, carefully; very tender, but carefully, as one exploring a rock-pool. 'I think,' he pronounces, 'it would be better if you *didn't* give that to Beryl.'

'Oh,' I cry, truly disappointed, 'does Beryl not like presents?'

'Beryl adores presents.'

'Well, then?'

But he is silent.

I look down at the little lovely circle.

'You mean . . . she would not like it.'

'She would not like it.'

I am crest-fallen. I say, 'Of course, I do *know* she too has everything. I do *know* this is nothing . . . but . . . I haven't anything else.'

'Why do you feel you have to give her a present?'

'Why? It's Christmas. Tradition. A rather nice one.'

'We take no notice of Christmas.'

'Oh, *that* I know! Do you remember the Christmas Day that Beryl was abroad and you asked me to dine with you? We had a boiled egg each. And the other time . . . at Regent Square . . . we had lychees. Which was – I remember thinking – more imaginative but not madly nourishing. If we hadn't been living on air we'd have got very slim indeed!'

He nodded smiling.

'But, Pitten, let me tell you about this ring. It was dug from the bed of the mountain stream – the "raging torrent", rather – the "crashing river" – beside which I spent my infancy. I was in terror of the river. And yet, again, I was unafraid. For from the Maoris I learned that the river was a god. And from the minister I learned – or so I took it – that gods were good. And so . . . and so . . . anything from the river was direct from the gods . . . a gift . . . and from Erewhon. I was just four years old when we left the Erewhon country forever. But my father had told me of the Englishman called Samuel Butler. Together we had explored as far up as one could on that side of the alp towards his plateau. I respected his gods. Often on winter nights I heard their wild music. With my friends the Maoris, I shared his awe. Perhaps – if you were to tell Beryl this ring is from Erewhon she would like to have it? Please give it to her from me. With my love.'

He looked at me quickly, strangely. 'What do you mean – your "love"?'

'What do I *mean*? Why, what does anyone mean who says that?'

'It's ridiculous.'

I sit back on my heels. I do not understand him – his sudden change of mood, his ... yes ... his anger. We look at one another. A long look – in the flickering, searching and concealing light of the fire. No; I am beaten. 'I'm sorry,' I say at last: and place the ring back on its shelf.

But he will not let it rest. 'Why did you say that?' he demanded.

'Say what?'

'Ask me to give Beryl your love?'

I am bewildered. 'Because I meant it.' Then, 'Not – oh, Darling – not *that*; not the love that is mine because *you* give it me – not "my love", that way ...' I am now hopelessly floundering and out of my depth. 'I couldn't give *anyone* that – I think I couldn't live without it ...' For a moment I am under with a splutter – then touch bottom, turn and struggle back to the shore: 'I ... I only meant ...'

'You "only meant ..."' he flings back at me and moves across the room. 'You "only meant".'

I remain, half kneeling, on the hearth-rug and I feel tears pricking sharp behind my eyes. But *I* am angry now.

'Yes,' I say, stressing the words, '"I only meant". I'll tell you what I only meant. I meant that I can – quite truly – send my love to Beryl and I do so.'

'You *love* her? You don't know her!'

'No, I don't know her. But I can love her. I love her because of you.'

'Because of *me*.'

'I love anybody and everybody who contributes to your life – who brings anything to it that's worth having – who stands with you for pleasure or joy – who piles up gifts, enrichments, at your feet. For this *I* would do, but cannot do it. Therefore I love those who can and who do. And I've *seen* them do it. Sometimes at the Burlington or the Tate, when I

[103]

move aside and your friends close in about you, I have watched and seen their faces – their pleasure in you, their delight. Once I ran down the stairs at Olivelli's and, with my hand on the door, saw you through the glass panel. You were seated at one end of a table, facing me, your back against a wall. Some seven or so students were leaning forward, their faces turned towards you, listening. Yours was radiant, wonderful. And theirs – those youthful ones – seemed lit from it, they shone so. Of what you were saying, of course, I could hear not one word. But oh, there was no doubt of it, they loved you. I tip-toed back up the stairs and out into the dark street. I walked on air. I too was alight with love – *not* mine for you, nor even *theirs* for you ... but *mine for them*.'

He is silent. Then he says flatly, but, like a child repeating a lesson: 'It doesn't make sense.'

'Oh, "sense"! Nothing wonderful ever does! And love – as *we* know, don't we? – is pretty wonderful.'

He makes no movement. No response.

A log falls sideways and I kneel to lift it into the glowing centre. Silence seems to have closed about us.

Then, 'What *is* "love"?' he cries suddenly in protest. '*None* of my friends believe in it – *None* of my friends!'

But I am back in Erewhon.

I am again four years old. I sit quietly beside my father; my legs, cramped and hanging from our pew bench, cannot reach the hassock. I swing them gently back and forth. I put my hands under my thighs to ease the ache ... and – to forget it – try to listen to the words that come drifting down from the pulpit. 'Love ... suffereth long and is kind ... Vaunteth not itself: is not puffed up ... Taketh not account of Evil ...'

I say now, 'Have you ever read the Bible?'

'Yes. What of it?'

He is scornful but he cannot hurt me for I am years away (how many years?) in time.

'Not just the bits about the whores of Babylon ...' – I pause, making slow return ... while he shuffles impatiently – 'It sometimes seems ... to hit the nail on the head.'

He is moveless.

I sit silent. I am thinking new thoughts. I say: 'I haven't understood. I haven't known that Beryl hated me. I've thought she didn't "mind" me.'

'Ah!' he exclaims now. '*That* was before she knew you were clever!'

Clever? I am surprised to find I resent the word – and feel vaguely disturbed that he uses it of me.

'I'm not clever,' I say. And add, 'And I'm *glad* I'm not.'

At this, he has sprung to his feet and is at the door. He turns and faces me. For a moment he is like a man glancing about a private arsenal for a weapon – a javelin perhaps – to throw. Then he has chosen – yes, a javelin – and hurls it. It is widely aimed, however, and falls short.

'It's not very nice to play second fiddle, is it!' he flings at me, and is gone down the stairs.

The enigma remains.

[19]

Challenge

One day he comes to me and sits silent. I know that something of significance is to be said. Presently, in the singularly quiet and even voice that is for such utterance, he says it: 'Beryl wishes me to tell you . . . that she would be willing to pay the fares for you, and your son, to South America – to Mexico.'

It would be strange if I were not astonished. But after an instant's pause – my voice no less quiet and even – I answer: 'I came to England because I wished to come to England. If I had wished to go to Mexico I would have gone to Mexico. This – London – is my home.'

He is not looking at me: instead his inner eye is hard at work with a confusion of images: he says: 'So. You do not accept. The answer is "No".'

'The answer is "No". You must thank Beryl for me . . . and tell her the answer is "No". Negative: decisive.'

Now he glances quickly up – and I see in his face a triple conflict: radiance, gladness, relief, at my decision: fear of what he must face on his return to Beryl with failure as her envoy: and disturbed speculation as to what will be the repercussions, for me, and for him – the long-term outcome.

Still, he is human: a man: who loves deeply – and it is this that ultimately takes over; a relief he cannot (and dares *not to care to*) control. He says – it is almost a whisper: 'I am *glad* you say "No".'

Quickly I kneel before him. He holds me close. The future may be prickly with alarms. But . . . Here and Now . . . (as always) . . . we are in love.

[20]

Ballet

But then he came to me in happy mood and asked me, 'Would you like to come with me tonight to Covent Garden Ballet?'

Delight surged. I felt it too in him. Also, what had happened? Were we at long last to be *seen* together? Was there to be open acknowledgement of our friendship? I felt the gyves about my ankles loosen, the horizons expand.

'Oh, but yes,' I breathed. And then – 'Will Beryl be there?'

'No. Beryl has a headache and has gone to bed. She has very kindly suggested I should take you and has given me her tickets.'

'Oh.'

'Well? Was that not kind of her?'

I felt ashamed of my secret heart-sinking. 'Yes, Darling. Very kind.'

Our seats were in the stalls, at the end of a row and near an exit door. The lights went down. I could scarcely breathe for happiness. At last my inhibitions about ballet were to be dispelled:[1] I realised that only so, with him – so all-comprehending, so compassionate – could this ever have been accomplished. I felt – I knew – Arthur too understood this well ... and presently he slid his hand across and took my own – 'It will be all right,' he whispered.

The lovely music lifted ...

There – with him beside me, the warmth of his healing love about me – the spell, the hideous spell, was lifted; the pain of

[1] My own career as a dancer had been cut short when I injured my spine at the age of fifteen.

memory moved from me forever. I no longer was the prisoner, pinioned, of my cracked and broken spine; with no future, no life to live but through that of others: I *was* Giselle. I moved in enchantment.

Suddenly there is a controlled commotion at the exit door somewhere behind us. Two women, blind in the darkness no doubt, stumble and feel their way into two empty seats immediately behind our own.

With a jerk Arthur snatches his hand from mine and says in an audible and sternly admonishing whisper, 'I think you must *try* to behave nicely.'

These words are greeted by a ripple of laughter at our very ears – Alas, how all-too-well I knew that hollow music – and a titter of whispered conversation.

Now, throughout the performance, we two sit rigid; Arthur leaning from me at an embarrassingly ludicrous angle, his only remarks in the nature of the 'I wonder if I might trouble you for your programme . . .' sort.

Misery takes possession of me.

Giselle moves – swims in a sea of tears. An ache of disappointment is in my throat. Try as I might I cannot be happy. Bewilderment clouds my mind. Is it a trick? Has he planned it so? No. I cannot think it: for I feel his agitation: he is as frustrated as I.

The performance over, Beryl and her companion disappear on a trill of high-pitched laughter. Its echo remains.

It is all either hears as we walk home in silence.

At length I ask, for I have to know: 'Darling, did you ask me . . . because Beryl couldn't come?'

He cannot resist the riposte. He answers coldly: 'Naturally. And you must admit . . .' his voice sinks, as a knife to the final incision, 'that you *were* a little boring.'

I run up the dark stair, let myself in and shut the door against him. Against him? Against her? Against them? Against it? Yes, '*it*'. I lock the door; lean against it, feeling now his pain.

And presently I hear his step, hesitant, pause ... then tiptoe down and away.

My Darling.

But I do not open. My tears fall on my arms, on the window-sill, as I watch him round the corner.

He does not look back.

[21]

First Encounter

It is 1953.

Arthur stands at the top of my stair: 'Beryl wishes to meet you.'

I had for some time urged that it might relieve the tensions, assuage Beryl's natural curiosity, lessen the pressures put upon him, were we to meet: but Arthur had seemed to think this unwise.

'I'm glad,' I say now.

Apart from my 'sightings' of Beryl, I had only the somewhat fantastic stories of the Balinese children[1] whose impressions were at such variance that I would be glad to form my own.

Arthur now added: 'She wishes you to come to tea on Thursday.'

At the steps of the house I encountered Gordon Luce.[2]

'You!' he breathed.

'Yes,' I laughed, 'so far as I know I am me.'

To this there was no response, and as I mounted the stairs, I observed a kind of anticipatory glee gather in his face and mien. Arthur received us and having, with the single utterance of my name, announced me at the door of Beryl's room, left me standing uncertain whether to enter, while he led his friend hastily into his library.

---

[1] Richard, Tamara and Edo Sie – Arthur called them the 'Three Little Seas' – were Balinese dancers who had stayed with me in Sloane Street.
[2] Professor at SOAS.

I was surprised to find the spacious room empty of guests. Beryl, however, was certainly decked and a'glitter to receive them; seated against a mountain of gaily coloured cushions she was actually in her bed. She had the appearance of a creased and leathered marionette, not quite real; and, perhaps because over-decorated, rather like the Javanese shadow-puppets exhibited behind glass in museums. Yet I thought, 'Strange. She is somehow ageless. Mythological.'

She looked me up and down. After a bemused silence she asked: 'Are you a Maori?'

The question was so directed and so odd-seeming – for I could not have resembled one less – that I took my time to make answer. 'Arthur tells me you are an anthropologist, Beryl. No . . . I am not a Maori. I am a Highland Scot: though there is still a French strand somewhere.'

As no comment came, I thought I might as well continue to fill the silence; which was of curious quality; heavy yet vibrant. It had to be broken. I said, 'I think it is concluded, isn't it, that the Maoris are an Aryan race – as we are – who travelled through many centuries eastward, pausing in Malaysia and moving down through the Islands of the South Pacific. Naturally, they would have become a rather dark-skinned people . . .'

I was walking about the room now, and listened for any welcome sound from the library next door. Then I went on: 'All the same, many Maoris are no more dark than an aristocratic Spaniard. Or, for that matter – and with a drop of Jewish blood thrown in – anyone's uncle who is "something in the City".'

Masks leered back at me from high cornices – and Beryl's own mask now followed my movements closely. I began to enjoy my abandonment to the past. I was breathing mountain air. Bloomsbury had faded.

'Early in his second marriage, my father took two young native chiefs into his household to educate them in the English cultures. It infuriated my mother. One – Parata, I think – yes – became a brilliant lawyer. Pomare – Sir Maui Pomare now – became a doctor. Both in time became

[111]

Members of Parliament ... and I met them, ages later of course, here in London at the house of our High Commissioner, Sir Thomas Wilford. They wore pin-striped trousers, morning-coats and silk hats. They were on their way to Buckingham Palace to be knighted for their services to the Empire. They were tall and god-like men – the Maoris of my childhood – and had soft, beautiful voices. For eloquence, they put the whites utterly to shame . . . .'

Suddenly I turned on my heel and looked across at Beryl whose black-as-agate eyes had never swerved from my pacing figure. An anthropologist? I thought of Margaret Mead and her work; even in the Solomons where my husband had been stationed.

'You know, Beryl, after all, there *are* others. Not everyone who comes from New Zealand has to be a Maori.'

Faces familiar, some even from childhood, flashed before me. The boy, Ernest, at Nelson College, who became Lord Rutherford after he had split that all-too-significant atom. The brother of my school friend, the poet-eccentric Count Potocki de Montalk. My brother's swimming-companion, Bernard Freiberg, vc, who swam the Dardanelles to cut the wire of the Iron Curtain and was later to be made Governor-general of New Zealand. Katherine Mansfield, who climbed the trees of our school playground that hung on the lip of an earthquake split we called The Gully and was out of bounds. The Countess of Seafield, who, when the Laird of our Clan was killed in the War, took the title. Frances Hodgson, the painter. Jean Batten, the aviatrix. And other names – Lowe, the cartoonist; Pickering, of Californian Space Research; Gillies, and with him McIndoe, who in Harley Street gave men back their faces ... One could hardly ask *these* if they were Maori. Yet these, all, were born in my remote land. Arthur had said, 'One has to be very careful where one is born ...' I began to see his point.

Oh, why was my rescue so long in coming?

But at this moment the two appeared: and, with a flutter of wing-like garments, the figure across the room came to life. '*She* is saying ... *extraordinary* ... things!' it excitedly cried

... as though I were an ape-creature taught lately to articulate intelligibly.

I was rather delighted at this and prepared to be amused, but both men ignored her words and seated themselves, rather gravely, on either side of the bed. Facing her and leaning slightly forward, they might have been two visiting consultants.

Beryl now waved an imperious hand. 'You ... may sit ... there,' she said, directing me to a far and dim corner where a sofa was pressed against a shadowed wall.

I had sent Beryl roses as a gesture to mark my acceptance of her invitation, so unexpected yet welcome. Now, investigating a strange crackling behind my cushions, I found them: still unwrapped, crushed and partially thrust down between the couch and the wall. Even as I considered their odd fate, there came a clamour from the stair-head and there entered a chattering troupe of young women.

'My guests! My guests!' shrilled Beryl, waving thin, braceleted and wildly-welcoming arms from her flutter of wing-like garments, as they clustered about her.

Perhaps since childhood I had formed the habit of viewing scenes and events through the wrong end of a telescope: and here was a scene that proceeded to intrigue. Beryl was pouring forth not too coherent chatter while her guests – all, it seemed, from Covent Garden Ballet – fell into groups. A few glanced my way. A few, I felt, I had seen before ... friendly faces ... but where? None remarked my presence.

Tea was not served: nor, oddly I thought, were drinks. A meeting then; but not a ceremony. The whole thing, for me, was a spectacle, a charade, in which Arthur and Gordon played a silent, but an esoterically aware, part.

Soon I moved to the door, paused by Beryl's bedhead and held out my hand. This was ignored; but, with an elaborate circling of her right arm, Beryl drew the attention of all present. In a shrill voice she cried: 'She ... COOKS ... divinely!'

This announcement was irrelevant and bizarre enough to

produce a sudden silence. I found myself bowing slightly, with 'Thank you, Beryl, for the party,' and left.

Before I reached the ground floor I heard steps hurrying behind me on the stair and, out on the pavement, found Gordon beside me. He did not speak – I felt he was waiting for *me* to do that – but kept pace; sliding his eyes from time to time to glimpse my face.

Presently I said: 'Curious. Theatre. A sort of ritual gathering.' And then: 'Tell me ... do you, all, in some way, "worship" her? Or you perhaps ... *love* her?'

'*Love* her!' The words exploded. 'I am *terrified* of her! *Terrified!* We *all* are!'

I considered this. I thought: 'Perhaps part of her obsession, a sort of challenge, which does not let her rest, lies in the fact that I am not.' But no: it had surely been no more than 'performance'. My interest – and surely my importance – was small.

Yet, at the corner of the square, my companion left me peremptorily and returned to the house. Could it be that the 'party' had not yet begun?

[22]

A Present

It is my birthday ... and Arthur stands in my doorway. I rush at him. 'I wonder,' I say, 'if every woman is as mad-glad as I to be born!'

He glances quickly up: shy, like a boy. 'I've not known *one*,' he says.

But my words rush on: 'Listen, Pitten! Music at the Wigmore Hall. French music. Mostly Fauré. Shall we go? No – better, better! – will you come ... just for once, come, as *my* guest?'

Arthur's eyes are warm with pleasure. 'I'd like that *very* much,' he says. And then, 'Have you got press tickets?'

'*What* a rude question!' I exclaim, laughing. 'Yes, of course! I'm just trying to fit you in. Anyone would do as well, but you just happen to be handy. I once went into the street and found an old woman to accompany me. She was almost ragged. She'd never been to a concert before. I expect wherever – and whoever – she is, she still thinks she dreamed the whole thing up. But this? No, it's my present to myself – perfect music, perfect seats, perfect companionship. Yes?'

'Yes.'

It was in the semi-dark of the second group of items that I saw Beryl: to the right, towards the front, silhouetted. I touched Arthur's hand – which closed over mine.

'There is Beryl,' I whispered.

He learned slightly towards me: 'Beryl is in bed,' he whispered back. 'She doesn't feel very well.' Then added, oddly, 'She is learning Persian.'

'The young man with her,' I observed, a channel of vision

opening suddenly and diagonally between the heads of the audience, 'seems rather ill at ease. Do you know him?'

These words had the effect of making Arthur suddenly rigid. Without even an attempt to follow my eyes, he replied primly: 'Certainly. He's a columnist from Fleet Street. A friend of Beryl's over many years.'

'But he hasn't *got* many years,' I murmured. 'Well, I suppose he *could* have twenty-six.'

And Arthur, cold with fury, withdrew his hand.

When, at the interval, the lights went up and, as is usual, people rose to stretch their limbs, meet their friends and exchange comments in the foyer, Arthur continued to sit, indecisive. Suddenly, however, his mind made up, he got quickly to his feet and made off up the aisle. All unsuspecting, I followed, feeling rather like a dinghy on tow on a rough Thames. Beyond the glass panels of the doors was to be seen a close and gesturing group – persons for the most part titled, esoterically informed and an important part of any first night of music. These faces, some I thought gravely embarrassed, glancing now through the panels and observing our coming, yet smiled welcomingly: but, to my astonishment, Arthur now did a clever (and, I thought later, a desperate) thing. As he passed through the swing of the door he thrust it back behind him so that I was trapped – at least until the surge of people had forced it – on its inner side.

Presently, inevitably now, I found myself pressed close behind him and, across a ballet of gesturing hands, observing in fascination the glitter and bird-like chatter of Beryl who held all in thrall. The young escort was nowhere to be seen. Arthur, his back to me, made no movement whatever. A few younger faces, observers as I, met my eyes with amused and speculative gaze. It was, they said, a not unexpected – or, indeed, unappreciated – *divertissement*. Slipping sideways, I made for the windy streets. When, the hall quickly darkening, I moved again in to our seats, it was to find Arthur already there, hands folded together, alert for the music and, of course, wordless.

The performance over, we seemed scarcely to wait until

the final ovation had died before we were hastening in the main-stream of the larger corridor towards the outer doors. At first leading the way, Arthur had at some point dropped behind, for when I reached the pavement he was not with me. Then suddenly, he was. He was saying: 'Beryl has dismissed her friend and wishes me to take her home. Of course I shall do so. Would you care to accompany us?'

The words that rose to my lips – slow, deliberate – and, I knew at once, unworthy – were: *'No. I would care to accompany neither of you. Anywhere. Ever.'*

'Of course.' I said.

In the gloom of the taxi, spot-lit, theatrical from shafts and flashes of passing traffic, Beryl, triumphant, directed upon me all her most flattering charm. While Arthur sat silent, we exchanged impressions of items and found our tastes in surprising agreement.

Arriving at No. 50 Gordon Square, the driver leaped down and opened the door. Beryl was helped to descend. While Arthur felt in his pockets and sorted money in the palm of his hand under the street light, I too was helped to descend. Duly paid, the cabby touched his cap and climbed back into his seat. Arthur took Beryl's arm and, moving slowly up the steps, placed his door-key in the lock. I remained motionless on the edge of the curb, watching; too *interested* perhaps even to feel involved – 'Goodnight!' I called.

Neither a head nor a hand turned in my direction. The door closed.

I ran through the sharp night wind – glad of its seering sharpness. Through the emptying streets, outstripping the moonlight. But sparks of tears stung my eyes. And certainly if another planet had been at hand I would have stepped off the one I trod.

Three days later, Arthur again stood inside my door. 'I was a cad,' he said, across the width of the room.

I replaced my book on its shelf. 'A cad? No. That's not a role you can easily manage. A zombie ... Yes, perhaps. Or ... an *idiot!*'

With a leap, Arthur had gripped my shoulders, swung me round, flung me back across the bed. Now – in a ferocity of fury – he was pressing upon my mouth crazed kisses . . . which I, indeed, as crazedly returned; and which I was for some days visibly to wear, with the peculiar pride and pleasure of a woman who knows herself to be loved.

[23]

Enigma

'John Hayward has rung to ask us to tea.'

'John Hayward has rung *you*?'

'Yes. It *is* odd, isn't it. I mean, for one thing, where would he get my telephone number when it's ex-directory?'

My mind was scurrying round our past encounters. These were mostly in odd galleries – Duke Street, the Tate, Burlington House – or when he was accompanied (his rare glandular disease made him chair-bound) by what I called his 'pushers-and-pullers'; and a retinue which Arthur, seeing it bear down upon us at Kew, has not always been able to evade.

Now Arthur stood irresolute, his face a mask: but, I could see clearly, his mind scampering as mine. I added, watching the effect of my words: 'And he wants me to "persuade" *you* to come.'

At this he jerked to life. 'I shall not.'

'Oh,' I said easily, 'are you sure about that? It might be rather nice. I've said I'll come: with Dorothy and Janey. And Simon, whom I've never met, is over from France. And then of course there'll be Tom . . .'[1]

Rattling on within the circle of his tight silence, I was yet not unaware of a situation in the offing. Above all things I did not want to embarrass or make difficulties for him. I knew well he would not plead. Perhaps, I thought, I should have refused, snatched at some excuse. But why? This had become now always the question: and unanswered. Arthur had swung

[1] Eliot and Hayward were sharing a house in Chelsea at the time.

away from the door and stood at the open window, gazing with unseeing eyes at the chimney-pots below.

'Oh well . . .' he murmured – to a private audience. And no more was said. I could not guess that, and certainly not how, for him complexities were building up. I *could* guess perhaps that in this matter of the strange invitation I was a pawn in the quasi-Bloomsbury game. As a jungle animal approaches, skirts, sniffs at a trap, I would go forward.

Dorothy and Janey were ready at the door of the Strachey house and Simon – I saw now, a very small dark and secret-seeming man – was with them. Even as I approached, the taxi they had summoned rounded the corner of the square and we set off.

It is strange, the company of Janey: a warmth, a sort of 'knowledge' of one another, yet a disturbing and unnatural muteness. Together, it is Dorothy who does all the saying: of Gide and her translations of him which, indeed, I admire.

Arriving at the Chelsea house Tom shares, we find our-selves, a small party, circled, backs to the window, about the figure of John Hayward, the great purplish mass of his body overlapping, all but concealing, the heavy frame of his invalid chair. It is thrust forward into full light, to centre-stage as it were, by Tom Eliot who then steps back into shadow and stands strangely at attention. It was some time since I had seen him – and it was to be some time before I was to see him again, rounding the corner of Tavistock Square: the face lined, leathery, uncommunicative as a tortoise; detached, yet made grey with some inner distress. A day on which I am to exclaim to Arthur, 'Good God! What has happened to Tom!'

Now, however, as guests we talk of many things. Not, I fear, of 'cabbages and kings' – articles innocent, innocuous enough for purely social purposes. More naturally, of course, of friends in the South of France – what written, what painted, and of Gide whose secretary Dorothy Bussy had been for many years. Whatever the significance of this *div-ertissement*, 'King's English' with Tom was not to be part of it. Over and around other subjects, this I attempt. Quickly I

am informed, not by words but by subtler means, that this is
not permitted: that any word I may address to him will be
quickly, dexterously, dealt with, flung back at me by John
Hayward. It is grotesquely like a game – not of tennis; for
the ball is never allowed to fall but is caught at the net, as it
were, by that thickened invisible hand. Eliot's efforts to
respond become quickly futile and I consciously interested in
the play – the so clever, so genial yet blatant intervention
that succeeds, I feel, a little too well.

For me, a disappointing occasion. For John Hayward, too,
in its way: for I had *not* persuaded Arthur – perhaps the sole
object of the exercise – to be present.

Drifting back, as we did, on foot some way along the
Embankment towards Westminster and the burghers of
Calais, I muse on the affair. No man, I am thinking, especially
one of genius, should be a lackey.

At what following period did Arthur bound up my stair,
buoyant with news?

'They're all at it – all the telephones are buzzing – they're
meeting to decide what to do!'

The words somehow throw up a scene from *The Cocktail
Party*. There is excitement in his face. But also pleasure.
'About what?' I ask.

'Tom! He's left! Just a note for John to find on the kitchen
table in the early morning – "I'VE GONE. TOM."'

I know nothing. Nothing of these two lives. Apart from
their work, nothing of each or either. But yet I know this
news is good news.

I snatch at Arthur's waving hand – it is as though it waves
to a ship in sail. I cry: 'Wonderful! Splendid! "I'VE GONE.
TOM." The best poem Eliot ever wrote!'

But Arthur's face is suddenly grave. 'Tom ... is ... a saint,'
he says enigmatically.

One doesn't, I force myself to remember, ask questions.

[24]

'A Lot to Undo'

On my return, after many weeks of silence, from the house in Essex where, in answer to her desperate call, I had gone to the aid of a friend whose child had fallen suddenly and inexplicably ill, I met May-the-maid. A plastic shopping bag hung heavy at the end of either lank arm.

'Oh Miss! I'm that glad to see you. Such a carry-on! Miss de Zoosa's bought a cottage in the country and the two of them's going off there to live!'

'Where, May?'

'I don't rightly know, Miss, but in from the sea, seeming, an' a long way off. She's having a road built special an' special floors an' oil central-heating an' the *things* as have come to Gordon Square apart from them what's been sent!'

'Is there anyone to receive them?'

'Not neighbours I'd say; but a woman she's got to promise to come days like though it's miles an' in the winter I can't think she will ... Still, I've never seen Miss de Zoosa so *set*. Silk sheets on the beds an' them turned back ready; like a honeymoon.'

'And Doctor Waley?'

'Him – 'ee don't say nothin'. Jest sits an' lets her babbly on like an' accepts the clothes she buys for him.'

Never had I been made aware of 'clothes' as a point of interest in the life and landscape of Arthur Waley ...

'What sort of clothes, May?'

'Why, everything – an' it's all got ter be *new*. His trousers ... "an' throw away them cords"; his jackets as 'ee's so fond of – all's got ter be thrown away now. His dressing-gown, the grey Cashmere, an' all them warm stripe-pyjamas ... "into the bin!" ... an' now it's silk with spots an' purple pyjamas an' all in folds of tishee paper an' fancy boxes ready ter go ...'

'And when will they move?'

'Oh soon now I think. Even without them there she pays the woman to go every day an' put hot bottles in the beds.'

I stood a moment regarding this newest bit of grotesquerie – and regarding, visibly, her antics; his silences ... impenetrable.

I had been home a week when Arthur visited me. He wore a shaggy tweed jacket; of loud design and a size too big: his trousers were of band-box newness ... and I felt a surge of backward-turning love for the Cambridge tradition, casual and informal. Arthur took his pipe from his pocket but, cumbered by the over-large cuffs, seemed not to find his usual comfort in the ritual of its packing.

I was interested to realise that I felt no alarm at what might now come – and presently, having at last succeeded and drawing deeply on its new steel-filtered stem, he announced: 'Beryl has bought a cottage in the country.'

'Far?'

'Yes. Far.'

I was silent – knowing that only so would I learn more – and presently it came.

'In Devon. At the end of a narrow valley that runs in from the sea. There was a mere stony cart-track, but Beryl has persuaded the authorities to let her have a private road built. The cottage has needed a great deal of repair and reconstruction – but it's finished now: paths, new roofing, parquet floors. Beryl has been very busy.' He added, 'She wants me to go and live there.'

I made no comment. And now he paused ruminatively, stood up, knocked out his un-smoked pipe, at once refilled it, and replaced it in his mouth. No attempt was made to light it.

'D'you know what happened, Hun? Our Hoot Owl from

Torrington Square ... he came and sat on the chimney-pot all day. How very old he was! Even so long ago, he was old, d'you remember? Well; yesterday he sat, sometimes turning his head towards this window, on that largest of the chimney-pots, but seeing nothing for the blinding sun. Then – just when I thought his gaze on me, so long, so still, *must* be a "seeing" one – he toppled backward, down into the black depths of the chimney. I've explored the whole house for him; but, long ago, the fireplaces have been all bricked up ...'

Arthur showed no sign that he had heard my story.

I looked at him – his scholar's brow; the shuttered eyes, their gaze bent on the unseen. Where – at this moment – was his world, I wondered: his esoteric, his essential world? Where ... his vast library of books, the dictionaries decked thick with notes; the British Museum, the School of Oriental and African Studies, contemporaries, friends, scholars, travellers of the mind from the far ends of the earth? 'Beryl has persuaded the "authorities" to let her have a private road built ...' A fact – not altogether irrelevant – flung itself up. I thought, 'Beryl is seventy-nine. Where must the road lead? For her? For him?'

He stood quite motionless, his face a timeless mask.

At length I said quietly: 'Do you *like* the country?'

Arthur removed the unlighted pipe from between his strong teeth. 'No,' he said, replacing it.

A silence. As under dim stars.

Then ... as echoing across dark water ... I heard my own voice: 'Shall you go?'

'No,' he answered with the same gesture, but this time striking a match with vigour and applying it to the fresh tobacco.

I lifted his hand and placed it against my cheek. 'Shall I tell you my dream?' I said.

'Please.' I had all his attention now.

'It was while I was away. It bothered me because I was awakened by a cry ... and couldn't know the end. But now ... you've told me.'

'I've told you?'

[124]

'Yes. I dreamed that I woke urgently and ran outside the house into dim starlight. You ... had clambered out of a dormer window high in a gable of the roof, slithered down the moss-crusted slates to a narrow foothold – not a coping even, just a sort of guttering – and were walking its length slowly and deliberately but without any fear and in fantastic safety ... so that I knew you were asleep.

'At that side of the old house there was an overgrown and neglected pond – the water black and sedgy with a few reeds at its rim. It didn't stretch far – only across to the roots of great trees that stood tall and close on its further sides – but one seemed to know that for generations it had been a place of fear: one did not like to guess at the secrets hidden, drowned or trapped there in the deep of its blackened centre.

'As I watched, silent, you leapt by means of a water-butt to the ground, and crossing the narrow grass verge walked deliberately and resolutely into the water. The ooze came up, quickly discolouring the place where you entered, and I real-ised that every step must horribly claim you. Against the weight of weed you moved slowly, but without pause.

'There was a ladder leaning against the house. Quickly I leapt at it and placed it at the pool's edge, thrusting it out towards your retreating figure. But already you had sunk to your waist and from your movements it appeared that each withdrawing of your feet from that brackish bottom was more difficult.

'Strangely I knew that, though you slept, you were aware of my presence and aware too of the rescue I offered, but, though the hideous dark of the water moved now about your armpits, you would not turn your head.

'Then ... "Shall you go?" I said. But a cry from the small room next to mine roused me and I sat up, alert to a sense of urgency. Leaving the tattered end of dream, I went quickly to my friend's sick child. But ... it was not for the child I was caring.'

He turned; took my face in his two hands, pressed my hair back fiercely so that it hurt my scalp; looked searchingly, deep, into my eyes. Then he released me with great gentleness. 'You won't be disappearing again?' he asked.

I laughed: 'I don't suppose so. Or anyhow, not for ages ...'

'I have to go up to Cambridge for a few days. There's a lot to undo. Would it not be nice to dine together on my return?'

Of buying an old Humber

All through the night the snow had fallen, making the little street, where no traffic came and walled by its Georgian houses, look like a valley. It was not a cul-de-sac but turned at right angles to the left to join again a main route, gouged thinly to channels of blackened ice. At the angle, obliquely, stood the tall iron gateway to St George's Garden – named (and still to be found so named in old maps of London) at the time of the Great Plague as 'Ye Olde Burial Grounde beyond the Citie' – a convenient spot for the dead-carts moving across the field-tracks from Spitalfields, Stratford or Westminster to deposit their grim loads. Here, now, a curiously-shaped plot with its lesser stones of the forgotten dead propped up against its walls of ancient brick, its whitened lawns and snow-heaped garden plots still as a Breughel beneath its few magnificent plane trees which flung a black net against the winter sky, it served only as a short cut for the pedestrian to Mecklenburgh Square. Cromwell's niece lies buried here, an early victim of the Scourge, her substantial tomb remaining undisturbed.

A delightful pleasance in summer, this – but now, sketched in charcoal on a white ground, it assumed the character of a remote village churchyard. No church stood near, however – and the small stone chapel at the gate had become a convenient storehouse for gardeners' tools ... and, it was said, for some forty or so bodies hidden by students at the time of the Blitz for dissection later at the nearby Medical School.

All night the snow had fallen thickly – layer upon layer –

until footpath and roadway were one and entrance steps were lost and indiscernible.

On that morning I made my way to Euston Road and leapt up to a top front seat of an 18 bus. As I sat, my mind slid into a vacuum – as though a globe of ice had closed about it and all thought had frozen. Remembering now what had happened, I can recall no thinking whatever – at this or at any other point of the experience – but, as we were passing Madame Tussaud's, action was instant: I leapt up in the swaying bus, hurtled down the stair, was grabbed by the woman conductor, thrust my 8d ticket to Kilburn into her hand and wrenching free, leapt clear.

Still without conscious awareness of my actions, I dodged all traffic and, colliding with a nursemaid and pram, turned a corner and fled like a hare for the main gates of the Elizabeth Gardens. Across the frozen grass to where the lake lay partially rigid – skirting the knoll, fretted and icicle-hung – up the slope to the rose garden: an arena flower-garlanded in summer, now starkly etched behind its white-looped and frozen rope barriers.

What drove my feet, unerringly? What flung me headlong to that spot? For I felt no emotion, no apprehension, no terror – not even my own urgency. The garden lay white, still, empty in the near-dark: meagre, drear as the surface of some cooled planet which life had long deserted.

I stopped to gain my breath.

From beside me on my left – an arm's length only – a black-coated figure moved slowly and fell into my arms.

Nothing was said.

On an icy bench we sat huddled, my black priest's cloak enfolding both ... shapeless, silent; how long?

Pain. Ah, pain. And release from pain.

And suddenly – bursting from its bubble of inertia – my mind reeled back from a single thought. Why was he here? Why? Why – recurring until it fell back, mercifully, into the void whence it came.

Oh my Darling ...

* * *

I felt him stir slightly in my arms and sigh, it seemed from the bottom of his being.

I pushed his head into a position where I might meet his eyes. They were wide open. Enormous. Unseeing. I seemed to enter them – as once in a dream, so long ago. Not shutting me out (and this is not to be easily explained) but – as in that dream – taking me into themselves, the limitless tracts of that dark inner landscape we all defend.

I took him home of course – to his house – to his door – opened it with his key, set him on the tall stair. No word at all had occurred to me. No word at all to him. Only our faces and our hands, from time to time pressed close, were warmed as with kisses.

I caught another bus to Kilburn, bought a second-hand Humber and drove it away through the snow and ice of the streets.

By what compulsion had we moved? By what had we been drawn? What had been enacted in that timeless place?

[26]

Flying Dutchman

'I *must* go. I must ... I *must*!'

I look at him. His face, bone thin, is ravaged: his eyes are points of fear. I think – tigers' claws ... only tigers' claws ... could gouge those channels in a human face. Oh, my dear. Indeed you must.

'Where will you go?'

'To Switzerland.'

'And Beryl?'

'She remains here.'

I think – yes, she remains here. She must. That is *part* – the vital part – of the 'must'. But this time, this time ... shall I ever see him again?

As usual, does he guess my thought?

'You can write to me. Write to me.'

'At what address?'

Now he hesitates. 'I shall send you an address when I arrive. I shall be away about six weeks. And you? What do you do?'

'I? Oh, I've got a job to do: write-ups for syndication. There's no real hurry, but I shall do them now. In Paris, I can see John at the Sorbonne. Then I'll go on to Nice. I'll take a month: and perhaps I'll visit Pic and Kate[1] in St Tropez. Anyhow, I'll get them quite definite – my addresses, I mean – and drop them in your letter-box tonight. They'll be there in the morning when you leave: don't forget to pick them up. And give me yours as soon as you know it.' An odd

[1] Charles Higgens and his wife Kate Olver, painters.

look has come into his eyes ... 'Please remember. It's so hard
to work well when one's unhappy.'

'I know. *Indeed* I know. Oh my darling, kiss me a thousand
kisses ...'

'And one.'

'I shall think of you constantly.'

At midnight I drop my letter through the letter-box of No.
50: it contains my three addresses – at Paris, in Nice, at St
Tropez.

Next day to my astonishment Beryl telephones me. I didn't
know she knew my telephone number, which is ex-directory.
Another small treachery, I feel sure, which will cause me –
and him – endless trouble. Why must he tell her everything
– everything – to the last detail? His promises are always so
absolute – 'Of *course* I shall not tell her if you do not wish her
to know,' and he adds, 'And I think you are quite right.'

But now she says, honey-sweet: 'I feel sure you are already
missing Arthur. Would you care to accompany me to the
ballet tonight?'

So. Here is kindness. Though it is difficult – but why am I
reluctant? – I gladly consent.

At Covent Garden, Beryl appears to know a great many
people. In the foyer, in the interval parade, her introductions
are continuous. But I can pay scant attention: I scarcely hear
what is said. And – behind all the chatter, the gestures, the
posturing and display – I feel her ... and yes, her friends ...
watching me. Am I ... being ... exhibited? I try to force my
features into some sort of passivity. But I am conscious of
the skin stretched on bone as of a mask and though, or
because, she never once utters Arthur's name I feel her to be
only too aware of the effort I find necessary to thrust it back
from my lips. How gay she is. And her friends ... how gay.

What words will come instead, for instance, when we part?
I shall help her from the taxi, dismiss it, take her arm to the
top of the steps, thank her for so pleasant an evening and
then ... and then ... might I now surely say, 'Did you hear

[131]

... have you heard ... did Arthur arrive safely?' No: I shall
not, for I shall not be able to face the mockery in her eyes;
nor will she find it entertaining to tell me the truth; her reply
could but make me more miserable.

'Goodnight, Beryl. Thank you for the ballet ... it was most
kind of you ...'

Let me get to Paris – that's my first address. There may be
– even at this moment – a letter awaiting me. Let me go.

Four days pass in Paris. No letter, no word, comes for me to
the Hôtel de Londres. My anxiety is great. Arthur, though
frail to breaking, has for long seemed more than ill. 'I must
... I must ...'

In Nice I loiter a week. Each day increases now my fears.
After all, how could he, how could anyone, travel in that
state? And ... what has happened? Has he collapsed on the
plane? Has he ever arrived? And where? Is he alone? Ill?

At last I send a card to Beryl: '*Old* Nice is worth all the
rest. Have you heard if Arthur arrived safely? Do let me
know. I move on at the end of the week.'

No answer comes.

Somewhere on the front I meet Janey Bussy and we climb
the long fire-escape to her mother's flat – an iron escalier that
zig-zags steeply up the shadowed wall at the back of the tall
building. Why do we do that? There was a reason but I have
forgotten it. What I do not forget – after Dorothy's effusive
greeting – is the contrasting *un*-aliveness of Janey's face. And
I am saddened. And angry. For I have seen, back in London
at No. 52, something she has painted. Something utterly
un-related to this face before me now: something alive: something that calls to one in a small voice, greatly daring: 'Me
too! Me, me, me! I, also, exist!' I glance at her as she leans
above her mother's tea-table. 'Yes,' I am thinking, 'you too
– you, you, you!'

She raises her eyes: our gaze meets and holds: and I know
that she is aware of my thought. Quickly she lowers them.

It is 'subversion'. She is – she will always be – 'poor Janey'
... Poor Janey ... to be found years later (but yet before

2. *Above* They made me Queen of the May. The photograph Arthur carried in his wallet.

1. *Above* The 'silent and retreated' child yet moved at speed ... as the darns in his stockings show.

3. *Right* The 'hatchet-faced Museum official' ... I forget (discreetly) whose comment. Arthur *circa* 1929.

4. 'Beryl was no climber . . .
but at some point she
would come.'

5. *Above* Why do
photographers say, 'Look at
the birdie' when there is none?
Furious resentment in a
two-year-old John.

6. *Right* From somewhere
under the rubble our organ-
grinder had reappeared,
May 1945.

7. *Above* Snow ... can resolve perspectives.

8. *Below* Even to stand upright again is a thing for wonder.

9. *Above* Together we hung the walls of the Sloane Street drawing-room with a private view of Georgette Boner's illustrations to Arthur's *Monkey*.

10. *Below* A sheet of hardboard, a strip of fishing net strung on a pyjama cord, two mincing-machines and some chunks of concrete are more than enough for expert table-tennis in a blitzed kitchen: the Balinese dancers, Richard and Edo Sie, with Ruth Kraus prove it. John scores while I restrain Queen Shara of Abingdon from retrieving the flying balls.

11. *Right* Au labyrinthe . . .

12. *Below* At last Arthur had a small family in his garden. My son John, his wife, Antonia, and their two-year-old son at Highgate.

13. *Above* Any weather, our Highgate garden was a delight, February
1966.

Day REPORT.   Thursday May 26ᵗʰ

Temp. 10am. 98°
                 8pm. 100°
Drugs. Pethidine 100 mgs. I.M. at 9.30am.
       Largactil   50mgs. at 11.30am.
       Valium 1 1.30pm & 5.30pm.

* Dr Waley's wedding day.

Fantastic and wonderful day — All
morning treatments over by 9.30am.
Dr Waley then carried downstairs and
driven to Wood Green Registry Office
where her and Mrs Grant-Robinson
were married. Then returned home.
Dr Waley was in fine form throughout and fully alert and orientated.
Exhausted when returned to bed
and has been left to sleep until 6pm,
when evening treatments were
carried out.
Has eaten and drunk little.
Urine scanty and rather cloudy.
Clot - clear!
Sacral sore = lots of granulating
tissue. Upper end still rather
unpleasant and there is still alot of
necrotic tissue here.
BM. O.
                    E.J.Thompson.

14. *Left* There are degrees
of light … sometimes there
is so much that shadows
are overlain. The nurse's
report on the day of our
marriage, 26 May 1966.

15. *Below* A profile can sometimes be … as a horizon, ageless.

her mother's death) ignominiously dead in a fume-filled bathroom.

I take the cup from her hands and lean my ear attentively to Dorothy.

Ada Chagall, at the Tate exhibition and again at her flat on the Ile de France, had said, 'Visit my father in Vence.'

When Marc Chagall enters the room his pictures enter with him. He comes towards me, his two hands outstretched: he is laughing with pleasure. Something of mischief prompts me suddenly to say, 'What do you think of the work of Matisse?' – for, in this man, who, as with all genius, is also a child, I can foretell the answer and promptly it comes: 'I like only my own!' It is the sure test. I laugh with pleasure.

Virginia joins us and we sit at the table in instant discussion of many things – happily setting up, knocking down, the world's furniture – dismantling its show-pieces – like irreverent children with coloured blocks. In our exchanges and interchanges we are hilarious. It is lunch-time: it is tea, dinner, midnight. It is somehow next day – breakfast, lunch – and we are still talking. For interlude we must move off to the preview party in Nice of Marc's show of illustrations of the Old Testament: but we are to return as though uninterrupted.

Marc draws me aside. 'What do you think of her, my wife, my Virginie? Is she not . . . *limpide?*'

Yes: that, indeed, is her supreme quality – and he has only one fear, he confides, as she helps their four-year-old son, David, in through the window: that some malign fate shall separate them.

In his adjacent studio Marc climbs the tall ladder to his murals and proceeds to paint with replenished passion, replenished energy, while Virginia gets out the car and whirls me through San Paul to Juan Les Pins.

For a moment she alights and we stand together watching the languid serenity of an opalescent sea. I repeat to her his words – his voice, his look, as he uttered them.

'Yes,' she says, very low. 'But I too am afraid of our

happiness. It is too ... rare. If anything – life, or death – should separate us now ... I would not wish to live.'

She turns the car swiftly and dexterously and as I watch its speeding return up the winding hill I find myself thinking – 'Is it always like that ... *must* it be ... for love "too rare"? '

Down the coast a little way, behind screened and shuttered windows, Gide lies dying. His son-in-law stands wordless on the gravel. Together, strangers to one another, we stand there, silent. Where, just where, I wonder, is each of us in that retrospective landscape of Gide's life? My mind is filled to its corners with one of Dorothy's translated titles – *Strait is the Gate*. I think, one can feel pity without feeling love: perhaps one can possess capacity for love – and pity – without perception.

The gravel crunches under our feet. The palm trees cast black caging shadows. The house, in their grip now almost invisible, is silent.

And now – St Tropez.

Pic is restless; is not well; cannot work. Katie paints from the flat roof-balcony one view – the glitter of sea – over and over. I crawl out among the crumbling chimney-pots, negotiate perilous slopes of loose and convoluted tiles, to tilt my camera into the dark chasms of the streets – a cat's view, a bird's view, is all the St Tropez I retain. Nor care about even that. For no note, no reassurance, awaited me, nor comes.

Katie wants only to paint: Pic to rove. We rove whole days: living whole lives within long hours in all the little villages along the glittering coast. We dive in the sea; we roast on the sands; we tramp for miles exploring the hinterland; we watch Picasso making masterpieces in wet clay with an impudent and inconsequent forefinger; we pretend to rent a cuckoo-clock house no bigger than a stage-set: we laugh irrationally. And – because I am, during all this time, that rare and wonderful thing, the perfect listener; since, crouched in the dark of my secret mind, though responsive to every nuance I retain only momentarily what is said – Pic, in some part no doubt aware of the happy circumstance, makes just use of it to relate the story of his life.

One day, arriving back after one such expedition, a communication awaits me: from Beryl. I open it in private; with apprehension. But – contained discreetly in an envelope – is a snapshot. It depicts a man who is afraid – the face tense, the eyes pointed with alarm – a man (could it be?) in the act of falling.

'I thought you might like to have this of Arthur', Beryl has scrawled briefly. I hide it away: forcing myself not to look at it, lest I give it power. But, in its way, it informs. It is time . . . I now know . . . to go back to London.

My life is static. And soon I am home. Where, however, is no letter, no card, no notice that a telegram awaits my collection. I wait a day: then I telephone the house. The maid answers.

'Oh she's gone, Miss. Went after him – like as usual. No, there's no news. And me with the table that's heaped with letters . . . and people ringing up and me not knowing what I'm supposed to be saying . . .'

'Perhaps you will let me know, May, if you should hear anything?'

'Yes, I'll do that, Miss – soon as I hear.'

Many weeks pass. At length the maid rings. 'They're back!'

And after yet another seven days of silence, there is Arthur standing framed in the doorway of my room. I am working at the window. The Tree of Heaven casts a reflected dappled light on walls and ceiling. As Arthur moves into it I rise and then, to my own puzzlement, retreat: for, yes – it is the man in the photograph: heavy, desensitised, even coarse. He glances at me rather quizzically. But he is alive, I am thinking . . . trying to ignore my mind's added whisper . . . 'If it *is* he?' . . . and he is back.

I stretch out two arms towards him. He glances down at them, half turns away, and sinks into his accustomed chair.

My heart is cold with fear: and loss: for what have I to do with this stranger? Almost I am embarrassed. Thrusting such feelings back, I get up and cross the room. He lifts his eyes briefly and again lowers them. I kneel before him on the white goat-skin. Kneeling there, in the silence, I feel oddly that the whole thing has happened before, that the scene is a Biblical one; that I am a sacrifice – that, indeed, I have already been sacrificed. There is no warmth in this man. There is scarcely even recognition. At what deep level of knowing, then, I find myself wondering, did he even find his way to the house: on what impulse seek me out?

I take a hand that hangs limp, without response. I say, 'It's been awful.'

'What's been awful?' he asks jauntily.

'Not hearing. Not knowing how you were.'

'Oh, that!' – he shrugs – 'I could scarcely let you know with no addresses.'

'I did as I said: I wrote out all my addresses abroad and put them through your letter-box at midnight that same night. As I said I would.'

'You must have *thought* you did,' he says indifferently.

'Still . . .' I answer, 'Beryl managed to use one.'

'Beryl?' he exclaims, sitting up now, as I reach to the mantel-shelf and bring down the photograph she had thought to send me.

He takes it from me and looks at it in silence: expressionless: with no comment. I say, 'Whose fireside?'

He answers, 'Ella Maillart's.'

A sudden notion jumps into my head, 'Have you seen it before?' I ask.

'No.' Did he, in fact, I wonder, *not know it had been taken*? And who – then – took it? But I say nothing. And he rises to go.

'Beryl and I are going into the country. We'll be away some time.'

'Goodbye – sailor,' I reply. And he shoots me an angry glance: for he knows the reference.

He turns and all but runs down the stair.

I lean over the balustrade, watching his descent. And think how, even as a very young child, the tale of the Flying Dutchman had so strangely moved my heart.

The Boxroom

Arthur bounds up the stair. He is hilarious and makes for my bedroom but I head him off.

'No. No! You can't go in there!'

He stands amazed – 'Why not?'

'There is a man in my bed.'

'A *man*? In your *bed*?'

'Ssh! Yes. He's rather odd. He howls like a Banshee and drools like a baby.'

'*Why?*'

'Because he copulated with his nursemaid when he was twelve and didn't tell his mother,' and I add, 'And he has "bad thoughts". You can only stay a moment or he'll have them.'

I had opened the boxroom door and we were now pushing between brooms and suitcases to the window under which was a couch comparatively free of litter. On this we embraced, as usual examining one another's faces in great detail, as though after a long parting. We are entirely diverted. Presently, however, a feeble calling commenced and we sat up, listening. I said, 'It's his bad thoughts. He wants to throw himself out of the window. I've left it wide so that he can.'

'You *don't* try to *stop* him?'

'Oh, no. I say I think it is a very good idea. Only that he'll probably be impaled like poor Nina on the spikes below. Or caught, with broken neck and lolling head, in the branches of the Sumac tree. Then he whimpers and covers my hands with kisses – almost licking them – like a dog.'

Arthur is entranced. Suddenly he asks, 'Do I *know* this man?'

'Oh, yes – probably. He's Dr Erik Fischer.'

'Dr Fischer!'

I have named a Professor, a German, an authority, a brilliant man.

Arthur turns and looks at me, incredulous, the corners of his mouth twitching with amusement. But all he says – I hope irrelevantly – is: 'I dote on you!'

'Yes, Darling. I too am in my dotage. It set in quite early.'

He grins. 'Tell me,' he says.

'About Dr Fischer? Oh. Well, about two years ago I went to a party; cocktails at Richard Tawney's flat in Mecklenburgh Square . . .'

'Yes, yes. And . . .?'

'Well, *she* was rather a darling, you know. Her mind, though, wandered a bit and sometimes got fixed on one thing. So this day she welcomed all her guests by whispering audibly in their ears; "Have you got any money?" Most of us kissed her and murmured, "No, darling, not a sou," which seemed to meet the situation perfectly happily: until she came to Dr Fischer. He arrived with a companion, a harsh and glittering blonde – very odd in that rather shabby company of radical intellectuals. He hadn't been initiated, as it were, to this business of the money, and when Mrs Tawney whispered in his ear he burst into tears, collapsed on a sofa and, covering his face with his hands, continued to sob uncontrollably. At that point Richard emerged from his study, covered as he always was in food stains and, showing some amazement at the room full of people – for he had of course forgotten there was to be a party – he pushed his way through to the cause of the hubbub and, sinking down beside your Dr Fischer, soon had him – while we of course all looked the other way – quite magnificently controlled. Richard then – God forgive him – introduced *me*, by *name and address* . . . and so . . . and so . . . the wretched creature's in my bed.'

'But . . . you said this – this party – was all of two years ago.'

'Yes. It was. But when a mind's unhinged it picks at things

– desperate – at any point in time. On the torrent, as it were, of *his* dementia he saw this scrap of intelligibility just drifting along and snatched it up. The sister in charge of the ward said he kept repeating it, so they got in touch. Actually he tried to write me a letter, which they posted, but it was quite indecipherable and probably wildly mad.'

Shouts and cries now come from the bedroom. I leap up and open the door. 'Now, you *must* be good,' I say sternly, 'I'm coming back soon and you must wait quietly. If you make that noise I shan't come back at all.' Seeing the poor creature cowering among his pillows, I cross the room, sit on the edge of the bed, with a handkerchief mop up the tears that endlessly course down his cheeks and smile. 'Will you be good?' He nods, and I return to Arthur.

'The sister in charge of *what* ward?' he asks.

'At the hospital ... they'd had him thirteen weeks. He'd been picked up in the street in this state outside a telephone kiosk somewhere in Paddington. He just cried and cried. He didn't get any better: and when they stood him up he just fell down. They had no clue as to who he was and no friends or relations had come along to claim him. By the time I'd turned up they'd decided to certify him insane; or the surgeon wanted to remove experimentally a section of his spine. I asked if that would cure him. Probably not, they said. So I went to the superintendent.

' "This Dr Fischer is just a nuisance to you," I said, "and what you really want is the bed, urgently, isn't it?"

' "That is so."

' "Then, if you will provide an ambulance I will take him to my home – now – and report back at the end of a fortnight."

' "Experimentally, I suppose we could do that; but we cannot consider him discharged in the state he's in; in a fortnight we must send an ambulance for his return and further examination. Agreed?"

' "Agreed."

'So – all was simple. But then ... but then ... Oh Pitten, the *craziest* thing happened!'

'What happened?'

'Bundling Dr Fischer out in his red hospital blanket and dressing-gown to the waiting ambulance, my high heels caught in the ramp and I fell to the bottom. I could not move. Both ankles were badly sprained. Seeing me there, with a strange animal cry your Dr Fischer tore himself from the restraining arms of the nurses and flung himself headlong beside me. The ambulance men, rather belatedly springing from their seats and seeing us huddled on the ground, snatched us both up, slid us into those tray things they have in ambulances, slammed the doors and were off. There we were, two strangers, rushing through London at speed with the traffic skidding out of the way and bells ringing. I lay and laughed till, for me too, tears streamed!'

'*Fantastic!* But what happened when you got here?'

'Well, much the same sort of thing. Both my ankles by this time were enormous and, seeing our faces wet with tears – for Dr Fischer, who no doubt felt he was trapped in some sort of Kafka nightmare, had never ceased to whimper – they placed us both in chairs on the pavement, took my door key and whisked first one, then the other, to the top of the house. When *I* arrived it was to find Dr Fischer laid out neatly in my bed. The men were very sweet but in a mad hurry of course. They placed me gently – and with commendable decency I thought – in an armchair, smiled respectfully, saluted and left.'

'Could you walk?'

'No. I had to drag round on my knees.'

'How long?'

'Oh, days.'

'Is he going to get well, do you think?'

'Oh, yes. Now that we've got all that copulation-cum-guilt thing out of the system.'

'How did you do that?'

'Why, by roaring with laughter. I assured him that it had no importance whatever and that he wasn't unique – that *every* child copulates with someone or other . . . and one never, *never* tell's one's mother . . . that, as a child, I'd copulated with the gardener.'

[141]

Arthur looked startled, 'But *had* you?'

'Good God, no, silly! I didn't know the meaning of the word and I was such a fiercely private small creature I'd have torn him to pieces had he laid a hand on me.'

'Where do you sleep?'

'On the floor by the fire.'

'When is his time up?'

'Wednesday of next week. I've found his digs and sent for his clothes. I shall take him back cured and sartorially perfect. He's better already.'

A thin stream of words came through the closed door ... 'When you are not in the room with me I have bad thoughts ...'

Some weeks later Arthur and I are lying on the broad bed beside the open window, its former lugubrious occupant felicitously far. We have flung back the sheets and the sun streams dazzling across our naked bodies. Our thoughts stray back.

'Did he pass muster?' Arthur asks.

'Dr Fischer? Oh yes – but fantastically!' I answer, resuming the story. 'I worked on him non-stop and hard, because he bored me so. I massaged his back, borrowed a radiant-heat lamp, made him do exercises, practise standing up ... rang up the hospital and told them the ambulance would not be necessary; that I would bring him in my car. The stairs were a bit of a thing – but I slipped a benzedrine into his last coffee and he was himself amazed at how he dealt with them. But he looked good too, in his best suit back from the cleaners. We'd rehearsed like mad, and outside the superintendent's door I gave him his final instructions. It was like an audition on which not work but his life depended: he sat up rigid as a colonel of the regiment.

'The door opened. He rose and went forward. There was the superintendent, the thwarted surgeon, the frustrated psychiatrist and two young house-doctors. Our Dr Fischer played his part magnificently. He bowed to the right, then to the left. He said, with his slight German accent, "Good morning, gentlemen". He walked the length of the room, straight as a bean-pole; then returned to my side and faced the doctors: "Would you care to examine me?" he asked, gently and composedly, and was led to a couch behind curtains. The two young doctors remained behind; we waited in silence.

'Then one came and sat on the bench beside me: "It is just *not the same man* ..." he muttered, and sat a moment with his head in his hands. Then, "How did you do it?" he said, "I am leaving to work in India next week and I want to know."

' "Oh," I said, "I think ..." – but what *did* I think? I *knew* nothing – "I think it has to be someone *caring*. Not with one's heart, of course; that's quite different – but with something I don't understand. *One* person; night as well as day – giving *all* the attention *all* the time ... without intrusion or interruption. And, you know, I'm sure it would work as well with animals; and no doubt does when it happens. The creature's got to *feel* the consolation of mattering *one hundred per cent* to some other creature, I think. It doesn't matter who. Just someone. But to the exclusion of all else – one hundred per cent. A sort of joining of strengths to make a miracle. It was lucky for him, perhaps even vital, that my useless ankles kept me at his side."

' "You don't ... love him?"

' "Oh, no, indeed! I don't even know him. Yet ... perhaps ... do you think that sort of *caring* – I mean *bothering* with a stranger ... is a *kind* of loving?"

' "Yes," he said slowly. "It's what we, in hospitals, can't give. A kind of loving ..."

'Dr Fischer emerged from behind the curtains: the superintendent approached me, smiling. "You can take him away," he said heartily, "there's nothing the matter with him." Then he added, curiously, "I can give you sixty more patients if you want them."

' "Oh no, no, no!" I cried, "this was just an accident."

' "A lucky one for him!" he responded.

'And, Sweetheart, can you *see* this? Your Dr Fischer

[143]

rehabilitated and German now to the backbone – *proffered me his arm.'*

'But what happened next?' asks Arthur, the eight-year-old child.

'If you want to know what happened next,' I laugh, quoting *Monkey*, '"you must listen to what is told in the next chapter".'

'Tell me,' he persists.

'Oh, well, I persuaded a friend to take him to his country estate for a bit. Then he went abroad to places and wrote from them – Spain, Switzerland – asking me to marry him. Can you imagine a fate worse?'

There is a silence. Then Arthur says, 'If I had to marry, you know it would be you I would choose – of all the world.'

'But you don't *have* to marry, do you Pitten?'

He is silent: then ... 'What if I were to tell you one day that I had a wife?'

Now it is I who am silent. I am back in that evening of long ago when the bombs were dropping ... *'Mrs Waley* ... invites you to dinner.' I say at last, slowly: 'I think ... if you had seven wives – oh, my dear one, my dear – I'd still wish to be the eighth.'

His arm tightens about me: his voice is very tender, but so low I must bend to catch the words: 'You may be promoted,' he says.

[28]

Taking the Air

At some moment of the fifties there was a great excitement – a great triumph – in the world of art. A Rembrandt hitherto unknown and of enormous proportions had been discovered, and we, 'the National Gallery for the People', had purchased it – at enormous, appropriate, cost.[1]

I don't remember that I ever saw it reproduced in the papers of the day – but many thousands of words were expended in its praise. And there was to be a 'preview' – indeed a '*pre*-preview' – so that those elected few who mattered might see, approve, applaud. Arthur, invited, insisted I should accompany him.

'I thought it would be nice to go with Eddie Marsh, who has suggested we meet him there.'

Duly, then, with the accustomed courtesy of exact punctuality, we climbed the steps of the National Gallery.

Yet Eddie was before us – with his air of height, patrician and handsome, waiting at the foot of the lift. As we ascended, he looked down at me with an especial tenderness: for had I not a young son who, for an hour, had enchanted him – and had I not had a half-brother who had known – in that dream-like and unlikely region called the South Seas – his beloved Rupert Brooke?

Perhaps this knowledge had come to him first through Arthur. Why else would he invite me, *tête à tête*, to tea at his house of memories if not to derive the sad delight of some

[1] *Is* there this huge Rembrandt in the National Gallery? I have searched since, but never found it.

first-hand knowledge: some picture, some missing portion from the one he cherished?

The invitation to bring my son, however, had come first. We had not far to walk from Sloane Street to his small abode so stocked with treasures that to step so much as a yard without pausing was impossible. Not a table, not a cabinet, not a space on the walls as we ascended the stair to his sitting-room but caught and held the eye with appreciative pleasure.

Sir Edward Marsh, one felt, was at that time – the Poetry Bookshop days so far behind – a very lonely man. He was delighted with his new encounter – this lad with his appreciation of the French cultures. Together they peered at engravings, examined snuff-boxes, quoted from the French of La Fontaine; Eddie then reading his own translation. Yes, Edward Marsh was charmed; John was charmed; the one to take a stride back into the cultural landscape of a beloved country; the other, to take his stride forward. The 'tea-party' had been a success.

Mine – mine, alone – when it came, held for him a different value: I could construct for him that part of Rupert's life in the South Seas: whence so many of his poems had come – could, with coloured words, provide a 'backdrop', as it were, to the Samoan scene, the Tahitian scene, to *Mamua*. And this, though the knowledge was not my own, but had come to me only through the eyes and experience of my half-brother who, young, blond and native-worshipped as that other had, and as that other found his death in the Dardanelles.

Gladly, but carefully, I told him all I knew of the strange venture – that dash-away of the too-lauded young poet; that (were he able to understand it) break for freedom.

The tale unfolded, my words came to an end and we sat together silent in the light fast fading from the room. I could feel Sir Edward's degree of pain – his degree of gratitude.

And presently he rose and, going to an almost imperceptible cupboard between the crowding pictures, took from an inner pocket a small key. The door opened, another was revealed and, that opened, yet another. From this now small space he took a box, removed something and, returning to the light of the fading window, opened my two hands. Slowly, with dream-like movement, he placed something upon my open palms. Almost inaudible, his voice came: 'A lock of Rupert's hair . . .' it said.

Standing there I was wordless, shocked, repelled, yet deeply moved. Blond, silken, half-curled it lay – like something living; a foetus – upon the naked skin of my hand.

I had loved my half-brother passionately: and the lock, so like, might have been his. For Eddie, the moment was illumined: a different kind of love; but a deep one, and real.

I saw now so clearly it was the bereavement of his life – no Christopher Hassall was to console him – and thought of Rupert's lines:

> I yet shall keep before I sleep
> your Ambarvalia

And of Rupert himself and his desperate escape from the claustrophobic exigencies of the male society of his generation . . . even, of Eddie himself.

Now we had arrived at the upper floor, entered through the door of the special gallery where, at its far end, they had hung the Rembrandt and where, now, a group of people stood silent before its great stretch of colour which seemed to fill the space from wall to wall. Slowly we three moved down towards the group and took our places in like silence before its majesty. It was of a family, perhaps in all five persons and children, portrayed in the usual darkened interior. All was life-size. One entered it.

On these occasions – as I had observed before – a silence falls: not necessarily of awe. It is that, for some reason, no tongue chooses to be the first to utter; each awaits the comment of another that shall set the mood, give the cue, as it were, for what shall be said. As we took our stand, I noted quickly how very *chosen* were the few – not fifteen in all – who were considered worthy to approach this wonder. At a short distance, Duncan Grant stood – silent. Beside him, Vanessa Bell – silent. My eyes scanned the vast canvas in its every detail.

But now the silence, suddenly oppressive, was broken by Sir Edward Marsh. Leaning his head gently, he addressed me: 'And what,' he asked in his high clear accents, 'do *you* think of the Rembrandt?'

My head had drooped over some sort of catalogue that had been thrust into my hand ... and, finding the eyes of all upon me, the silence broken, the direct question – thoughtful, a little startled – I raised it. I said simply: 'Me? Oh ... *I* don't think it's a Rembrandt.'

Astonished that my opinion should be sought, my answer was spontaneous and sincere. But my words seemed to rattle round like pebbles in a metal drum.

Into the all but audible gasp of silence that followed them, Arthur's voice rose to its highest Bloomsbury cadence. Close beside me, he took my hand.

'I think,' he said, 'we will take the air.'

And 'take the air' we did.

In the sunlight of Trafalgar Square he paused. He stood quite still and turned to me. 'What,' he said, 'made you say those words?'

'Because,' I answered, baffled, 'I don't think it is. The left-hand bottom corner is – but then the brush strokes, the techniques, begin to vary across the canvas. I think others, perhaps his students – did he have students? – went on with it; finished it off.'

Arthur gazed at me, confounded; but I was still in retrospect examining the canvas.

'And it wasn't his signature ...' I concluded.

We had crossed the street before he turned to me again.

'But what made you *say* those words?'

'Eddie asked me what I thought. They were what I thought.'

He stopped: looked at me despairingly. 'In England ...' he said, 'one doesn't always *say* what one thinks.'

[148]

I felt quenched. And hopeless. But Arthur drew me to him like a rebuked child – and there, amidst the flowing pedestrians at the foot of the steps of St Martins-in-the-Fields, kissed me with great tenderness.

[29]

The Rigged World

I am seated on a bench inside the railings of Tavistock Square. An open letter is in my hand. What it says has left me nerveless. Then I am aware of a shadow across me – and look up into Arthur's questioning, compassionate face. Mine apparently requires no question, for he sits quickly down beside me, slides his left arm along the back of the seat and draws me close so that I am, as it were, in the very shelter of his armpit. Then he takes the letter from my hand and reads it. John, it says starkly, is posted to Korea.

We sit wordless: trying, both, to penetrate the screen of the inexorable future.

John – the Sorbonne behind him – had been due for Magdalen College, Oxford. Picking violets with Boase[1] in his garden, I had said, 'Yes, he's been conscripted. But couldn't he come here first?'

Boase had answered, 'But then, if he were to be killed, we would have wasted our money,' and, with a smile of great charm, had handed me his posy.

But, his officer's training completed, John had been posted to Germany; was even now preparing for departure. Suddenly headlines are across every paper – 'MANY MORE BATTALIONS FOR KOREA.' 'GLOUCESTERS WIPED OUT.' 'WAVE UPON WAVE OF CHINESE FLOW OVER THE HILLS ABOUT PUSAN.' Plans had been switched. John, in company with five fellow officers, is among those forming battalions to stem the flow. Departure is – now.

[1] Vice-Chancellor of Oxford University.

The notice flutters to the ground. With his right hand Arthur tips my face up to meet his eyes.

But mine are seeing other things; in distance, far; in time, too close. A child lying flat on the forest floor, beating with fists of pain – because the cattle have trampled the tall beauty of the foxgloves and now 'the buds ... the ... buds ... can never come out.'

Gently Arthur lifts a streak of hair from across my unseeing gaze. 'You *do* need looking after,' he says and tightens his arm.

Only days later, I am seated on the bed changing the badges on John's uniform, sewing on the 'active service' flashes of his new regiment, when Arthur bursts into the room.

'Would John like fifty pounds?' he says.

Fifty pounds! It is a fortune to either of us.

'How?' I ask, amazed.

'There's a prize for an essay. I choose the subject. And judge it. I thought of Genghis Khan.'

He is excited, I see, and hopeful. I am bewildered. I say, 'John will be on a troopship, training Borstal boys, non-stop, not to be afraid of the dark. And to twist a bayonet in a Chinese gut. How could he write such an essay?'

'Oh,' he says, impatient. 'He wouldn't have to *write* it. *I* would write it.' Then falters as he meets my direct look.

'*You* would write it? And ... give him the prize?'

'Yes. It's not as though he wouldn't win it anyway. Only, as you say, he'll be busy on a troopship. I only thought he might like ... could do with ... fifty pounds.'

'What happens to the prize if he should refuse?'

'Oh – it lapses. It seems a pity.'

'I think it unlikely that he will be interested. But I shall put it to him, and let you know.'

I give a final twist to the thread and, lifting the heavy jacket to my teeth, snap it off. For a moment I smooth it out, gazing at my inexpert handiwork – the tabs and tags, the highly burnished buttons of a young officer of the Queen. 'A rigged world,' I murmur.

[151]

Arthur, who had seated himself beside me, springs to his feet. His face is white. He is very angry. 'Oh well!' he cries, between exasperation and contempt, and is gone.

I remain with the jacket smoothed over my knees. And gradually, as my mind pursues Arthur's retreat, rocketing down the stairs and out into the empty roadway, a question rises quietly to its surface. Had there – in *fact* – been a prize offered? Or was the whole thing an invention? Had he longed to give himself the double pleasure of a departure gift to John and the fun of dashing off a youthful-sounding essay on the Genghis Khan? I glance up, smiling, as though he were still with me. But I've made him angry, I think sadly. And now I shall never know.

When John comes in, I put the whole thing to him. He, too, smiles. 'I think it had better lapse,' he says.

And when these words, in their turn, are conveyed to Arthur he accepts them with the comment, 'He is young.' But adds gently, 'I am glad he is like that.'

[30]

'Yes, There is That'

'Oh, poor Beryl – poor Beryl! She has a tumour on the brain!'
There is a note of hysteria in the voice, which I break with,
    'How do you *know* this?'
    'She has written to tell me. And she has been turned out by
her friends . . .'
    'Again?' I thought.
    'She has been to the British Hospital and the British Em-
bassy – and to a convent: but even the nuns, who took her in
for three days, turned her away. She is wandering about
Trieste alone and ill. I must go to her at once.'
    'But Darling, *why* do they turn her away? The hospital,
the embassy, her own friends? It's inhuman and quite incredible. Convents, I seem to recollect from somewhere, as also
monasteries, are under some religious obligation to give shelter – refuge – to any who asks: and this for three days. But if
the creature who appeals is also ill – why, I do think truly
they would not cast her out on the world again. Unless . . .
unless they have reason . . .'
    'What reason could they possibly have for being so cruel –
so monstrous! A tumour on the brain is a terrible thing –
terrible.'
    'I don't know the symptoms,' I answer reasonably, 'I've
known only two persons with tumours on the brain. One was
raving mad – homicidal: the other lay in a coma. I just don't
know.'
    'I'll fly early tomorrow morning. Will you look it up for
me? About tumours on the brain? The medical dictionaries
are just inside the door of the Reading Room . . .'

[153]

'I know. On the right.'

'Tell me all that's said. Take careful notes. I can't give you an address. But keep it for me until I can. I shall bring Beryl straight back here of course. I shall see you again very soon.'

He holds me a moment in a tight embrace and, as sometimes, I feel his mind stirring. Then he runs down the stairs, pauses, and looks back: 'You don't think ... it's a *ruse* ... do you?'

For an instant I am repelled. *Could* it be so? That is a thing beyond my imagining: a thing I cannot know. But there is another which presents itself: appears to be evident. I sit down on the top step. I say: 'Did Beryl wish you to accompany her?'

'Yes.'

'You refused?'

'Yes.'

'She was angry?'

'Very.'

'Did you give her a reason?'

'Yes. I could not leave you.'

'I see. Well, but now. You *are* leaving me: you *are* going. There is that.'

'Yes. There is that. That ... I *must* go.'

'Yes. And of course you must. I understand it. And don't be unhappy about going. Just ...' Alarm breaks suddenly in my mind, so that I know it is in his, 'Oh, promise, promise ... to return soon.'

He runs back up the stairs, and sits a moment quietly beside me, an arm about my shoulder. His eyes – and mine, though less effectively – are on Trieste. He says: 'I can't imagine what I shall find.'

No. Not I – nor even he – could have imagined that.

[31]

Flight without Face

Time passed. And passed slowly. A silence hard to bear.

At length came news. Arthur had searched Trieste. Beryl, it seemed, had taken a train to Venice and he had found her in a luxury suite on the Grand Canal where she had been for some time in deadly conflict with the proprietors. 'We move from one hotel to another. I am trying to persuade Beryl to come home.' – 'It is terrible. Terrible. I have taken Beryl to five specialists. They are all useless. Why don't you write?' – 'I am doing all I can to get Beryl home but she refuses to get on a plane.' – 'The sister of a friend of Beryl has offered her villa at Bertinoro. We will go there. I long to have one word from you.' – 'I think of you constantly. Constantly.'

Where, then, were my letters, my notes from the medical dictionaries, my almost daily cards of exhortation? My communications seemed to have misfired: and in his I began to sense a note of panic. But how *could* he – or she – be friendless in such a place; or, one might think, anywhere? That it *was* so, wrung my heart with pity. I would wait no longer: I would go.

Telling no-one of my plan – indeed I had no plan – I moved now as in a dream.

The manager of Air France in Lower Regent Street received me in his office.

'In return for articles, illustrated with photographs, in overseas journals, will you give me a free flight return to Nice?'

Perhaps the directness of the request amused him, the

corners of his mouth twitched; but when, glancing up, he saw I was deadly serious, he said kindly, 'Why do you wish to go?'

'The man I love is in great distress. I must.' And from my pocket I handed him three of the unsigned cards, the handwriting on each increasingly revealing.

The French are many things: one of them is perceptive. Here was a man in his forties; handsome, experienced, intelligent, and sympathetic. Sitting before him, I had no doubt whatever that he would understand. Silently he took them from me, shuffled them slowly back and forth, held them still an instant and suddenly closed his eyes. I thought, 'He is reliving some parallel dilemma: perhaps in a personal world.' I waited. His head dropped a little; in some pocket of time he had forgotten me. I felt my nostrils tauten. Then, without raising his head he opened his eyes and lifted his gaze to mine. He said quietly, 'Yes, of course you must go,' and pressed a bell on his desk.

Within minutes, a ticket – 'GRATUIT' – was in my hand.

From Nice, then, a card direct to Bertinoro – *'I am here. Say if you want me to come'* – with Marc's address.

No answer. And a great urgency possesses me.

Nevertheless, I force myself to wait and it is days before, for my blind journeying, Marc and Virginia are pressing fifteen pounds into my hands and I am on my way.

At Genoa I send a card – and at Pisa – giving as address the American Express at Florence. At Pisa I sleep in a railway waiting-room and loiter a long blazing day. I am not unhappy. It is as though, even consciously, I keep my mind empty, as to receive a sign. For now his distress is with me like a heavy burden – in flower-gathering meadows, in the dark-shadowed doorways where I stand to watch the hourlong expert chipping of stone angels' wings. I climb the twisting stairway of the campanile. My feet drag with fatigue. Suddenly, some twenty steps from the top, I hear (as how often) my telephone bell at home in Handel Street and the familiar, 'It's me! It's me!'

'Yes, yes – I know,' I cry aloud, 'I am coming ... coming!'
and pushing past a youth who blocks the way, I leap up the
final flight. The sky is vast – empty – silent. 'Utrillo,' I think
– 'and there are larks.'

Alarmed, the youth has followed me close and, leaning at
the parapet, he asks in French 'Is anything the matter?'

'No,' I reply. 'Just the telephone bell. But there was, of
course, no bell; you heard no bell.'

'No. I hear no bell.'

'Just the message,' I say, 'that it is important I should
continue my journey.'

Running to the station, I fall in with a young priest. I stop.
'I see you are of an order that observes silence but I think
you are permitted to listen. Can you pray for help – and
protection – for one quite unknown to you?'

His head bows assent.

'Then I beg you do so,' I say, and run on.

Florence. And the American Express. And no message.

I feel now that money must be used sparingly, if indeed at
all, and make my way to the Youth Hostel at the top of the
barracks. There are mattresses on balconies; and a huge
cauldron. Each evening we descend – any age, any national-
ity – for a scavenging raid on the market and return with our
contributions to the communal stew.

Little Monique, a French Canadian, and I take upon ourselves the job of chief cooks; the boys are dispensers. Some
come, others go. Enormous rucksacks litter the floor. All is
movement and change; yet it is as though we are a family,
known to one another at some primitive and basic level.
Through the days we pursue each his way. Through long
hours I prowl the galleries, stand entranced, loiter about the
fountains, chatter on the bridges, lie sun-drenched on the
narrow fringe of shore that juts out into the waters of the
Arno, watching the dreamlike gestures of the young boatmen
as they scoop the mud from its bed with fifteen-foot spoons.
Often I am companioned only by the ten-year-old Simple
who fishes diligently with one hand while with the other he

holds aloft the spokes of a sunshade divested utterly of its rags.

Nothing at the American Express.

In bookshops I find Arthur's translations and, reading them over with delight, feel I hold him close.

I make acquaintances. There are two American students on a 'bourse'. A young countess has lent them her villa in which to have their child. They are very young. And deep in love. One day they will have their degrees. One day they will marry. Or not.

Up on the hill, there is Harold Acton. But I do not seek him out. More to my purpose, and to Arthur's need, is Father Pietro in his poor-boys' sanctuary. One day I climb the rocky way to where he sits and place in his keeping not only Arthur and Beryl but my son, John, on his besieged Korean hill. He extends a hand – 'Priez pour moi.' His voice holds peace; the limitless serenity of the spirit. I run, light-headed with the certainty of safety – of purpose – of the unknown end – and, to mark it, to acknowledge, buy from my ancient wizened silversmith in the black cave of his stall on the Ponte Vecchio his delicate heart of antique silver.

My sandals break. I stir the family rice-pot while the shoe-mender, robustly refusing any coin, sews them up again: it becomes a daily task.

But . . . the American Express.

This time, I telephone through an interpreter the postmaster at Bertinoro over the hill. I explain that I shall post to him a letter within a letter. The inside one will be merely an envelope addressed in a certain hand to a certain person. He is to examine the handwriting, destroy it; and await my further call. Two days later, again I ring. Has he recognised, as familiar, such a letter: as resembling others that have come? Certainly: and they have come with some regularity. Have they been delivered to the villa on the hill? Certainly. Ah! – and are the English couple that have been occupying it alone still in residence? No; they have departed this very morning. Very early. To Milan.

*　　　*　　　*

So. To Milan. And to the strong feeling of near-proximity. Yet followed quickly by the urgent haste to London.

I am home again. Home again. And, waiting, I make no move.

I busy myself with the matter of the photographs – with the placing of the articles for Air France.

Arthur's letters – odd paragraphs, odd scraps of paper – many times re-directed – begin to drift back to me. Each is articulate as a cry. None is from Bertinoro.

It is to be many, many months before I am to know how it was for him – the long desperate weeks in that close-shuttered villa; in loneliness, in isolation, in terror and in near-despair.

'Beryl would not let me so much as move into the garden: she believed I had you concealed behind every bush.'

'Ah, Hun – had it only been true!'

But he looks grave, and I add, 'Or would that have been – disastrous – for you?'

'Very,' he says. And I see again my foot quickly withdrawn from the step of the little bus that, in twenty minutes, would have taken me to him; hear again my father's childhood injunction – 'Intuition comes from deeper and further off than thought. Never ignore it.' There are indeed (how well I know it) means of communication other than words – spoken or written – between those who care. Just as – audibly summoned – I had fled in haste through the little town of Pisa, so then, in Florence, though my heart was in full flight, had my foot paused. 'No.' The single syllable had seemed to vibrate, hang, visible, in the glittering air.

He says: 'On the way home ... in Milan ... I searched the streets for you. Odd: I felt you were there.'

'I was there. And I searched the streets for you.'

Silence.

And now he says: 'It is strange. Beryl was very generous. I couldn't control her: wherever we went she gave away large sums of money.'

'Whomever to?' I ask, astonished.

'Well ... to the gardener's wife at Bertinoro, for instance;

she handed her forty pounds as we left. I must say, as a tip I thought it a bit much; don't you?'

'Yes.'

From now on Arthur began to receive in his mail communications with unlikely postmarks – 'Can we eat here together this evening, seven thirty?' – 'Shall be in Reading Room till closing time, then home' – intelligible enough; but franked Aix-en-Provence, Heidelberg, Sydney, NSW, or even Monte-Video over the appropriate stamp: any postmark indeed that, filched from some business waste-paper basket, I could convincingly copy.

'But *how?*'

'Look close, Hun – and you will agree that one of my so-neglected talents might well have been forgery.'

He is incredulous. The envelope is snatched up: the stamp, the date, the wavy or broken lines – all is held an inch from that microscopic eye. Then he smiles broadly. 'You are *very* clever.'

'Well ... it's less troublesome than posting slips of paper behind bricks in blitzed churches, Honey ... with the weather as it is, altogether simpler. And ... safer, don't you think?'

[32]

Return

But now he stands in my doorway, beret askew, his coat which seems a size too large flapping wide like the great wings of a bird. His face is ravaged. There is no greeting.

'I've got Beryl back. We've been back several days. I came round at once. You were not here. I'm taking Beryl to a private place in Exeter – run by a woman she apparently met in Switzerland, a Mrs C. You did not send the notes' – for an instant the eyes he lifts to mine are heavy with reproach, but there are other more urgent matters – 'Will you find out how much a hire-car to Exeter would be and book it for Thursday.'

He has moved to his accustomed chair. I gaze down at him. The change in his face is alarming. There have been many weeks but even so they have taken strange toll. The bones of the cheek and jawline seem almost visible through the skin. And he is a man cut down, mentally and emotionally, to barest essentials; a man, as it were, involved in a military operation of magnitude and of imperative importance.

'I *must* get her to Exeter,' he repeats now. 'It's where she wants to go. And you must help me.'

I think, 'In his mind has been no interval of time, no parting. I am a vital piece of equipment he has left here, in this room. And here, in this room, naturally, he has found it. The wheel grinds on; gathers speed. Beryl is the hub; he is the felloe; the spokes . . . No, I am but the space between. "Spaces between the spokes of the wheel . . .?" Then, in the split second that it takes for thought to move over lands, lives, philosophies, a voice springs within me. It is saying: 'Yes.

You must always be where he can find you now. Always. You are no longer free. It is, after all, your choice. You have made it.' 'When?' I murmur – and I see again the small metal table at Antoine's; the steam-belching pavement. But the voice tosses this aside as tiresome nonsense, and I know that many centuries have been flung over the shoulder like a bundle of twigs. And the voice goes on: 'You are his island. He is a swimmer in strong tides. You are his rock in the Indian Ocean ...' I think – a rock over which those same tides must flow. 'He will need footholds,' the voice moves on, 'even finger-grips. There will be typhoons. They will lay you bare. And there will be times when you – and he – will be all but submerged. But – you must be *there*. He must know ...' But here another voice chimes in – laughs happily: 'But that is what he *does* know! That is what he does not doubt. And shall have no need to doubt. But there will be times of limitless brightness, ineffable peace – times so still, so lit, lit as only in dream, that sea merges with sky: times when, in shining wonder, horizons are lost ...'

He has sunk deep in the enfolding chair; his arms flung wide; his hands hanging in exhaustion. I run to him; kneel and lay my head in his lap. He lifts my face to his: 'What were you thinking?' he says.

'I wasn't thinking: you know I try *never* to think.' I laugh, 'I was *being*.'

He is with me now: a gaze so loaded I can scarcely meet it. 'What were you being?'

'A rock in the Indian Ocean. There'll be storms. I'll always be it.'

He presses my head down into his lap as though he would submerge me. His fingers loose my hair and play lightly with each strand as it were weed afloat in a tide. He lifts the long dark ropes one by one, pulls them out to their full length as though measuring their adequacy, kisses the end of each before he lets it drop back into place.

'Hawsers,' I mutter, wriggling up now between his knees and – back in the moment – demand with mock imperiousness: 'Do you love me?'

He does not smile at the oddness, the banality of the question. He lets his hands drop again to his sides. His voice is as still as the sea-bed as he answers: 'Don't you *feel* I love you?'

Beryl is ensconced at Exeter. Yet every day or second day, Arthur is with me. We go together to No. 50. 'She wants her gloves;' – 'She asks for her belt;' – 'She needs her black tights;' – 'She must have her . . .'

All is insane, of course; but indeed I am delighted. What Beryl wants, what she asks for, what she needs, what she must have . . . all must be attended to if it brings him up to town. It occurs to me too that the long train journey, the hours seated alone gazing at the now winter countryside, are perhaps his only respite: so needed, so replenishing. But always it is London for but an hour and the next train back. May-the-maid complains that these visits mean the place is turned upside down, drawers emptied, contents scattered in the haste of the search. 'What she needs all them things for down there I can't think! Having the time of 'er life, by all accounts. Nothing the matter with *her*, I'd say, Miss: jest play-acting.'

Christmas is upon us: comes, goes. I see nothing of Arthur until the New Year. Then . . . he is there.

'Beryl is very much better. She was the "life and soul" of the party. She has the young men patients in her room to sit on her bed and talk to her. But the matron – or, well, Mrs C – is not very pleased. Beryl is "not good" for them, it seems. And she goes down and wakes that lady up in the night and in the small hours of the morning to repeat chants with her. Now she wants to see Beryl's diaries. She thinks they may help her to understand the case. I suppose there could be something in the theory. I'm taking them down today. I shall spend the weekend down there and be up again on Monday. Shall we have dinner together on Monday? I could be here by six o'clock . . .'

He stands a moment. He says: 'Beryl is certainly much

[163]

better. She came to the station to see me off. But she did –
said – a strange thing. She ran after the train as it moved out
and called up to me, "Remember! Alison is Quint Number
One." What do you think she meant? She also said, "Is she
human?"'

'Human, yes indeed – but "Quint"' I repeat, puzzled. 'Is
it a word – or a name . . .?'

Suddenly he is staring at me. But unseeing. His eyes enormous as with some new comprehension; colour fled from his
face. He is rigid.

'What is it?' I cry now in alarm, beating my fists on his
chest. But he takes them and moves me gently aside. And not
to me, but to himself he says in dead and level tones:

'It is the name of a man in one of Beryl's favourite stories
. . . a story about children . . .'[1] and turning, is gone.

The door below has slammed, echoing up the empty stairs. I
have been leaning over the stair-rails to watch his descent,
but now . . . I am seized with sudden panic. I fly down after
him and catch him as he rounds the corner. I am out of
breath. I jerk to a stop beside him.

'Darling, Darling . . . Oh, my dear one . . . Don't go! Don't
go!'

'Don't *go*?' he queries mildly, with the gentleness one uses
to a distraught child, 'Don't *go*?'

I say; 'They are waiting. Waiting for your return so
that . . .'

The words that come out of my mouth are as meaningless
to me as to him. But, then I am aware, more so. For though
the voice is soft as velvet and wraps me about with its toler-
ance, one at least of the ears of his mind is pricked, is listening
attentively.

'So that . . .?' The words are repeated and hang in the air
between us, waiting also.

'So that . . .' I stumble on . . . 'Oh, I don't know – I don't
know! So that they can *persuade* you – something is being
planned, plotted – to *do* something: something wrong and

[1] *The Turn of the Screw* by Henry James.

dreadful. Oh, promise – promise you won't: *promise you won't do it.'*

He unlooses his hand fastidiously from my arm and glances at his watch. 'I shall miss my train,' he says flatly.

'Oh, but don't you see it's *better* to miss it? – that then you won't have to face them ... won't *have* to face them? *Missing* it – *not* going – will be your answer!'

For a moment he stands on the edge of the pavement, silent, with head flung up to the brightening sky. Then quickly he leans and kisses me, dives between a lull in the traffic and is again gone.

Slowly I retraced my steps to the house, climbed the stair, my heart numbed with its nameless fear. What was it? Was I, too, insane? For I could *hear* their voices. A flock of attacking birds – a ceaseless conflict, in argument, in dissension, beat upon my ears, beat a way into my brain.

But there was more than fear; there was danger; and for him. The combatants were strong and pressing and in the midst he stood, assailed; defenceless. The din was horrible. I was amazed he couldn't hear it. I have thought since, he did. Something was being planned, plotted ... It sounded crazy. But suddenly all doubt had gone from my mind.

Snatching up a coat, thrusting money into a pocket, I fled again down the stair and into the street. At a signal a passing taxi slurred into the kerb and I leapt for it – 'Paddington Station'.

A train stood at a platform. It was about to depart for Exeter. A platform ticket took me through the gate and on to it. I knew only one thing: that I must find Arthur, somehow, if necessary travelling down with him, daring his and every other fury, convey to him my now certain knowledge.

Swiftly but systematically I moved from compartment to compartment, from corridor to corridor. There were of course the lavatories, sometimes locked, and these I could not search. Only at the engine did I descend, desist. Was I defeated? Could he – yes, it was just conceivable – have caught an earlier train? I enquired of the engine-driver: yes, one had departed ten minutes before. From another platform. I stood still now while, with their series of jerks, carriage after carriage commenced to move, rapidly gathering speed. I watched until the last one had disappeared into the distance. And knew myself defeated . . .

On the Friday, Mrs Richmond, an elderly lady, came to stay with me. She had injured a leg and had lowered her heavy frame, with what looked like some degree of permanency, on to the divan in the front half of my room behind the heavy dividing curtains.

Suddenly a clatter on the stairs and Arthur was with me. His looks were wild, his voice high, strident. He cried: 'It is terrible. Terrible. I came only to see you. But I must go again immediately. Yes, yes, we shall still dine together on Monday – but now I must go.' Then with sudden force, 'Don't you understand it's *cruel* to keep me?'

I had made no move. Had said no word. I waited until I could no longer hear the stumbling step on the stair. Then I went in to Mrs Richmond. What had she heard? The heavy curtains between us had been closely drawn, but now she was sitting up, supporting herself on one trembling hand, agitated.

'What was it? My dear, what has happened? That man – whoever he is – is in a terrible state – is on the edge of breaking!'

On Monday, a telegram arrived – NOT MONDAY BUT TUESDAY GORDON SQUARE AT SIX.

So. Mrs Richmond stayed on. She lay, reading, aware of my comings and goings, an eye to my preparation of the evening meal which I had decided to assemble, pack into a basket and take with me to No. 50.

Once, as I passed close, she put out a hand. 'How happy you are, my dear. You love this man. It is always a great joy to prepare for the creature one loves.'

Yes. I was happy: it was as though I were folded about by the awareness – the storm of conflict abated – of his love.

I smiled – picked up my basket and went off to our rendez-vous. 'Don't you *feel* my love?' Yes, *indeed* I felt it. Throughout the afternoon as he had approached in the train: and now, as he awaited me in his high kitchen, his love enfolded me. I moved, cocooned in its certainty.

Both doors were ajar. For a moment, as I entered this vast, dim room, I could not see him. But yes, there he was, over there, in the corner by the sink. I crossed to the broad table: unpacked my things, set them ready, and moved to the armchair by the fire.

'We've a marvellous feast, Sweetheart,' I said.

Wondering, but not disturbed, at his silence, I looked up and saw him moving slowly, like a shadow (like Orphée, I remember thinking, in the Cocteau film), along the far wall. His face, white and staring, was towards me. His eyes were like hollows in a mask. He crept, came stealthily, as though I were a wraith, insubstantial.

I rose, pulled out our chairs, and sat down. 'Shall we eat?' I said, 'while it is still so delicious?'

At the end of the table and still without a word, he took his place and fell to. I looked at him. We had neither touched, nor kissed, nor greeted one another. He was eating as though ravenous. Back to the window, face in shadow, he was eating like a starving man.

My food was untouched. I rose and stood behind him, putting my cheek against his hair. Sliding my hand across a shoulder and down a busily-moving arm.

'I suppose you know,' he said now, between one mouthful and another; 'I suppose you know. We are never to meet again. I'm giving you up.'

The words, spoken casually and like a schoolboy, had no meaning. I laughed gently. 'That's silly, Darling. We can't give one another up.'

His voice lifted suddenly into the strident key. He said: 'She says I've got to give you up. She says I must choose. And *that* is how I want it' – and continued to eat with the rapid motion of an automaton.

[167]

I moved back to my chair where I could see him. But his face, shadowed, carved in stone, told me nothing. He did not meet my eyes.

And suddenly I understood – and knew this verdict was true. So. The conflict . . . with whom, and how many? . . . had come to an end: and terms negotiated. I felt I might faint. I went to the hearth-rug and crouched there, my head bent to the floor. I had forgotten him. My fists beat helplessly on the rough stuff of the mat. Words came out of my mouth: 'Oh, Christ. Christ. I can't. I can't. I can't bear this pain.' I lay inert; blinded, unfeeling.

And then a great cry burst from Arthur. He stumbled to his feet and reeled about the room. 'No! No! No!' he shouted, as he lurched, clutching at chairs, table, cupboard; 'No!' Great sobs shook him. His whole body seemed buffeted, as in a gale at sea. Leaning back against a far bench, his head jerked down on to his breast: 'It is *my* turn to cry now,' he cried between deep-rising sobs. '*My* turn. *My* turn. *My* turn to cry. And I think my tears will never stop.'

I rose and flew to him, all but carried him to the armchair, sat down, drawing him on to my lap, like a child, encircling the now frail body with my arms. Tears streamed down the sunken face; the mouth trembled in its agony of suffering. 'Oh! Oh! Oh!' The words shook from him like a groan.

Wiping the tears aside with my bare fist, I pressed my lips against the bowed head; with broken words, broken kisses, showered the loved and broken face. 'Hush, my Darling. Oh, hush. It can't happen. Things like this don't happen. It won't, you'll see. Oh, I love you, love you, love you.'

Suddenly the sobbing ceased; the body slumped as though lifeless, deep into my arms; the head lay on my shoulder. From closed lids the tears continued to flow . . . endlessly, endlessly.

Above us was a kitchen ceiling-rack on which May-the-maid had hung socks to dry. With my right hand I reached up and pulled them down. With the damp woollen things I wiped his face – cheeks, eyes, matted hair – again and again; and then my own; our tears mingled in the damp wool. And soon I became aware that the pounding heart was quiet; tears continued to ease themselves from under the closed lids; but – he was asleep.

How long we lay, huddled so, exhausted, feelingless, I do not know. Silence, as of death, had invaded the room when at length I slid from under my burden, covered it with a rug, and tip-toed down the stairs, letting myself out of the front door and into the night street.

My flat was in darkness. There was no stir from Mrs Richmond. I pulled off my garments and slid, naked, into the wide bed.

It was many weeks, months, before – the room, the world, tipping slowly from right to left; small explosions in the skull; wings of caged birds beating through all my arteries; groping a way back to nights and days – I was able at last to leave it.

Of Arthur nothing was heard or seen. He had – as he had said, and faithful to his word – given me up.

People, doctors, came; went. At some point Mrs Richmond must have departed to her home in one of the western counties. I have no memory of the event. Nor ever heard of her again.

Only in the well of pain in which I found myself were we together; and one. Knowing the pain was his; exact; I lay still – waiting for time to pass.

[33]

A Twist of Paper

John was home. John ... was safe. And he had gone to
Heidelberg. With but twelve pounds in his pocket, and no
single word of German ... to grope his way back from his
besieged hill in Korea ... he had gone to Heidelberg.

But, before he had gone, lifting one foot to a chair to lace
a shoe, he had paused, straightened his back a moment and
said: 'D'you see Waley?'

'No,' I say, trying not to let him hear the depth of pain in
the single word.

'I saw him this morning. I have seen him several times.'

'John. You have seen him? Where?'

He crosses the room to the open window, stands tall against
the topmost branches of the Sumac Tree; the Tree of Heaven.
He says quietly, 'Swaying in the traffic ...'

'Swaying in the traffic.' At once I am in the lobby of the
British Museum. The swing-doors revolve slowly. A group of
doormen glance up and whisper together. 'Here comes Waley.
He's on the slide. He looks like a man who wants to be dead.'
Then I am in the snow of the rose garden ... running, running.
The lake – the lakeside in the frozen park. The solitary
black-coated figure ... swaying beside it.

'Thank you for telling me, John.'

When he is gone ... for whole days together I wander the
streets. Each day I find myself, unaware, at some beloved
spot. The 'marriage-tree' in St George's Garden. The
mallow-fringed island. The secret garden ... and here on our
bench at the farthest end, a nun is seated telling her beads. I

stand quiet, unnoticed, watching her. Tell them for me . . .
For us . . . for us, I plead in my heart. Tell them . . . No, no,
not us . . . for him. And I creep away.

Round the northern corner of the square, I stand still.

He is there.

Behind the tall iron railings. Pacing slowly the path beyond
the new-dug border bed of shrubs. He is within speaking
distance. His hands are clasped loosely behind his back. His
head is bowed. His face . . . is surely the saddest in the world.
'. . . like a man . . . who wants to be dead.'

No! No! my heart cries out and, taking a scrap of paper
from my pocket, using my crouched knee for desk, I write the
words: 'I love you. Please love me.' I fold it about a pebble
and fling it . . . so that it falls at his feet. He stops, startled.
He walks on. He returns; and as he passes again the scrap of
paper, he touches it with one foot. But his pacing continues.
Down. Up. Down. Up. And now it is almost as though he
were guarding it, carefully, from any violation. At length he
stops, stoops quickly, reads the message, crumples it, and
tosses it over his shoulder. But in that instant he has seen me
– my face pressed against the bars; our eyes have met and
held.

Now he has his back to me again. I reach for a long stick,
a thin broken branch, and try to draw the tell-tale message
towards me. It lies on the garden-bed, midway between the
path and the railings. 'Darling,' I am saying now in my mind,
'Darling, it's not safe to leave it there – not discreet.' We are
opposite James Strachey's house. I glance up at the windows.
'Alix . . . might pick it up . . .' I say.

Now he is returning slowly. He steps on to the freshly
turned clods of earth. Stooping swiftly, he snatches up
the twist of paper; folds it, places it in an inside pocket,
and – without another glance in my direction – moves
away.

I wait, hidden by the bushes and only long enough to see
him resume his walking. But . . . is the face not that, after all,
of one who yearns to live? I watch him with a warmth of
certainty. So. We are still together. We are not alone. I turn

and make for the back streets. I make for home. I run like a hare. I run for sheer joy.

Three days later, I turn my head on my early-morning pillow. I fling out an arm. It touches something familiar: tweedy . . . and smelling of pipe tobacco. I open my eyes. Kneeling, he is there . . . his face buried in the strew of my hair. It is over. It is finished. Tears stream suddenly across my face, to my mouth. I lick them away. Their salt is nectar.

[34]

The Electric Tea-Party

Now weeks flow by. Quiescent. Without communication. Without, indeed, the need for this. For I move in a dream of acceptance; a sea becalmed, a sea unruffled by fear, by doubt, by even hope or desire.

For what has happened? We have been driven, together, to a deep of suffering whence, returning, we can never again be separated. We are as two who, side by side, have lived out some momentous battle, some blitz of the spirit, some crisis of human experience, some deep of dark and light, that thereafter finds them bound in a special relationship. Savagery ... has failed. We are, now, inextricable.

And though the days go by as silently as before – though no further gesture is made on either side of communication – content, a healing tranquillity, envelops me. I know – and it is enough – that never again can such deeps be plumbed; that Arthur, somewhere and somehow is busying himself, and with all the wisdom he can muster, to find a solution to our dilemma: a reconciliation of spirit, perhaps, between myself and Beryl ... for both, by enigmatic fate, have become the fabric of his life. In this pursuit I trust him – and am warmed by that trust. Whatever, indeed, the outcome – of life or of death – it seems now to matter curiously little; even, scarcely at all.

Spring days come, glitter, move back to make room for summer. Still he does not come, nor write, nor make a sign. To know nothing of the creature one loves is great privation and I know well that for him, too, this is true. News drifts from the odd sources of course – Old Lom;[1] Charlotte-and-Jean;[2] May-the-maid, whom I find one afternoon seated on a bench in Tavistock Square, in tears, with an old blue felt hat in her hand, a 'gift from Miss de Sousa' which she thrusts now deep into the litter-bin beside her. 'Oh, him, Miss ... I'd do anything in the world for him. When you read in the paper of things that happen to people ... good people ... you wonder why ...'

I leave her there, cross the garden and, turning a corner, almost collide with Arthur coming my way. We look at one another now with only gladness.

'Are you free on Saturday?' he asks. 'I thought we might go to Kew. Beryl's going to her sister. I'll call for you at ten.'

I walk on air.

Late on Friday afternoon he comes up my stair, but with lagging step I think, enters, sits down and states: 'Beryl would like you to come to tea with her.'

'Come to *tea* with her?' I am amazed. 'Is it a party?'

'No. I don't think so.'

'Oh dear!' I murmur stupidly, uncertain of this new move. I consider in silence.

Arthur says, 'I think it would please her if you would accept.'

And that would make life easier for you, I am thinking: I say, 'Yes, of course – will you accept for me? Tell her it's very kind of her and I shall be pleased to come. Next week sometime, is it?'

'No. Not next week.'

'But there's almost none of this left. Or do you mean Sunday?'

'Saturday.'

'Saturday? But that's tomorrow ... That's *our* Saturday ... we're going to Kew!'

He is silent.

---

[1] 'Lombardo': Alfred Lomnitz, an artist with a studio on the second floor of No. 50 Gordon Square.

[2] Charlotte Gaffran and Lady Jean Stuart: the joint leaseholders and occupiers under the Bedford Estate of No. 50 Gordon Square.

'You mean . . . you really wish me to say yes? Oh Darling!'

Still he does not speak. He sits abstracted. I go to him and touch his arm. 'All right,' I say. 'But it's very hard to be happy about it. And if the sun blazes out as the radio says it's going to, it's a *dreadful* way to spend an afternoon. . . . It's . . . immoral.'

He smiles at the word, but ruefully: 'I'll tell Beryl you'll come. At four.'

Next day Katie rings to invite me to take lunch at her studio. The sun has indeed 'blazed out' and – thinking how whole cycles of flowers have been missed at Kew, thinking of the corner of the bricked wall of the kitchen garden where a blackbird sings always for us alone – to lift my spirits, I go.

Somehow they do lift. Pic walks with me, afterwards, to the door in Gordon Square. I know his native curiosity makes him long to come in – and wonder, now, if the pattern of our lives had been changed considerably had he done so. Pic has known Beryl – 'The Babbler' – abroad at Kitzbühel, and for many years. 'Well,' he grins now, 'keep your fingers crossed.'

Charlotte opens the door to me – rolling her eyes upwards as she does so. Her meaning is all too clear: there have been 'scenes'. I leap for the stair where, half way down, Arthur is leaning over the banister. He turns now and we climb in silence. I hear myself say, inexplicably and without conscious thought, '. . . As a lamb that is led to the slaughter . . .'

Before me, three steps up, he sways, clutches the rail, pauses for a moment and moves on. At the door of the sitting-room he stands aside. Even in the half-light of the landing I see his face is white; his mouth, slightly open as though to speak, trembles; his eyes are pointed with alarm.

I smile, hoping to reassure him; to convey to him that I do not share it.

And then, standing there, I do a curious thing. I do it – again without conscious thought – an action not at all in my habit and almost inconsequent, I make the sign of the cross.

The result is instant and strange. Arthur turns and disappears into the kitchen . . . I enter the room alone.

The windows are heavily darkened against the mid-afternoon sun. The air is curiously electric, as before thunder. I fancy I can hear the faint crackle of my hair. A great silver witch-ball hangs from the ceiling, reflecting back the room and its contents. Gigantic masks mouth and leer from cupboards and corners. Beryl sits in an armchair before a round table, decked and laden as for an important occasion. I know the lace and linen to be the household's best – the china, the silver, the whole array to impress – I wonder who is expected.

Beryl greets me with a raised hand aglitter with rings and I see that she, too, is unduly decked – jewels and beads, earrings and brooches, glitter as she moves. Her face, too, is heavily made-up, her mouth bright with lipstick, and her eyes gleam and dart like small black animals in ambush. Her voice is honey. She at once, without waiting for others to arrive or, to my surprise, even for Arthur to follow me into the room, draws the cups towards her. But I notice that her hand seems suddenly agitated and I leap to my feet.

'Dear Beryl,' I exclaim, 'do let me pour my own. I'm rather odd about tea. I take it so weak as to be hot water,' and, without waiting for comment, take the cup nearest me and pour my brew.

Arthur now enters and sits primly on the edge of a couch. He receives his tea and Beryl extends to me a plate of small cakes.

'I am the most miserable guest,' I say now, 'but I confess to being quite unable to eat a morsel of anything. I lunched well with Pic and Kate and normally, in any case, take nothing in the afternoon. Please forgive me.'

There is an angry rattle of tea-things. I look up to see, with astonishment, that Beryl is trembling from head to foot. Arthur springs to his feet and goes to her. Leaving me astonished, in silence and half-supporting her, he leads her away and up the stair.

I wait. Then I pour myself another cup of tea and look again about the room. It is, I think, a 'theatre-set' for a palmist; or no, rather for some not-to-be-underestimated worker of spells. It is a lovely room – and I amuse myself mentally hurling everything out, flinging up the blinds, opening the windows wide to the sun and letting its long radiance traverse to its very corners to make childish nonsense of the wooden and jewelled images, the enormous and horrific *papier-mâché* masks that clutter the place. I think again of Kew. I wonder if our thrush is singing his heart out in our secret corner by the high wall. I feel suddenly tired.

Arthur appears in the doorway. 'I think we will take the air,' he says sternly.

I rise happily enough but I whisper, 'What is happening? ... What is it? ... What has happened to Beryl?'

He does not answer and I follow him down the stairs. Out of the house and along the pavement, in silence he strides with me all but running at his side.

When we enter the corner gate of the park I venture a hand on his arm. He shakes it off. I move away on to the grass and, at some distance where it is long, sink down at full length, my arms flung up above my head, my gaze on the serenity of the moving sky.

Arthur comes and sits beside me. When I look up at him I am amazed at the fury in his face. Is it fury? Or fear? He begins to talk, rapidly, the words pouring down upon me.

'What did you *do* to Beryl? You have made her very ill. What did you *say* to upset her so? Tell me. You must tell me at once! What did you *do*?'

'I did nothing. I did nothing to offend her. I explained ... I apologised and explained that I had just dined late with Pic and Katie and could not eat. I poured my own tea. I poured my own tea ...'

Suddenly I cannot bear it – the burden of his fury, his injustice and his hate. Tears spring in my eyes and stream down my cheeks on either side until they fill my ears like wells. My throat is constricted to the point of choking. I cannot continue. I close my eyes and breathe deep to hold back the sobs that I feel pressing against my ribs. Soon I become aware of the cool grass-stems between my fingers and that the warmth of the sun has moved from my face. I open my eyes and sit up. Arthur is nowhere to be seen.

Somehow the night passes, and the day. With the evening Arthur is standing in my doorway. He is in a state of greatest agitation. He says, 'I have written to John to tell him it would be better if he were not to live with you. For two years.'

'Not live with me? You mean here? But this – attic – is the only "home" he has.'

'I have explained to him that you are mad. You *are* mad, you know. But you will get better.' And, with odd repetition, 'In two years.'

I look at him now with some curiosity. He is perfectly serious. I say, 'But . . . he won't believe you. He was here only a weekend or so ago and we had a *very* happy time together. I think it was rather silly to write that. And unfortunate. He's sitting his finals, as you know, and your letter will upset him,' and add: 'Not for me, but for you.'

There is a pause. 'You mean, he'll think *I'm* mad?'

'Of course. But I'll write and tell him to think nothing at all, just to get on with his work; that it's all a mistake; all nothing.'

'Nothing? It's all nothing?' Suddenly his voice is scarcely audible.

What is moving in his mind? Or out of it? He looks at me in sudden calm, almost with a sort of hope, a question.

'Nothing at all, my Darling. Shall we make love? I long to lie in your arms.'

Like a child turning from the memory of nightmare, as freed from a spell, he now loosens his clothes, tramples them to the ground, slides naked between the cold, sane sheets and thrusts out his arms to me wildly, wildly. 'Am I *cruel* to you, my Darling? Am I *cruel*?'

'Yes. Often. Dreadfully cruel. But I love you and so I want you to be *you*; how you *are*.'

'But the *cruelty* is not *mine*! You *must* believe me! The cruelty is not mine – *None* of the cruelty! None of the cruelty!'

'Hush! . . .' I whisper. 'I *know* it isn't, Silly. Or how do you think I could love you at all? That I *do* is proof that I believe you. That I *do* is proof that it isn't. I *know* it. You don't *have* to tell me.'

For answer a hand creeps up, the fingers tangling in my hair; twisting it once round his wrist – like a hawser – he draws me to him.

[35]

Omens and Portents

One day, after an unprecedented silence from Arthur and some seemingly unreasonable anxiety, I visited No. 50. I knew what had been the intentions for the immediate future: May-the-maid on her annual holiday and Beryl, so I understood, insisting on a visit to her sister in Forest Hill. Yet ... one never knew what might, or might not, be happening in that house.

I climbed the stairs to the flat: the cupboard door of the topmost stair stood wide and the landing in great confusion. I glanced to the left where the door of the large kitchen also stood ajar – and saw Arthur. He was standing, facing me, in shadow, on the far side of an ocean of shoes: slippers, boots, mules and high-pointed things of ancient design littered every space between. The whole room looked like a stage-set for a madhouse. I suppose, now, the scene might have been comic: had not all in that place been made of the very stuff of tragedy ... and Arthur's face, staring, wordless, across at me so frightening.

Some very ordinary instinct – simply to clear a pathway – made me bend to pick up a shoe.

'Stop!' he shouted at me. 'Don't touch them. They must stay as they are.'

I put the shoe carefully down – he, watching – placing it exactly as it had lain.

Then – fastidiously as a child who must not 'tread on the cracks' of a pavement ... as my Siamese at the end of her red lead, picking her way between the 'French letters' that

sprouted overnight from the grass of wartime Grosvenor
Square ... I made my way across to him.

I put my two hands on his shoulders. But he appeared
rigid. I turned and glanced at the table.

It was as *interesting* as one of those enormous trays in a
Victorian child's party game – when, each armed with pencil
and paper, one is instructed to gaze for the space of a single
minute, turn away and scribble down the things seen. Except,
yes, there was a difference. For here were jewels and trinkets,
of great and of lesser value: bracelets, chains, pendants, rings,
brooches and minutely carved ivories. They stuck upright in
the butter; they sank into the marmalade; they draped the
honey-pot and festooned the flower-vase.

For an instant my mind caught up with Dali's painting –
his flattened watches ... but Arthur was swaying at my side.
Yes – yet again – there had been a 'scene'. I pushed him
gently into the large fireside armchair – curled on to his knees
and, heads together, as ship-wrecked mariners on a raft, we
slept it off.

At my attic flat there was an escape hatch to the roof that
opened slowly on a hinge as a ladder, hooked to the ceiling,
was pulled down into place. This roof, in summer, became
our second world. Behind the front coping I had placed wide
boards across the central guttering from one slope of tiles to
the other: so that a platform was formed of good enough area
to sunbathe, to pass long sun-drenched hours with goat-skin
rugs for flooring, cushions for comfort, books and ourselves
for company. At the far end, boxes and planks supported
tubs of flowers and trailing things which, sheltered from the
north and thriving on London's soot and the high cleansing
breezes, made a kind of hanging garden. Arthur and I had
collected these from time to time in the little car from country
gardeners and there, miraculous in colour, they glowed and
multiplied.

We called it 'Babylon'.

One morning, alone with my books and even shaded a little
from the sun's hot rays, I knelt up and peered over the coping.

Arthur was crossing diagonally to my door. As welcome, and lest, not finding me in the rooms below, he should go again, I snatched up one of my light red slippers and, aiming carefully, dropped it to fall a yard or so in front of him.

He stopped. He stood stone still and stared at it. I was forced to call: 'It's my slipper. Bring it up with you.'

It seemed a very long time before I heard the creak of the ladder and he had sunk down at my side. His empty hands and the expression on his face prompted me to lean over the coping yet again. My slipper lay precisely as it had landed. I sprang to my feet, ran down the stair and retrieved it.

When I returned, Arthur said: 'Did you *mean* to do that?'

'Throw my slipper? Yes, of course. It was all I could snatch in time to attract your attention.'

He made no comment, and we lay quiet in the sun.

After a long time had passed, he opened his eyes and I said: 'Tell me, Darling – why did it, how did I, offend you?'

Then he related some Eastern myth about the population of the world. The gods, it seemed, curious to know something of mortals, sent down their younger gods to investigate earth. Their instructions, however, were explicit. Any who found himself seduced by a mortal would have surrendered his purity and his godhead – and, sullied, debased and contemptible, be no longer acceptable among the immortals. Many, it appeared, on this expedition succumbed and found themselves, in disobedience of this law, in such predicament. They had forfeited their virginity, their purity; they had become less than earthlings.

After which (and here my memory becomes vague) the legend created a custom in the East. The deepest insult one could give a man was to fling one's slipper in his path. The meaning was clear to all. He had fallen from grace; was culpable, contemptible and no longer acceptable.

Listening, I was enthralled. Delighted. 'And *that's* why people tie an old shoe to the carriage or the taxi of the bridegroom at marriages today? He's going off to copulate – to lose his virginity!'

'That is so,' said Arthur, grave still.

'But they also throw rice for fertility – and rose-petals for happiness . . . it's not *all* insult!'

Arthur was silent.

'You know,' I said, 'I think gods are a bit smug, don't you? And a bit boring. Half-gods are a thousand times nicer. And I'm going down to make us some China tea.'

'That man is at breaking point . . .' Mrs Richmond had said. Breaking point . . . even then? And now yet again, he stood before me at the head of my stair: beret askew, coat buttoned awry, eyes imploring, despairing. He murmured: 'I can't do it. I can't do it alone. I can't go on. You'll have to help me . . .'

A question? A prayer? How puzzling it all was. My mind ran on into idiocy . . . 'It's your life; it's your choice . . . And if you chose to keep a crazed Orang-outang and hand-feed it on rose-petals . . . I'd help you. If you CHOSE.'

I said: 'Tell me – Did you *want* Beryl in your life? . . . Under your roof?'

'No. No. But she insisted . . .'

Can a person insist? I thought, if it's grandeur she wants . . .

'Could you afford to set her up – perhaps in some luxurious hotel with a trained attendant?'

'It would be no good.' His gaze retreated now – moved inward; back down years, and scenes, unknown to me; returned as slowly . . . like an exhausted traveller. 'It would be no *good* . . .' he repeated. And this time the words had a flatness, a finality, that left no doubt of their truth.

'I will help you,' I said.

[36]

Old Lom

The huge Old-Testament eyes follow us . . . up the steps . . .
down the steps.

'Who is he?'

'Alfred Lomnitz. He has the flat above Charlotte. He is an
artist.'

Hesitating, shaking, there on the top step of No. 50, the
eyes – deep, Jewish, suffering – bore into mine: and I see that
he has Parkinson's disease.

It is some weeks later that, coming upon him alone, afraid,
in an empty street, I take his arm and attend him to the door
and safely into his flat. I tell Arthur. I ask Arthur if I may do
this. Beyond a rapid glance that says much or nothing, there
is no answer: and so, when the encounter recurs, I continue.

It is a happy acquaintance.

Before the war, before the internment camps . . . what tales
he has to tell of Paris: a Paris I had been born too late to
know. 'Between the wars.' I come to feel I had been born into
a limbo, a no-place . . . Why? . . . and must straddle two
worlds.

He is not only an artist, but a sensitive one; and now,
though his life recedes, his visions do not. His studio is
stacked with large canvases that are never to be used . . . that
are to be, together with unfinished works, easels and gear of
every kind, piled on to a builders' cart to be taken away – 'to
make space'. But now he stands, for comfort, at a tall sloping
desk and, with his good left hand and a long brush, puts on
blotting-paper microscopic jewels of colour. Somehow the
results manage to be infinitely eloquent. But where will these

end – these glimpses into the fading spirit of a man? I think, wryly, 'There is a pig-bin at the corner of the square . . .'

One evening, dining alone with him – the essential ceremony of silver and napery spread on the refectory table of his studio – there is a sudden sound above us. It freezes him. His arms, his hand, his head – all freeze. The sound increases: and across the board our eyes meet. Heavy objects are being moved. Scraping slowly – slowly – to and fro – on the floor above. I, also, am riveted by its strangeness: for what could make that sound but furniture pushed, slid – slowly, menacingly – hither and thither? Old Lom's eyes grip mine. 'C'est une maison maudite,' he murmurs.

It is difficult to proceed with our feast. For both, images assail and fasten in our imaginations until we have neither interest nor recognition of what is on the dishes before us. Lom lifts his eyes to the window at the far end of the room.

'I do not sleep,' he mutters, 'I do not know . . . which one of those two will come hurtling past the panes.'

I look at him, appalled.

'Oh yes,' he says in answer to my troubled gaze, 'you think it is nothing? But I have heard her threaten him, "I will push you from the window . . ." From corner to corner she pursues. From him there is no sound. There was a day when I left my door ajar. I was alone. My light had failed. With difficulty I climbed on a chair. My arms were above my head: my hands – I could not control them – were frantic to insert a new bulb. That was her moment. Her voice close behind me was low and menacing as the hiss of a snake . . . "So. *You* are *her* friend." I did not actually fall: somehow I clambered from that chair. I had dropped the bulb and broken it. I was in the dark. But my door had quietly shut.' He paused. 'Can you think what it is to live so?'

'But it's me!' I cried, sickened by the scene. 'It's *me*. Don't you *see* it's me? I mean my *coming* here. Oh, how could I guess my friendship could so harm you! I must not come again.'

'Yes. I think that is true,' he answered levelly. 'But even

so, you must come again. I can endure ... even the water poured between the boards of my ceiling ... for your companionship. You recognise what I paint. You understand what I am trying to say with my brush. There is only you. I have a son but for him what I paint is nothing. I beg you to come.'

I think: 'Oh, Lom – dear Lom – with your beloved Paris behind you, and mine but a dream ... Of *course* I'll come.' I reach across, take his jerking hand and kiss its thin, white fingers.

Together then we rise from the table. I guide him to the window, flung wide to the summer night, and we stand – each locked in the world of mind and spirit. Separate and together we stand ... Suddenly a cry sounds. It is not only close, but immediately above us. If we were to lean from the window we could see the face – beseeching, afraid – of him who makes it: 'No! No! Don't ... Don't do it, don't do it ...'

Instinctively, I thrust my fists across my mouth lest I should cry his name. My breath strangles in my throat and I am rigid. But somehow Lom's jerking fingers grasp and hold my wrist, restraining; his great eyes enjoining silence, while he drags me a step or two back into the room.

But now again there is no sound: and, while tears of terror and of sorrow stream down my cheeks, his voice is murmuring, 'Oui. C'est vrai. C'est une maison maudite.'

There came a day when Old Lom was carried from the house, slid into an ambulance and driven to a hospital. No-one on stair or in hallway had so much as touched his hand in passing.

'Where is he, May? Why?'

'Don't rightly know, Miss Alison. Some Italiano place, I think. There was nowhere else could take him in the hurry.'

I fled there. The *Ospidale Italiano*, Queen's Square. In a small room, its walls its only view, Lom's eyes embraced me as I entered, held me as I seated myself beside his bed. The right hand lay, at last unjerking, on the tight-stretched coverlet.

'The nuns,' he said at length, 'are very gentle.'

I nodded. 'Dedicated. You were right to come here. Lom,' I continued in a rush, 'Get better: get better enough and we'll go ... I'm poor as a rat but I'll "companion" you if you like ... and we'll sit in the sun, high up on the hills and look down on the sea.'

A soft, warm light comes into the brown depths and together we seem to move – with the speed of that light – through all his Jewish childhood, his wild, gay youth, his loves with their griefs and their betrayals, his internment, his lonely age ... through all that he had told me and much that he had not ... full circle to the place of his desire, set high above the sea.

He says gently, 'I'm looking at it ...' and we look together.

Still haunted by those glinting, weed-shadowed deeps of the Mediterranean, I go to bed early and sleep soundly.

In the night I wake; am instantly *wide* awake. Tears are wetting my pillow and I am saying, 'Oh Lom, Lom, did you *have* to go? Why didn't you wait? It *might* have happened ... Lom?'

At eight, the phone rings: it is the *Ospidale Italiano*. It is to say Mr Lomnitz has died.

'I know,' I say, 'he died in the night.'

'Well, yes. We found he had died when we went on duty this morning. You may see him, if you care to ...' and I knew they wished this. Religion is harsh, I thought; unsparing. But perhaps they're right.

I find Lom, perched rather high and partly covered by a sheet. His sensitive lips are torn back in the snarl of an animal; his gentle face is contorted in terror.

'Lom,' I whisper, 'it's savage, isn't it ... religion. Even dedication has to be savage ...' For I have noticed they had had to break the finger-joints, to fold them in an attitude of prayer.

Divertissements

Time moves forward with its superb indifference to trivialities. At Gordon Square, Old Lom is not mentioned. But one day, a step behind Arthur, I enter the large kitchen. An instant's glance shows that it is blackened: ceiling, walls, are burnt black; flames have leapt across them; the long window curtains are shredded ash. I make no comment. Nor, as he goes about the arranging of our meal at the scarred, discoloured table, does Arthur. Never, in the months that follow – and they are many before repairs are set in action – is any reference made to the curiousness of the circumstance.

It is from May-the-maid, shopping bag swinging with a certain truculent elation, that the explanation at last comes: 'Oh, tried ter burn the place down she did, Miss, an' him in his bed if you ask me. When I come, there he was dancin' on the table, throwin' buckets o' water at the ceiling as all come back on 'im o' course an' her shriekin' and laughin' like she's never been so pleased before. An' there's that big waste-paper basket as he keeps by the fireplace put over under them curtains – as is all ashes o'course. An' then the firemen come an' takes one look an' says about "public danger" an' ter put 'er away: but 'e says an accident an' all the laughin' an' dancin's just shock ... an' well, I don't know ... but it's a God's miracle there's either of 'em alive this day!'

Snow comes early and thick that year. For many days ice piles itself against the iron railings and the steps of the entrances. And it is now 'house arrest'.

Arthur's voice comes, muted, over the phone: 'If you could

manage to come to the corner of Bedford Way ... if you should see me at my kitchen window, raise a hand ... I may make no answering sign ... but I shall see you there ...'

And so, see me there he did.

Over how many hours and days of blizzard only the neighbours, curious – only the watchers in the wings can say. I am not good at freezing: and often I froze to the very pavements on which I moved from one stone foot to another. But what significance had that when – at times more fortunate than some – at a high window, a solitary hand was lifted ... and slowly lowered ... in answering sign?

[38]

Mexican Art

Oh but I was tired – tired of the nonsense – tired of the wickedness! I looked at her. That incredible mask . . . where had I seen it? Over and over . . .? Why, only that morning at the Tate. The sickening grimaces, the gyrations . . . that could be, as I had witnessed many times, so expertly and so instantly controlled: this all-but-fabled creature who yet boasted 'possession' of the mind of genius.

Now, before me in the midday street, she trilled and smirked and spun like some exotic tropical bird. It fascinated – this zoological dance, this flirt and glitter, in the dark noon-shadow of the grimed doorway.

'You want,' she was saying, 'to congratulate me?'

'Perhaps,' I heard myself answering. 'Perhaps.'

And I thought 'Yes; she is successful – and success calls for congratulation.'

'You wish,' she trilled again, 'to congratulate me on my book!'

Her book – that agony of *Arthur's* toil . . . *A*, of course . . . I had forgotten that.

For an instant I was back in her fantastic room bending, with Arthur, to pick up the torn and indecipherable scraps of paper that littered it like confetti. Of these . . . must he make a book . . . (It was surely a task in a fairy tale – to weave a cloak of feathers – to scrape away a mountain with a spoon – to empty a lake with a thimble!) A book: that she might sign it with the flourish of her name. And the appended scrawl: '*I* am the poet! *I* am the genius!'

'Your book? No. I was thinking of . . . your life.'

My words were my thoughts, thoughtlessly uttered.

But now I was amazed at the result of them. Their effect was that of a hot and searing wind. For the creature before me withered, shrank, was fantastically and instantly still. Just as a spider, touched by a curious finger will furl, shrink, wither, feign death – lie 'dead' as dust to be blown aside, but yet is alert, aware, ready to flash to safety at the moment danger moves on – so now Beryl leaned, grotesque, rigid, moveless against the grimed lintels of Tavistock Place ... awaiting my departure.

I remembered the words of Gordon Luce long ago – 'It is a jungle play.' I knew jungle well enough. *And* its law. But this was London. And no law applied. Yes, indeed.

I felt only the sickness of distaste and turned away. I turned on my heel again for Tottenham Court Road. At the corner I glanced back and, without surprise, saw her dart across the road; alert, vigorous, and in haste she hurried towards the square. At the first sight of the railings – in the gaze, as it were, of the windows, this strange being took on yet another all-too-familiar character. She became, no longer a frightened crone, but a gentle, timid, pitiable 'old lady' – uncertain, unhelped, making her way slowly and with difficulty to the doorway of her home.

I did not need to see round corners. I knew, so well, what now was happening. Arthur from the upper windows had seen her approach. Clambering at speed down the stairs, leaving the door ajar (much to the fury of Charlotte and Jean) he runs to her – 'Oh, my poor one!' – and supports her now seemingly nerveless head on his shoulders, all but carries her up the steps.

From behind the curtains, the bushes, the railings, the quickly-lifted hands of the passers-by, come the same words uttered: 'Those two! Just look at those two.'

Next morning I am awakened roughly by Arthur sitting on the edge of my bed. 'What did you do to her? Tell me at once. You have made her very ill!'

But I am aware that he is not really angry with me; only

A Half of Two Lives

that he must *know*. I sit up. I say quietly: 'She was "perform-ing" in Tottenham Court Road. Workmen were laughing at her. I followed her a few steps – she saw me and asked if I wished to congratulate her on her success. I had forgotten all about her book – but suddenly there flooded in all the non-sense of the years – the humbug, the play-acting – the "play-acting" that you'd always said you detested.

'Do you remember when I saved a child's broken back in the Italia Conti School, because I knew what to do, what had been necessary to do with my own broken back at the age of fifteen? And after, when, as a sort of reward, I was offered the job of understudy to Madeleine Carroll – I, who knew I could be brilliant, who loved the work and was penniless – how you entreated me to refuse the offer ... because you "detested actresses": because you "detested" every kind of play-acting?'

'But I do, I do! I *detest* actresses – I *detest* play-acting!'

I look at him. In that long moment I feel like a suicide. And also like a murderer. I say: 'Your whole life is play-acting. And Beryl is a superb actress. It was on that – *that* "success" – that I congratulated her.'

He had turned white. He looked at me, not so much with hate as with a kind of horror. He stood up. He said quietly: 'I shall never speak to you again.'

He went to the door. Then he turned about: 'If you were to put on some clothes we might walk across the square to-gether. I'm going to the British Museum.'

I pulled on some garments. But I had accepted his ulti-matum – and my heart was like a stone. I went to the kitchen and threw some water over my face. Then I followed him in silence down the stair.

In silence still we came to Russell Square. In silence we walked the diagonal path that led to Montague Street. How could such pain – such parting – be? What gesture would break the horrible spell that seemed to be upon us?

'I shall never speak to you again ...' Yes. His face was ice-cold; detached – indifferent; his eyes opaque.

The scent of wall-flower from the beds beside us was

stifling-sweet. Suddenly I plucked a single bloom and held it out to him. The effect was startling. He seemed to take a veritable leap into the air. He danced and stamped beside me. 'How can I *know* such a creature – so vulgar, so barbarous as to pluck a flower in a public park! How can I *know* you! How can I *ever* have known you!'

He rushed away, I trotting at his side, and, as though now quite desperate to escape me, he hailed a passing taxi.

As the door swung shut I panted up and, reaching to him through the open window, proffered again the single flower. I breathed, for I had little enough breath left: 'Take this – to hate me by.'

As the taxi spun away he was adjusting it with considerable care in the lapel of his coat.

It was at least three mornings later that I became aware of a shadow obstructing the sun's rays from reaching my pillow. I opened my eyes and twisted my head sideways. Yes. Arthur was there. A faded wallflower drooped in his buttonhole.

He said, bending over, ineffably tender; 'I love to watch you sleeping. I love to look at your face . . . upside down.'

In silence, I considered his: 'upside down'. I said, 'Yours . . . is wonderful for me. Forever. Any sort of way,' and opened the bedclothes.

[39]

Conveyor-Belt

We walk on the Embankment from Westminster to the Tate as we like to do – leaning from time to time on the granite wall that separates us from the great weight of water that, this day, buffets and pushes its way to the estuary.

We walk, as we love to do, into the sun – and also, as in London one so often must, against a high wind from the west. It slaps at our cheeks and swings our heads aside: it snaps our eyelids shut. It catches us with buffets that turn us right-about-face, coats flapping, scarves strung out like pennants – a head-down running battle.

From the bright sky the wind seems to slant and dive visibly – hacking at the surface of the water, the brown-grey-silver-gold river water, that subtlest of colours that has no name – hacks with such sharpness, such surprise of strength, that it is chipped into a million small fountains that, gazing up-river, seem shot through with light, appear again as a sea of dancing feather-like flames. Leaning on one of the ancient, black granite bays, we pause to watch.

Silhouetted – black too, and bobbing on the chipped fragmented surface – comes a wild duck with her brood. The tide has turned, is running strong for the sea; behind them the wind drives relentlessly. The mother-bird makes no resistance more than to move from one to another of her scattering chicks that, themselves, fight instinctively to remain in some sort of formation.

They pass close and as we lean to admire the swiftly-moving, gay flotilla – the brave flutter – the small bobbing balls of feather – one, raised sharply on a sudden crest, is hurled out of the main stream into the granite bay below. And here – alone – bouncing – swirling – it remains: lifted, beaten against the dark towering wall, trapped in its angle – lifted and dropped, lifted and dropped – with no hope of regaining the main stream; the family already far down the river, the mother duck fighting the tide to remain abreast of the calamity.

'The seventh . . .' I exclaim, '*and* the smallest: it would be! *Is* there really something magical in numbers?'

'Yes.'

A young soldier has joined us. His face, watching, is all anxiety, urgent. 'What can we do?' he mutters to himself.

Swung on my shoulder by its cord is my 'dilly-bag' – the light wool-woven thing one carries abroad or on air travel. 'M/V ESPEROS' is woven across it.

'This,' I say, emptying the contents on the paving-stone at my feet. 'Quick, Pitten – your pockets – string – you always have string – or red tape will do.'

Arthur's hand, delving deep, brings it out – the tangle of string and assorted lengths of red tape. I begin rapidly to knot them together. 'We'll need a weight,' I call to the young soldier, 'a stone.'

But where on the Thames Embankment is a stone?

'Here!' he says, thrusting into his tunic, 'It'll have to be this,' and he brings out a torch.

'Excellent!' I cry, dropping it into the bag and securing the lengths of string to the handle-cord. 'Here. You do the job. It's an urgent one – it's desperate – and you're the soldier!'

He blushes with pleasure at the inferred superiority and trust, and, leaning far out from the wide coping, lowers the bag gently beside the bouncing and near-exhausted duckling.

Patience. Accuracy. Down the bag goes into the opaque waters, the mouth widening out as it fills, under the chick.

But with the jerk that would have been the heave to safety the little creature but rides the over-spill, helpless, back into the flood.

Patience. Accuracy. 'Timing,' I say quietly, and he nods. Again. Again. Again.

The fledgling, with each jerk against the granite wall, battered with ferocity, is losing strength.

Once more. We are now – all three – holding breath. Down. Not too far. Nor too full. Watch the movement of the water. A wave, that lifts high, a spurt, a splintering, a crash. A wave ... that lifts ... NOW!

And suddenly the chick is becalmed. In a lake no bigger than a dinner-plate he is floating – breathless – all-but-beaten.

But now ... paddling ... paddling with diminutive, webbed, and frenzied paddles.

And far below, down-river the yellow eyes of the mother creature are fixed on us: her strength, too, all but gone, her feet, too, working desperately to keep place in the tide.

We all three race along the river wall.

We all three lean again. The young soldier lowers the dilly ... gently ... slowly ... into the water beside her: the chick glides out against the strong maternal wing and in the next instant they are away. Away ... close and swift ... on the giant conveyor-belt of Thames ... rocking, rocking, but swimming too, towards the bewildered, deserted brood.

We watch until – afar off under the bridge – all are again together, tightly circling: a reunion of all but human excitement and congratulation: of achievement: of survival.

Now the boy is wringing out my dripping dilly and handing it to me.

'Your torch is ruined,' I say.

He shrugs, glancing up.

'Government Supply,' he grins: then blushes deeply. What has he said? – For he is unwinding the myriad short lengths of knotted pink tape that had emerged so instantly from Arthur's pockets. Who ... *is* this 'Gent' – so quiet – in the sober black overcoat? Lumme! From what *Ministry*?

But Arthur's eyes are shining like a boy's.

And, '*Operation Rip-Tide*' I shout against the wind, 'Ex-

pertly carried out and one hundred per cent successful!' – and
he grins his relief.

The young soldier straightens up, salutes smartly, and
marches off. For a moment we gaze after his trim, khaki-clad
retreating figure: then turn again to one another.

'How ... *lovely*,' murmurs Arthur: and we move on to the
Tate.

In the galleries we habitually part. Never far afield. And,
finding a thing we must share, we seek one another out.

Coming together in this way, I observe a group of persons
who seemingly are interested in our movements. It is not
unusual – and also not peculiar. I think, Arthur is, at the last,
'bien connu'. Then I espy Augustus John; and move across
to speak with him.

'Will you not come with me?' I fling back to Arthur.

'No.'

Surprised, I turn to look at him, but he has disappeared
into the crowd: is fantastically nowhere.

Soon we find ourselves together again and Arthur is tug-
ging gently at my sleeve. I know this for an urgent signal,
and we turn towards the doors.

Outside, as always, from the high, broad steps, the world
is just another canvas: a series of canvasses. The silken river,
still wind-gashed but scooping up the last of the sun; the
bridge; the elevated railway on the far side, with its toy train
of nursery blue – each in its frame: seen: captured – and
recorded forever in that best of catalogues, the mind's eye.
But, this evening, Arthur will not pause; moves rapidly down
the steps, with me, reluctant, following in his wake.

We walk in silence. Presently he says; 'Who were they?'

'They?'

'The group of people in the Gallery.'

But he need not have explained, for I too was wondering
the same thing. Were they ... general public? Art world?
Ackerley 'Gang'? Covent Garden Ballet?

'I didn't know them. But it's not *peculiar* that they should
know *you*. Perhaps they were friends of Beryl's.'

We have walked now the brief length of Millbank; past Lambeth Bridge; past the delicately-tessellated drinking fountain marking the abolition of slavery; past Rodin's splendid six burghers of Calais; past the Houses of Parliament – and are standing on the pedestrian-island at the bottom of Whitehall. Awaiting our chance to cross, I glance over my shoulder at the corner we have just left. There – grouped in almost identical manner – are the strangers: four men and a woman. At the same moment Arthur too has recognised them – and, to my horror, has flung himself into the traffic. I dive after him, while vehicles grind to a halt with a squeal of brakes. Arthur reaches the far side; is already on the pavement. I stretch out a hand and touch him. He wrenches free and, half turning, thrusting me violently back into the roadway, runs towards Trafalgar Square.

I stand again on the kerb: dazed. For I am three persons – one is shocked; one is puzzled; one, which remains within and uppermost as I follow at discreet distance, is filled with compassion for a fear I cannot know or explain.

With some forty or so yards between us, we continue the entire length of Whitehall. Past the Cenotaph. Past the Guards. Past the Admiralty. At the top, on the corner of the great swinging Nelson-dominated square, Arthur waits. Without looking round, he stretches out his right hand behind him. As I slip my fingers into it, his left signals a passing taxi-cab. Quickly it swerves to the kerb; he has opened the door, pushed me in and given direction: he is pulling me roughly towards him: he is covering my face with kisses. Remorse? Relief? I ask no question. And I cannot care. We are alive – and puzzlement is an irrelevance to which we can give scant attention. And the tide of this, I think amusedly, this thing called life, is bearing us as surely – as helplessly bobbing on its stream – as Thames conveyor-belt the brood of ducklings.

But this is a tide too, I think more seriously, depthless beyond our knowing, on which we must travel blind, unguessing, as pathless a way as they . . . To what haven? Or disaster? To what estuary, or open sea?

[40]

Manacles

By this time Arthur's visits were brief and spasmodic. There was no time when he might not appear – when his feet might not be heard stumbling on the stair, his hands groping at the door. He would enter ... swaying to the nearest seat; he would say no word: he would gaze with unseeing eyes, or seeing only what was visible to himself alone. His emaciated cheek bones bore fevered red patches; he was unshaved; ill-clad. He sat slumped with the right hand flung – rather curiously – over the left. What is this? I began to think. And watched carefully. Was it a clue? Yes: there was no doubt – 'this' ... was something.

One day, he arrived, sat a moment thus ... jerked to his feet and made for the door.

'Stop,' I said. And was amazed to see him stop ... as automatically as if I had turned a switch.

'Turn round,' I said.

He turned.

'Come here.'

He came towards me.

'Sit down.'

He sat: again in the low seat.

My mind ... had strode into horror and was struggling with the unthinkable. I stood above him: looking down at him with unbelief. Oh no, no ... my heart was crying. He did not raise his head ... his eyes stared at nothing at all. As I wrestled for a solution to this strangeness, he slowly lifted his left arm, then the right: folding the one wrist over the other he held the drooping hands towards me . . . he sat, so, motionless.

'NO!' I almost shouted, 'No! No! You are *not* a slave . . . you are *not* manacled. Oh, no . . . no . . . no!' My mind seemed to sob, 'I cannot bear this . . . I cannot bear it,' as I fell upon my knees before him, thrusting his arms apart, crowding into them between his knees, taking his unresisting face, covering it with tears and kisses.

His body was slack now, as though nerveless. I lifted him to his feet, led him to the bed, laid him down. He lay inert, with eyes closed. I stretched myself full length beside him; never ceasing to murmur, to kiss, to caress with my right hand, to whisper . . . 'Sleep now . . . sleep, my Darling. But listen . . . I'll sleep too. We'll go to sleep together. You shall not go alone. I am coming too. I am with you. Always. I shall never leave you . . . my Love, my Darling Love. Oh, there is nothing to fear . . . ever . . . ever . . . ever again.'

(Ah, but there was. And did he guess? And how could I?) But now, motionless he lay. And slept. And at his side, my limbs, my breath, my very consciousness wrapped about him, enfolding, holding . . . I slept too.

He woke to fantastic normality; looked briefly at his wrist-watch, kissed me with tenderness . . . hurried away.

John came in. I told him, with tears, the story. 'Look,' I said, 'his hands . . . I've drawn them, so that I wouldn't keep on seeing them. What does it mean?'

'But it is terrible. Horrible,' he said, '. . . and you must never do it again.'

'I know . . . I know,' I cried. 'Horrible. Terrible. To be *obeyed* in that way . . . it's the most hideous thing that has ever happened to me. But, John . . . perhaps it is now the only weapon . . . the only one which can save him?'

'Weapon?'

'Yes – weapon: this monstrous power over him of another – perhaps *any* other – to command. Can his susceptibility have reduced him to this?'

He looked at me sternly. '*I* would never use it,' he said.

'Oh . . . Oh . . .' I moaned, '. . . and perhaps I *must*.'

For suddenly I had remembered Oliver[1] stopping me in the street: 'We – his friends – can do nothing for Waley . . .' and he added, 'But surely *you* are a match for Beryl?'

What was he saying? My answer was scornful, loaded with contempt: 'No – I am no match for her; I have not her weapons. And, if I had, I wouldn't use them.'

Wouldn't I? Had I not, already perhaps, used one?

And I remembered the overheard words of a Jesuit priest when I was a child: 'One is sometimes forced to fight the Devil with his own tools.'

No. No. A second time I swore I couldn't do this thing – *would* not – ever, ever again.

But . . . I did. Oh, many times. And in many ways.

The strange thing is that the *consciousness* of doing so was spared me: was never with me. It is only now that I begin to know why – that, with my Puritan morality obstructing the matter, nothing could have been accomplished: the way ahead lay strewn like a minefield: only *blindfold* could I dare it.

And – blindfold – together we dared it.

[1] Oliver Strachey.

[41]

The Emissary

Arrived at the little St George's Garden, Gordon Luce, slightly out of breath, seated himself on a wooden bench outside the Gents. He leaned forward carefully on his stick: his plump face wreathed itself – carefully – in smiles: and I waited, interested, for what might come. What came was an exact and detailed reconstruction of the previous afternoon's session, 'performance', at No. 50. He had, of course, no need to set the scene; it was one with which I was familiar: the shuttered room, the leering masks, the suspended witch-balls, the glitter, the fulsome excesses of affection, the ceaseless and hypnotic chatter.

'Beryl made Arthur read *The King of the Dead*. He read it beautifully.'

Yes. He read it beautifully. Seated in the glow of my fire he had, always, read it beautifully . . . 'Had it not been for the light placed . . . he would never have found his way back to the Land of the Living . . .' And was it not I who had placed the wrought-iron brazier at the head of my stair that the starred rays from its lantern might welcome him up?

'Beryl made Arthur read . . .'

Gordon's voice ran on, relating, in careful detail, the Buddhist cautionary tale of children building sandcastles on the shore: their savage and merciless attack on one who in innocence infringed the rights of possession and trespassed.

I knew the tale. And took his point. He glanced quickly sideways to see if I had done this: for it was . . . a warning. But my face revealed nothing. I had taken a long twig and was drawing meaningless – purposely, to intrigue him – lines in the gravel before us; he found himself nowhere and could not altogether conceal a certain irritation: for, after all, he had to report back. *Something* had to be said on his return . . .

So now was offered an inventory of Beryl's special qualities. This, I think, proved a bit embarrassing: for, as always, and in his agitation, he went a bit far. When he had run through those relating to the brilliance of her intellect, he launched on her compassion, regaled me with her kindness and gentleness in all things and finally – with an abandon of rather theatrical enthusiasm, even excitement, I thought – her fantastic sensitivity.

I made no sign. But before my inner eye flashed up, like stills in a projector, the scenes over the years. The past months. The immediate weeks. And Arthur's words: 'She will not permit me to write . . . my own work. For two years . . . not one word.' – 'She will not permit me to sleep . . . I wake to find her hanging over me, muttering . . .' – 'If you could see, could see, what is happening here . . .' And that cry of fear, as Old Lom and I stood, appalled, in his flat below, that drifted down to us from the open window above – 'No! No! Don't DO it! Don't DO it!' – and Lom's breathed, 'Une maison maudite . . .' Then, strangely, Arthur's curious words: 'I have never known Beryl cry . . . I have never known her shed a tear.'

Compassion.

At length the *recitative* faltered to a halt . . . while he looked obliquely at me. Mixed with my anger, my disgust, was now almost amusement and even a kind of pity. '*You'll* get it!' I thought, 'if you don't take back *something* with you!'

But now – gamely, or perhaps desperate – he tried again: 'Beryl is so *sensitive* . . . She can hear the movement of the sap in trees . . .'

'But not . . .' I said, breaking my silence but without emotion, 'the drip . . . of a human heart.'

He started. His eyes widened. His mouth opened slightly, and oddly quivered: but no word came.

He said at last something rather flat and stupid, I thought. But after all, he was, shall we say, in the position of a failed emissary. And he was exhausted. He spoke in a totally different voice: 'What ... do you think? What do you *think* ... of all I have said?'

Well, I thought, it is my turn to be compassionate: he shall have, after all, *something* to take back. I made a final deep mark in the gravel with my stick. He stared at it. Was it ... in its way ... significant?

'What ...' I said, my words ice-cold, 'what ... do I think?' and from my mouth leapt two words that I think, perhaps even for him, might have been unequivocal – have left no doubt: 'I think ... *balls and bull-shit.*'

Trembling from head to foot – but with eyes strangely gleaming – he snatched up his stick and ... disappeared into the Gents.

I had no interest in his return. I went home.

But ... he had received ... beyond all expectations – that for which he had come.

Plaw Hatch

The old Humber was nosing through the Sussex lanes against a driving rain: the sky beyond the tunnelling trees was black with storm: and we were running out of petrol. I never carry a map. I take what comes. But for this night, indeed, I was ill-prepared. As the engine all but sputtered to a stop, a light showed on the right of the road. There was just enough power left to ease into a drive-way and come to a halt. A private house, it would seem, and all but hidden in shrubs. But perhaps – it was possible – petrol could be obtained here. My companion and I approached the wide doorway and, feeling foolish, rang the bell. The lady who opened the door did so with a generous sweep and standing back against the cheerful glow, at once invited us into a wide square hall. Great rugs were flung on the floor and a huge open fire crackled under freshly-piled logs. When, then, she flung out a hand towards a deep couch we knew fatigue had already claimed us. Petrol? No. But the storm? Surely we could not continue our journey to London: why not stay till morning?

'Stay? But is that possible? You see, we don't in the least know where we are!'

'Of course it is possible – if you don't mind sharing a large room in the annexe: this is Plaw Hatch.'

Dinner was excellent. Other guests appeared to be, in general, elderly women but later jolly-squire-types from far and near congregated in the bar – a lavishly appointed room of real comfort and taste.

All this time, however, my very skin was *aware*: behind the hospitality a thread of words running in my head kept me preoccupied: Arthur's words, spoken on the day immediately following the 'emissary' visit – 'Gordon has found the perfect place. I shall take Beryl there tomorrow. If she likes it she may stay some time, but I shall be back on Monday. It was advertised in the *New Statesman*. It is called Plaw Hatch.'

Exhausted, we retired early. The room in which we found ourselves was approached by lengths of passageway and stairs and seemed, by its silence, to be quite cut off from all the activities of a guest house. Facing a wide window that looked on to a forest of laurel and rhododendron, dark against the even darker back-screen of tall trees densely planted, was a broad bed. Tucked into a corner, with curious irrelevance amidst the lavish furnishings, was a narrow camp stretcher. Glancing at it without apology our hostess said: 'I'll leave *you* to sort out your sleeping arrangements.'

Since the responsibility for the adventure was entirely mine, I insisted that my friend should lie in comfort; and felt, indeed, that no bed, that night, could keep sleep from me. Little did I guess the trap this narrow couch concealed.

Had I known, indeed, I might have warned off the evil with Wang Yen-shiu's poem,[1] but as it was, I suffered a night of unimaginable horror. Sweating with un-nameable fear, I tossed this way and that in a vain effort to fend off the further terrors of sleep. My friend in her wide bed lay quietly slumbering, immune to all demons, while, beset by every torment, I jerked up time and again. The moonlight and torn cloud scudding in the night sky seemed to offer a heaven of safety I could never hope to win. I was conscious of being ice-cold. I wondered if I were dead. Silence and dark. The sound of an ocean roared in my ears. And suddenly I knew where I was: what I suffered: and with whom. 'You!' my mind cried silently, 'you, you, *you* suffered this! This room – this bed – this living hell! But why? And how? And by what hideous cruelty?' I propped myself up, shivering, imploring the dawn. Daylight. Sanity. The lash of the sea receded. I heard at last the first stirring of birds.

[1] 'The Nightmare' translated by Arthur in *Chinese Poems* (Allen & Unwin) 1946.

'You look frightful,' said my friend on waking. 'Did you sleep badly?'

'Sleep? I think sleep had little to do with it.'

She looked puzzled. 'Shall I get your breakfast sent up to you?'

'No. Just excuse me. I want only to lie as long as possible.'

Soon a maid was tapping at the door and entering with apologies. I guessed that she was Irish and would not be averse to chatter.

'Tell me,' I said without preamble, 'about this room.'

For a moment she looked startled. 'This room? Oh yes, Ma'am, it's for special cases – them as likes to get away as you might say. The lady that was here last, she seemed bad at first, very excited she was. But in the end it was the gentleman.'

'Was he in this bed?'

'Yes, Ma'am, in that bed where you are now. Not at first he weren't. At first he would have a room of his own but she insisted: said she couldn't be alone, couldn't be left like; and in the end she got her way and had that camp-bed put in here with her. Poor gentleman.'

'Poor gentleman?'

'Well, you see, Ma'am, after a bit he never left the room though *she'd* come down and be very gay. But she'd come to the kitchen late at night and mix things up for him to drink. He'd be sound asleep as often as not but she'd make me help her rouse him to make him drink it. She did take great care of him, I'll say that – but once the gardener found him away in the woods in his pyjamas sitting on a mound and playing a pipe and another time he run down the lane like that to the Green Line bus to stop her going away.'

'Going away?'

'Oh yes, Ma'am: she'd go up to London. This time though, she just had to get off the bus and come back.' She was well launched now and her words were sickeningly vivid. 'We used to wonder what she did to him – the high words and cries an' that – and when at last he did come out, to go away like, his poor face was like it was clawed by tigers and him such a nice quiet gentleman.'

Ah yes, yes, yes, I thought: well indeed do I know those runnel-marks of torment.

But, 'What a curious pair,' I said, as casually as I could. 'Did they not have friends? Get letters?'

'Oh letters, yes, Ma'am – *She* took charge of the letters. Except . . .'

The door opened wider: a second maid appeared to help with the beds: and possibly, I thought, to break a conversation. I dismissed them both until I should dress. When I had done this I stood long at the window looking out at – but not seeing – the still dripping trees. I saw instead the dark wash of a receding tide: against the white spume a solitary figure standing motionless.

'Except . . .?'

The salt weed lay again across the palm of my hand: white and pink and green.

From the gravelled path below a voice called up. Petrol had been supplied. We were ready to go.

[43]

Nettles

Oh so long ... with no word, no gesture.

It is morning. The telephone rings.

Arthur's voice. It says – in tones of a calm that, more than any hysteria, strikes fear – 'If you could only *see* what is happening here; if you could only know.' And the receiver clicks down.

I sit frozen: then hastily replace my phone: perhaps he will be able, somehow, to ring again. Aeons seem to pass before I am lifting it a second time – and again his voice. It says; 'What she is doing is criminal. What she is doing is worse than murder ...' and this time the words fade out. I wait.

I wait. And with all my mind – for indeed what other weapon is to hand? – and with all my love I seek to defend, hold safe.

Time passes. And Arthur is on the stairs. He enters the room with leaden step, crosses to his chair and sits. He speaks no word at all, his face is expressionless, dead: his glance unseeing. I am alarmed – and puzzled. I go to him, kneel on the goat-skin rug before him. With my two hands folded in my lap, I wait. Slowly he leans forward, clasps his hands about my throat, presses me back upon my heels, the grip ever tightening. I make no movement to release the loved fingers. Instead, I let my hands fall loosely to my side. I say, 'Would it help you, my Darling ... if I were dead?' At once the hands fall, a look of bewilderment is in the face before me.

Quietly I raise him up; and, my arm about him, lead him down the stairs and out to a Gray's Inn Road bus stop.

*   *   *

We have entered by the little gate that leads to what remains of the old orchard of his uncle's house at Kenwood. On the sloping, broken paths that must have known him in childhood, Arthur's feet now stumble; his head is bowed; never once does he lift his eyes. I think, 'He is like a sleep-walker.' On a slope of the long grass, in a space hedged with nettles, I spread my coat; on which now – like a child, obedient – he lies. I lie beside him, imploring some benediction – some respite from our two-fold suffering.

Presently he turns on his side – and again his hands are on my throat, the fingers tightening.

'Love casteth out fear' ... I do not 'think' these words – that echo up from some deep of childhood memory: I think nothing: and indeed cannot – for in my mind, as in my heart, is room for nothing but compassion – and the fingers drop away. Arthur has flung himself from me into the bed of nettles and is beating his face into them again and again ... crushing deep and deeper into the stinging leaves.

I wrench him back to me: hold him close: with kisses and tears, both, soothe those features that, of all men's, are the most noble; and whisper, 'Oh my Dear One ... I love you, love you. And listen; you must listen: *everything's quite all right*. But we are so tired, and now must sleep a little. Sleep ... sleep.'

His eyes are with me now – dazed, sorrowful, but emptying visibly of distress: and, I pray, of memory. With neither word nor question, he places his head on the coat beside me ... and is asleep.

[44]

Urgency

I have found in the telephone book the name of Arthur's favourite brother, Hubert, and he will come and talk with me. He arrives at eleven – with, I detect, some apprehension – and ascends the five flights to my long, low room.

We have never met. I tell him of myself – of my husband, Hugh – of my son, John . . . but it is evident that my concern for Arthur is real and deep.

'You must forgive me for confiding the matter to you – and it is one I do not understand, know nothing of – but I beg you to help him if you can; if you will. He loves you dearly, as I feel you must love him; and he is very unhappy.'

'Arthur's position is no different from that of any other man who wishes his wife would die.'

'His wife?'

'Well, no – but they have known one another a long time.'

'Oh, please understand. Arthur does *not* wish Beryl to die: his every energy is given to her. But it is he, he for whom I fear.'

Hubert's eyes roam round the room. A photograph of my son in military uniform, meeting the eye with steady gaze, seems to arrest him. Then he stands up; goes to the head of the stair.

'We dare not be involved,' he pronounces as, with finality taking his coat on his arm, he descends from my sight.

Gordon Luce, I think now, must be found.

I find him in a temporary annexe of the School of Oriental

Studies: a room of a Georgian house in the adjacent Woburn Square. He is not alone but on my arrival several Indian students rise silently and vanish. Recalling our meeting in the little St George's Garden, I know his feelings for me cannot be other than hostile but what am I in this matter but one who seeks help for his friend? I speak, directly, urgently, without greeting: 'Arthur badly needs help, and I think it must be yours. I am nothing. I can but exist for him: a sort of dressing-station behind the lines. I can but staunch his wounds; but you have superior power; for you know the *reason* for them. If it is true that you have cared for him, please care now; for the need is urgent. You are his friend: and you are Beryl's friend; you have known her, even as long as he ...' But now my thought is invading foreign territory – before my time ... I think – my words peter out.

Suddenly my attention is caught by the plump fingers that flutter before me in the air and I observe that his gaze, too, is on them. There is neither reply nor comment. I think, 'Either he is listening intently or he is not listening at all.'

Suddenly I say: 'Do you *love* Beryl?'

'*Love* her? I am *terrified* of her!'

Astonished at the vehemence of his tone I yet pursue my hope. 'Nevertheless you have known her deeply over many years: and I am helpless, useless in the matter. Please – I beg you – appeal to her.'

'There is nothing in Beryl to "appeal" to!'

I am abased. And suddenly I know with sickening illumination that for him all this is 'theatre' – and pleasurable. He is audience, actor, and onlooker. No vestige of human communication exists between him and me. I rise wearily and take my leave in silence.

To the specialist, who I know has attended Beryl at Gordon Square. Yes, he will receive me. He listens to my few and halting words.

'I agree: Waley is in a formidable state,' but adds, 'I advise you to leave the matter alone.'

Of whom is he thinking – of Arthur? Or of me?

'I don't understand you. The matter, the situation, is desperate.'

He is silent. And again I am wondering, can it be for my sake that he wishes me to extricate myself? For now he is using subtle words.

'The situation is of *your* making. So long as you support him, you make his stand possible. Without you he would collapse and the situation would resolve itself.'

'*Resolve* itself? – In death? In madness?'

'How can we know? But at least it would not continue; *some* end would be. While you stand beside him you prolong the conflict: it is you, therefore, you who are responsible for his sufferings.'

I take this idea and examine it – and am aghast to find it sound. I hear Arthur's voice, 'You *are* me; I *am* you.'

'You speak as though the *desired* end were defeat and death. Does he then make this superhuman fight for nothing? I do not know what is in the balance – what indeed, the fight is all about. All I do know is what is evident to all – that he struggles against appalling issues. And will continue; for he will never give up. What those issues are is not important. But there are times when the strength of one person is not enough and must be augmented by another's.'

There is no answer and I am aware that we are moving across the room. I am in the corridor. He stands behind me holding the door ajar. He says now, '*No-one* can help Waley: *no-one.*'

But I answer with quiet finality: 'Even so; I shall never leave him.'

The door shuts. I stand alone.

Slowly I return home through the familiar streets; slowly I climb the stair.

The door of my room is ajar. On the bed Arthur lies sleeping.

Silently I slip off my outer clothes, shake the pins from my hair, slide alongside ... as a tug might slide alongside a foundering ship. He shows no awareness of my coming; his body is tense and rigid; he makes no stir.

I thrust my left arm under his shoulders and draw him to me. With a single finger I caress the sunken cheek, the temple, as one would that of an exhausted child.

Presently a hand lifts, gropes for my hair, knots itself firmly in the dark coils; holds; clings, as on a thrown rope. A deep sigh; and slowly, perceptibly, the tensions relax: folded so in my arms, he sleeps. Like a child, he sleeps: and as always, I pray he will not dream.

I think: 'I am a raft. On what sea do we toss? To drown? Or drift to safety?'

[45]

The Vast Skies of Freedom

'I am going to Norway. For a month.'

'Oh, splendid!' I cry. 'Oh Darling, but *what* a happy thing! And perhaps you will ski . . .?'

'Certainly I shall ski,' he says. 'X will stay, with Beryl.'

I look at that frail figure. But I know him. Already in his eyes I see the mountains, the vast skies of freedom. In the brown depths they stand, visible. Yes; he will ski. I am dazed with gladness.

May-the-maid, her feet planted flatly to produce that queer jerking gait, her thin body weighted sideways by the black water-proof shopping bag that just clears the pavement, is crossing Tavistock Square. She sees my approach. With her free hand she is gesturing, signalling me to wait, and is watching her chance to cross. Long before she reaches my side I see she is greatly agitated.

'Miss . . . Miss.' She pauses to get her breath and to give a glance in several directions before, leaning her face nearer to mine in curious confidence, she continues in a whisper that I can scarcely catch above the traffic.

'Miss. Them two! That young man and Miss de Soosa. You'll have to write to him and tell him to come back. They're at one another all the time – screams and quarrels. He'll have to come. Dr Waley'll *have* to come.' The words are garbled.

So. Was it – as time and again it had appeared to be – a ruse to snatch back his vital respite?

'No, May.'

'But it's *terrible*, Miss. You can't think . . . you've no *idée* how it is!'

'No, May. He must not be summoned home. He must stay the full month out.' I speak with quiet finality, and she glances into my face the more clearly to take my meaning.

'I do see what you mean, Miss . . .' and she adds, 'And 'e *do* need it.'

'Yes, May. And Miss de Zoete is well able to defend herself . . . as you know . . . when she has a mind to. Dr Waley will need every day of his month to recover his strength – and meanwhile, dear May, you mustn't distress yourself – it's not long now till his return.'

'I s'pose you're right, Miss. But them two . . . You've jest no *idée* . . .' And nodding gravely, she moves away towards her home, her loaded bag bobbing to touch the pavement as her slight body ducks and dodges between the passers-by.

As I watch her out of sight I wonder just how serious it is – this bit of 'theatre' between the 'friends' who would seem to have discovered such a degree of enmity. Well; not from me will come the word that shall shorten Arthur's period of escape by so much as a single hour.

And then . . . it is a midday of bright sun . . . I am driving through the square when the little open car swerves into the kerb to come to rest beside him. For there without doubt he stands – bronzed, straight, glorious.

'Honey! Oh HUN!' I whisper, gazing unbelieving; gazing my delight. 'But you're . . . magnificent. What a miracle-place is Norway!'

His face, too, is radiant: 'I'm back,' he says, quietly.

Laughing with happiness, I touch the seat beside me. 'Jump in!' I say, 'I'm going to Tring. Come!'

'*How* I would like to do that!' he smiles. 'But I cannot. I must go in. I must say goodbye to X . . .'

I speed, I speed on those northern roads. The little car bounces and purrs, takes to the lanes, climbs the heights, runs between the bracken. And seldom, it seems, has the county of Hertfordshire unfolded so much beauty.

*　　　*　　　*

Next morning I sleep late, drowse, am reluctant to relinquish my dreams, when the telephone rings beside my bed. Silence. And then a whisper. 'Miss ... Is that you, Miss Alison?'

May's voice is very small, hesitant; then again silent. Yet I fancy I hear her breathing rapidly; and sense disturbance.

'Yes, May. What is it? Say it quickly.'

'It's him, Miss. They've took him to the hospital. Last night.'

'*Suffering is one long moment.*' My mind goes taut. I say, 'May. Which?'

'University ...' The wire goes suddenly dead.

A girl clerk flicks over the pages of the files.

'WALEY? A.D.? Yes. Brought in yesterday. At 4 p.m. But he's not here. He discharged himself this morning.'

'Discharged ... – He went home?'

'Can't say, Madam. He discharged himself. Can't say where he went.'

Reassurance? Three days pass. During them I haunt the streets, the adjacent squares: I am looking for May. I loiter on corners. I peer inside pubs and put my head in at the doorways of the little Marchmont Street shops: I am looking for May. I defy the curiosity of the tradesmen. And I dare the 'vigilantes' of the square itself. I am looking for May.

And then ... a scrap of paper, thrust into an envelope, and somehow posted. The writing is all but indecipherable. It says: 'There has been an accident. I shall come to you as soon as I can.'

Below, in the empty house, I hear the front door open: and presently close. Then silence. I lean over the narrow banisters. I can see no-one. I run lightly down the stair to the dim hall.

Yes ... he is there. If it is he? For the figure that leans against the wall in the narrow space is a grotesque one. Its beret is awry. The laces of one shoe are undone. Its coat is buttoned wrongly. And something is wrong also with the arrangement of the body, so that it sags to one side. The right arm hangs straight. The face, with its Norway brown, is ravaged with pain. The eyes are enormous – and, in them, more than pain.

Quickly I slip my right shoulder under the left armpit, circle the waist to take the weight as one succours a wounded man and slowly, in silence, we move up the stair.

We have negotiated the five flights – the last, my attic one, narrow and difficult. 'Does he suffer physical pain?' I ask myself: but then, 'Never would he permit me to know.'

I seat him carefully on the edge of the low, wide bed. I kneel before him and sink my head face downward on to his knees. For a while we stay motionless. I say: 'How . . . did it happen?'

I have to wait for the answer: and then it comes; 'The mat slipped.'

But there are no mats. For years . . . no mats; lest Beryl should do just that. I am silent, and he says now, trying again: 'May had polished the floor like glass.'

But the floors are scrubbed to dullness. For years, scrubbed to dullness; the linoleums scarified for maximum safety.

My mind is leaping. But still I am silent. And I hear again his voice as from afar off. 'I slipped . . . and fell.'

But now I am not even listening. My mind is occupied suddenly in fighting off a curious weight of exhaustion. I turn my face on its side. The fingers of his left hand come up to touch it. They touch it with an eloquence – an appeal – which I must respect. For he knows I do not believe his statements. Not one word. Not one word. And again the exhaustion that is the fringe of despair enfolds me; and suddenly the tips of the fingers that move so lightly, tentatively, over my cheek are wet with my tears.

[46]

'Witchcraft'

Now began eight months of rigid routine. Each morning at ten I drove to the corner of the square where he waited and took him to the Outpatients Department of the University College Hospital.

Those benches on which we sat ... how many hours? ... our gaze, seeing or unseeing, fixed on the slow-moving procession of the crippled and the infirm arriving, departing on crutches, in chairs, for their therapies ... on which we sat close, waiting also, for all of a summer and far into the winter of a year.

Beryl's shrill laughter would echo down from the windows.

'She doesn't believe that I go to the hospital: she thinks I go to see you.'

I was silent. And exhausted. What poor Beryl thought or believed was long since beyond any influence or control.

I said quietly, 'There is nothing we can do about that. If there were, we would do it.' And at once the tensions, the torments, left him.

I thought, 'He lives in an insane world' – and I thanked the gods (with what wonder and humility I thanked them) that I had but to lift a finger to beckon him out of it. I thought of Clement and her furiously reiterated 'You are a witch! I've seen it working! Even in crowded places, you have but to lift your head – to meet his eye. In the most dreadful hubbub he will hear *your* voice: *we* are all forced to listen with him. What is it? What do you *do*? What is your secret?'

I laugh at her. Yet I too have been disturbed. 'Dear Clem! I DO nothing. And as for my "secret" ... has love become a secret? (Better for us if it could be kept so!) To love with all one's heart?'

One morning he is seated, collapsed, on the steps of No. 36, his old address with its door in Endsleigh Place – the flat he occupied alone when I knew him first. He looks ... derelict. What has happened?

His clothes are awry, his face ravaged, his eyes full of a desperate fear ... I leap out and, taking his weight across my shoulders, get him to the car. His story is incoherent – 'an overdose' – of sleeping pills? Of pain-killer? By whom administered? By intent? I was never to know in any detail what had happened during that weekend, but certain it was that he was very ill indeed.

The many weeks passed, in dreary routine. With hope. Without hope.

'Did what the doctors did today hurt?'
'Terribly.'
'Darling ... is it getting any better?'
'No.'

And at last, after the eighth month, the final verdict: 'It will never be different. You will not be able to write again, use your right hand, or even lift it from your side. We are sorry.'

That English word – 'sorry' ... Five years later, the fur-hatted man who crashed our car stood, Arthur lying on the pavement – spine broken and crumbling, paralysed, his life's work over – at his feet, and said it: 'Sorry.'

He stood now before me, with difficulty lifting his arm but a hand's-width before him.

'The doctors have done all they can,' he said. He spoke low, so low I could scarcely hear him. 'My life – my intellectual life – is over.'

Sadness hung between us, visible, unendurable. Words came to my lips ... remembered? ... I don't know. I said. 'When half-gods go, the gods appear.'

'What does that mean?'

'I don't know. I think I'm trying to say . . . Where doctors leave off, the miracles begin.'

'Miracles?'

'Yes. They happen.'

In the days that followed everything was tried, everything was invented.

We found that if the table was low enough before him, Arthur could bend his arm to a writing position. The next thing was to close fingers and thumb on some sort of pen, and this proved impossible.

About this time Michael Cardew gave his exhibition of African pottery in North Audley Street Gallery. He presented me with some porcupine quills and some small loofahs which he had brought back with him. In my search for something Arthur could grip, I had heavily-wrapped and tried every sort of thick-handled pencil and pen – but now I forced an ordinary Biro through the body of the loofah. Arthur found that his hand could close about the thick sponge-like substance, and before long he had mastered its manipulation well enough to write with tolerable legibility. A great stride forward: and a good deal of his built-up pessimism dropped from him.

One night after we had dined together as usual at my Handel Street flat, he rose to go and came towards me with his left arm raised for an embrace. I stood at bay. 'Not good enough.' I said. '*Two* arms.'

He looked deeply sad. 'You *know* I can't,' he whispered.

'I *don't* know it,' I answered, standing before him. 'Come, Darling. Do it. Two arms or nothing.'

Startled, fascinated, we watched the right arm rise. The left was already on my shoulder. Now – inch by inch – the right lifted towards that same level. The hand descended. Both arms were about me.

We stood; trembling, weeping, laughing, in a full embrace. The impossible had been achieved. The 'miracles' had taken over.

A House of One's Own

The University of London has made its decision. The historic properties bounding the east side of Gordon Square that have housed for several generations the literati of Bloomsbury are to be vacated: not for development; they will remain but be put to other, academic, uses.

And so it is that Arthur Waley, greatest translator of the century, ailing though he so conspicuously is, must find himself – together with his great library of rare books and horde of precious documents (and the dying Beryl de Zoete) – another abode. Where? How? Together we contemplate this appalling contingency.

Together, now – as, like leaves from a tree in autumn, the days drop from the calendar – we snatch at already exhaustion-heavy time to make our search.

A house is suggested in Islington's suddenly fashionable Canonbury Square. We visit it: and are received by its owner, an Indian lady who mentions an extortionate price. But Arthur's dilemma is a desperate one. I say nothing and, returning from this expedition, he requires my judgment.

'Not the price – but certainly the house – is beautiful,' I say.

He considers. 'And it is not far for you to come.'

My impression was that the square was a veritable nest of sycophants. I could see Arthur, his years falling behind him, a man trapped yet again in cunning-set snares from which, this time, he would have little hope of struggling free.

'I . . . shall not come.'

'You . . . will not come?'

I shook my head.

'Have you a reason?'

I laughed. 'Not a logical one. Perhaps a zoological one. Well, anyhow, a jungle one.'

He looked at this statement with his usual intentness, and one felt, as always, the stir of his mind. 'I shall not go,' he said simply.

We turn towards the north – as giving easy access to Bloomsbury: to the British Museum, the School of Asiatic Studies, the Courtauld Gallery, the parks and gardens and squares of our native haunts, yet offering also escape beyond the city's boundaries: to Essex, to Aylesbury, to Ca⁓bridge even.

Returning from Hadley Wood, there, fronting the common at Barnet, is an old farmhouse. Wooden, gabled, its concealed garden sloped to the dipping sun. No. It is too far, remote, alone. The years – our years, mine, his and certainly Beryl's – forbid such a venture.

Still returning, we pass up North End and turn just before the Highgate School where Tom Eliot had taught in his prime. Another turn to the right and the car, almost of itself, comes to a halt. For there it is. The house: the house of all our searchings. Cut through a square edifice of late Regency architecture is a narrow, arched tunnel, its darkness framing at its far end a beyond of leafy sunlight. A vista so surprising in its loveliness that at once we are out of the car and have entered its deep-shadowed and stone-paved way. A twist of worn steps descends to a further tunnel of young limes, from which the rear façade of the house is scarcely visible. Thrusting the branches apart, we see that this is balconied and tall-windowed and netted over, even to its roof, with flowering wisteria. A small gate is set in a garden wall. Perhaps even here we are trespassing; and, wordless, we make our way back to the pavement.

'Look!' I cry, and clutch at Arthur's arm – for, newly-erected but tipped sideways into the arms of a tall white lilac, is a board. It reads, 'FOR SALE'.

For answer, Arthur is looking at his watch while I am scrambling back into the driving seat.

The office is about to close for the day. Typewriters are properly covered: the staff already departing.

But Arthur, seating himself and folding his hands in his lap, awaits attention. Curious glances are being exchanged. The agent himself emerges from an inner office, pulling on his coat as he comes. Seeing a stranger sitting primly, the scurry of departure arrested, he pauses. In the hush that falls, Arthur's voice rises, clear, fountain-like: 'I wish to buy a house. No. 50 Southwood Lane.'

The agent remains standing: glances at me: bends slightly. 'You would wish to see over it, Sir? Perhaps tomorrow ...?'

But Arthur interrupts with a single word: 'Immaterial.'

'Would you care to know the price?'

'Immaterial.'

Now the baffled man leans aside to me and murmurs: 'Is he serious?'

'Certainly,' I answer.

We have about us a small audience. For those last-departing ones are now held, tethered, by curiosity. It is, surely, a curious business.

But Arthur has removed his wallet from an inner pocket – and the silence is broken. 'Will you take a cheque?' he is asking, 'or would you prefer cash?'

[48]

'Who . . . is Beryl?'

One day, soon after this, he comes to me, bemused. I wonder
– as I so often now do – and in silence, what is working in his
mind. But then, as usual, he comes to the point. Following
me to the kitchen where I go to prepare our meal he seats
himself on a chair at the end of the table, watches me for a
while and then draws from his wallet an old snapshot. It is of
a group of little girls arranged on the grass against the façade
of a house. He hands it to me and I pause to scrutinise it. I
comment, simply, 'She's tall, there, for her age, isn't she.'

He looks startled. 'Who is?'

'Why, Beryl.' And add, 'But it's very like her.'

He stares at me. He says, 'Beryl . . . is the baby seated in
front.'

I answer, smiling, 'Oh no. Look again, closely. Beryl is the
one standing at the back.'

He takes the photograph from me and, holding it to the
light, himself scrutinises it with his 'blind' eye – that
strangely affected eye that appears so normal, yet sees
only microscopically when, as now, he holds the object very
close to it. Then he puts the snapshot down on the table and
slowly raises his gaze to mine. He says, his voice tip-toeing
as it were back over years: 'She has always said she was the
baby.'

What can one answer? I do not answer. He says, again as
to himself, 'She told me she was six years older than I.'

He is puzzled, and deeply sad: yet the thing now has to be
faced; we both know it. I squat down on my heels beside him
and take the photograph again in my hands. I say gently;

'Darling – the baby is about two, I'd say: and the little girl standing, about eight. So Beryl meant she was *twelve* years older than you,' and add, 'Women are often odd about their ages. I've never understood it.'

He says nothing, but replaces the snapshot in his wallet. I rise and go on with my cooking. No more is said.

About a week later Arthur appears and seating himself promptly as usual, pronounces, 'I've spent three whole days at Somerset House trying to find out who she is.'[1]

'Who?'

'Beryl.'

I am astonished. I say: 'But – you've known her more than half your life ... what do you mean, "who she is"?'

'She tells me she is Jewish. Do you think she is Jewish?'

'No.'

'Why not?'

'Because she has none of the Jewish qualities ...' I hesitate, and then, 'And because *you* are a Jew. I cannot believe that one Jew could so persecute another.'

'Ah,' he says quickly, '*there* you are wrong!'

'Ah, well,' I murmur; for so much is, and has been, beyond my conception that I feel sick, incapable and disinclined to consider the matter.

But presently Arthur, who has never left it for an instant, returns to the puzzle. 'What do *you* think she is?'

'Me? Oh, I've always thought she was chichi.'

'Chichi! What does that mean?'

'Oh, *half*-something. Mexican-Indian perhaps. She looks it. She has the vivacity, the bird-like aptitude for languages, the absorbing interest in magic, the ...' my voice tails off, and then, '... the immorality.'

He says sharply, 'You mean "amorality". If you mean amorality, I agree with you. Beryl is the most *amoral* person I have ever known!'

---

[1] Beryl's birth certificate at Somerset House records that she was born on 17 August 1879, the legitimate child of her parents Edward Frank and Drusilla de Zoete. She was ten years older than Arthur.

I do not answer and he says now, fiercely, 'You mean "amorality", don't you.'

It is not a question.

I look at him. I meet his gaze. It is challenging, almost threatening; certainly warning. I say quietly, 'No, Darling. I don't. I mean "immorality".'

The effect of my word is, as so often, surprising. He springs to his feet. He says; 'You mustn't say nasty things about Beryl or I shall not come here any more.'

There is something so strange, so child-like in this outburst – even in the tone of voice; and, yes, something also so forlorn, so pitiful; a kind of fear – that I am baffled: I can say nothing.

He waits a moment, staring up at me, in the hope that I will take the word back. Then, since I do not, he literally springs for the door and is gone down the stair.

Yet ... he comes again. And days later.

Seating himself in his usual place, and with no greeting nor so much as a glance at me, he says: 'Her mother ... was *very* low: *very* low.'

Vividly now, and from a long way back, I recall a similar snapshot he has shown me, of Beryl's parents: taken perhaps in that same garden, even at the same time. They stood together side by side – the father, the Dutchman stock-jobber, thick, insensitive; the mother, slender, intelligent, cultivated – an essentially 'good' face. 'That woman,' my mind hands me now with certitude, 'was never "low".'

My silences have always acted upon him like eloquence. *Nothing* was always the worst thing I could say. And this time his mind leaps from me, obliquely, clearing whole chasms. He cries out – as it were from the other side, at great distance – and with a passion of defiance: 'I don't *deny* she's cruel. I don't deny she's vicious. I don't deny she's *grim*. But I like it!'

What does it mean? Is it a defence, a loyalty? ... or a confession?

I gaze at him, impassive. It is my turn to speak and I do, as to myself. But I say aloud ... quoting his own translated

[227]

words . . . 'They gave him their food to eat . . . and he forgot he was a son of Kings.'[1]

If I had dealt him a stinging blow it could not have had greater effect. Indeed, he leaps to his feet and with a hand across his eyes as though to screen the very sight of me, reels to the door.

I sit exhausted: too sad, too fearful now, even for tears.

When I was a child I had a recurring dream: it was that I came and stood at the edge of the world. I feel now that we both stand there – gazing into the enormity, the awfulness, of space.

[1] From 'The Song of the Soul', the Syriac hymn translated by Arthur.

[49]

That Other Mind

At this time the paroxysms are constant, continuous – and are the business of nurses, a day nurse, a night nurse, with sedatives and injections. But they, too, rebel – for, as in all such cases, one alone is not enough: the terrifying strength of this creature-of-wires that is now Beryl requires the controls of more even than two. And – contemplating the situation – the frothing jaws, the blackening and writhing spider's-body, they are required to tend – sometimes after a mere hour or two, silent, pursing their lips, they re-pack their bags with resolution and thud down the stairs. And Arthur, his mind shut adamantly against all persuasion, all alternatives . . . and I, whose mind is in this matter, as resolute as his . . . are left with no other ally than the telephone and our shortening list of untried agencies.

'It's not, of course, a mental case?' a suspicious voice enquires.

A mental case? What is a mental case? Where . . . is Beryl's mind? In what ante-room of hell . . . Who can guess?

Seated beside her, Arthur offers the only magic he knows – to soothe, beguile, that lost and lashing spirit. His voice moves with its ceaseless music of words and images: while the eyes beside his flash fire, roll unfocused, pinpoint with an extreme of terror some tangible thought, hanging in air or fixed, relentless, confronting her alone. The noises, inhuman, defiant, that jerk from her might be speech, and what might pass for laughter were it human . . . while froth streams from the gnashing empty jaws and the enormous cavern of the mouth fills with a greenish foam. Oh Beryl – dear Beryl –

where ... indeed ... is her mind? That mind, so lit with shafts of splendours, of triumphs and of frightfulness; that mind that she used so ill and has so cruelly tortured.

Now no mere bed can contain the jerkings of this frenzied body – unrecognisable as such; a puppet of darkened leather. The bone-thin arms, jerked by relentless strings, flay the air: no more than claws, the fingers pluck forever at the gyves that would restrain her: all is soon matted, torn, hurled aside. As for rest – sleep? What are the methods used by nurses to achieve these? Neither Arthur nor I can bring our minds to meddle with the matter. He retires at ten, rises at eight – and, even under such rough regime for ever-changing supervisions as the flow of outraged and quarrelsome attendants can afford, he becomes rested. For he is a man who has fixed his purpose, has supported it to his utmost, will stand immovable – indeed, unassailable – to the end. And now – the ultimate, both of horror and endurance, reached – no more, no further effort can, humanly, be demanded. And this – in its way – is peace. An end is reached of human contrivance and human powers. No; once again, it is a case for 'miracle' – and perhaps, in compassion for Beryl, the only miracle is that final and most merciful one we choose to call death.

Even so, there comes a day when Arthur appears in my room and sits in silence. I am puzzled. It seems an odd time – a time I have learned to know as 'between nurses': a time, too, when he may hope to snatch a meal.

I say; 'Have you eaten?'

He makes a negative movement and closes his eyes. 'I've left her,' he presently says, 'I can do no more.'

'Left whom?' I exclaim.

'Beryl. There, on the floor, gyrating. I couldn't lift her. I couldn't get near her. Nothing was any use. So I left her ...' his voice tails off dreamily and I see suddenly that he is at the point of exhaustion.

I glance at my watch and go quickly to the telephone. The ringing sound continues ... and continues. I have a key to the house in Gordon Square. Will Arthur let me go alone? I think not. And could I do what he has failed to do?

But now at the end of the wire an angry voice is answering. The night nurse of the moment has come on duty.

I say, assuming a voice of quiet normality: 'Oh, good! you've arrived. Yes, we came out for help. She is quiet now? Sleeping? Oh . . . that's splendid . . . exhausted . . . Yes, indeed: her strength seemed limitless. Dr Waley will be home about nine.'

I return to his side. He appears not to have heard: he gives no sign. I bend down and whisper: 'Beryl is asleep and peaceful. The nurse is sitting beside her. You are going to curl up and sleep too for a little, my Darling – and when you wake we'll have a small meal together on a tray by the window.'

Without comment, he stands up and, his eyes scarcely seeing, moves to the bed: and, lying down, is at once asleep.

I pull the quilted coverlet over him and lie alongside. A last slant of the day's sun lights for a while the temple, the closed eye fringed with the motionless lashes. I think . . . 'How young he is – and how beautiful. He is like a child trapped in a fairy tale . . .' and, sliding soundlessly off the bed, go to the kitchen to prepare our supper.

How many days later am I removing my shoes as always in Charlotte's hallway and tip-toeing up the six flights of stairs? As always, too, the flat door is ajar and, creeping soundlessly into the kitchen, I signal Arthur not to disturb his writing, lift my basket to the table and unpack its few delicacies. Presently, however, he lays down his pen and draws me to his side.

At the same instant the urgent tinkle of Beryl's small hand-bell sounds above. I stand back, and Arthur leaps for the stairs. For do we not know – do we not *both* know – that, for long now, she has been incapable of co-ordinated movement?

It is many months since I have seen Beryl except through the eyes of others. Very soon Arthur is back. He stands just

inside the door and leans against the wall. He says in a voice
scarcely audible, of incredulity, of bewilderment: 'She ...
knew ... you were here.' Yet, I had been soundless. 'She
wants to see you. She wants you to go up ...' There is a pause
while, in shared silence, together we contemplate the mystery
of this thing. And had she *spoken*? *How*? For that, too, has
been impossible.

He looks across at me and adds, 'You won't – of course.'

'I won't? But indeed I *will*! Oh, Darling ...' and it is my
turn to leap for the stairs.

The door of her room is open; her couch against the wall
behind it. It is wide but seems no longer than a cot. I tip-toe
in and kneel at the open side.

Beryl – propped with a dozen pillows – regards me with
wavering glance.

I take her wildly jerking hands in mine and they are suddenly still. Looking only into her eyes, now fixed on mine and
strangely glowing, I say: 'Hullo, Beryl ...' I lean forward and
kiss her brow – sweat-soaked, dark and strange under its
flying wisps of white. I sit back on my heels and lay my bare
arms along her own – no more than withered sticks: but our
eyes hold. And in that long moment we are known to one
another so that nothing stands between. In some no-place, in
some mid-heaven, a truce is called: all is as it might have
been. I feel only a surge of love and joy that from that
grotesque mask the eyes – oh, but unbelievably – are *smiling*
into mine.

Gently I lay her hands on the coverlet and descend again
to Arthur.

He is standing as I left him. 'What was it? What happened?'

'Why – nothing very much ... or was it ... everything? I
knelt down and took her hands. I said "Hullo, Beryl" and
kissed her. Darling ...' my words are careful, for our awe had
entered into them – 'she's not mad. *She's not mad* ... And her
eyes are beautiful.'

Again the bell rings. And Arthur leaps up the stairs.

I wait. Where he waited. Motionless.

And presently he is back. He moves slowly into the room and leans against the wall. I go to him: I say, 'What is it?'

He says in a voice very clear, very low, 'I don't . . . understand. I don't . . . understand. I know . . . nothing. I *am* . . . nothing.'

'Of course. We are all . . . nothing.' I smile, 'And . . . everything. Tell me what happened.'

He says – and he, also, speaks carefully: 'She made me kneel down and take her hands. She made me lean forward and kiss her. She was . . . somehow . . . smiling. And she said . . . she said . . . "Alison's nice".'

'*Nice*'. How commonplace a word – yet, in this utterance of it, what riches for three earth-bound creatures.

'Oh, but what a *blessed* word – the best in the world! Oh, *dear* Beryl . . . And, Darling, did you see? She's not mad; not mad any more . . . and her eyes are beautiful?'

'Yes,' he whispers as I lead him now to the big chair by the fire. 'Yes. You are right.' And he repeats; '*She's not mad. And her eyes . . . are beautiful.*'

So we stay. In wonder. Uttering within ourselves those clumsy sounds which seek, so uselessly, to put shape to silence. She . . . has made her peace. With me. With him. With us. With herself. With the world. With life. How valueless are words: that can but smudge the feeling and the knowing. We cling, wordless.

The night nurse again is ascending the stair with heavy warning tread. Quickly I lean and kiss his hand and turn his face to mine.

'Don't you *see*, my dear one? – don't you *see* what Beryl has done? We are – all three – *blessed*,' I whisper, and snatching up my empty shopping-bag I am gone.

It is somewhere before noon next day that Arthur comes. He sits on the edge of the bed. He says gently: 'Darling, Beryl is dead. I went to bed at ten as usual and the nurse tapped on my door at eight to waken me. She said there was no point in disturbing me . . . that Beryl had died in the night.'

I crouch down beside him. Our arms about one another, we remain a long time.

Up in the kitchen, May-the-maid voices a protest: '*I* want to come to the funeral. *I* want to come. And he won't let me.'

'No, May. He must be alone.'

Indeed he must be alone with her. And with so many ghosts.

Arthur comes and beckons me into the next room: 'You will take me in the little car?'

'Yes. I will take you.'

There is no hearse to follow: only the arrangement to be made, the hour to fix. And punctually at the appointed time the little car drives through a deluge of rain and comes to rest beside the chapel of the crematorium. Arthur gets out and, bending against the downpour, enters the doors. I remain in the driving seat; thinking how strange a thing is life, of which we know so little; and then, how strange a thing is death – of which we know nothing at all.

I think: 'Beryl is eighty-six.' Then: 'What are years?'

My thoughts are back in a distant past, groping along the track, unknown to me, of her flamboyant youth.

I am hearing again Arthur's so strangely-spoken question – 'Who . . . is Beryl?'

The rain beats against the windscreen and I wonder if the wipers will work.

Now I am posting her letters – her hundreds of letters, on the back of each of which is scrawled in frenzied circular sweeps of the pen, '*I* am the Genius! *I* am the Poet!' – to as many addresses in almost as many capitals of the world. 'Replies flood in. Shocked,' Arthur had said. 'I read some. I put the rest in the waste-paper basket.'

I am thinking, 'Where are her thousand acquaintances? Her hundred friends? Her hundred enemies? Where are her "lovers" – those fascinated, those in terror? Those enchanted, those in thrall?'

*　　　*　　　*

There is a small angular gash in the car's roof fabric and the water drips heavily on to my knee. I cover it with a corner of my cape.

Apart from the clatter of the storm there is no other sound.

Now the doors are open again; Arthur is emerging, crossing the paved way and climbing back into the seat beside me. As I am starting up, a black-clad figure dives through the rain and beats wet knuckles against the streaming glass. I lean across and wind the window down. A head is poked into the opening.

'Shall I . . .' the voice sinks to a note of suitable solemnity, 'Shall I . . . scatter the ashes, Sir?'

Arthur is staring straight ahead. 'Immaterial,' he says now. 'Immaterial,' and, turning to me, 'Drive on.'

I press my foot on the accelerator and we leap forward into the storm.

At that moment Beryl fills all our thoughts – and with the ultimate of tenderness.

We never speak of her again.

Nor need to. For thereafter our two thoughts are one.

PART III

Homecoming

1962–1966

Like the waters of a river
That in the swift flow of the stream
A great rock divides,
Though our ways seem to have parted
I know that in the end we shall meet

12th century.

[I]

The Stage is Set

Gordon Square.

The sun sweeps the tops of the plane trees and enters the room in a gale of light, exhilarating to a point of intoxication. Every object, so long shuttered in darkness, now is curiously and intimately fingered by its rays: stressed, left lacquered, its long-forgotten presence at last asserted. David Hawkes[1] and I look on, bemused with delight to see Arthur dancing in a pool of it, dropping his bath-towel, snatching at his shirt, while words – released from the intolerable tensions of the last many months, babble forth in a strange elation.

'I've made my Will. David, will you be my literary executor? Alison and I are going to Richmond for a month . . .'

David leans back on the cushions, boyish and pleased. 'Of course, Arthur. I shall be honoured.'

Looking at him, I think: 'That's a good thing – David is, has always been, like a son to him.'

A knock on the slightly open door and May-the-maid announcing: 'A lady to see you, Sir,' while at the same time a strange voice, as it were 'in the wings' – high-pitched, admonitory – pronounces in doom-sounding tones: '*Laughter in the house of death.*'

Can we have heard aright!

Arthur snatches at his trousers and, dragging them on as he goes, disappears.

David and I – for the euphoria holds us, all three – rock with silent mirth. At once Arthur returns, still tucking in the tail of his shirt.

[1] Professor of Sinology at Oxford.

[239]

' "The Dreiver",' he says, in brief if obscure explanation. 'She wanted Beryl's cuckoo-clock. She's got it and gone.'

I glance down from the high window to make sure that the little car still waits beside the railings of the square.

'*I'm* the only driver today,' I say. 'Come – let's go!' and we are racing down the stairs like school-boys at end of term.

But May-the-maid beckons me back. She pats my hand, nods her head comically and whispers; 'I work for *you* now, Miss!'

From the Admiral's Suite – a whole small étage, the bedroom equipped with high bunks on lockers of polished mahogany, at the annexe-end of the Mor's Head[1] – we look down and away over the stretching plains of three counties of England. Each day our long roofed balcony with its patterning iron-work receives the full arc of the sun. At dawn the river mists lie below obscuring all but the tops of the tallest trees, so that they emerge as myriad islands.

'India,' I say, 'the plains from the hills.' And at once we are there.

Each day we go the rounds of our 'estate' – the great park at our doors – until each horizon, each outline, each family of deer, each pool, each burnished clump of rushes, is known to us: is ours.

When the wind strides, we make for Pembroke Lodge and picnic in the warmth of its western façade, the tall youthful ghost of Bertie Russell moving between the squirrel-live oaks and the slender birches that rise from flowery lawns.

At evening we descend from the heights and walk the water-meadows beside the winding silken Thames. And re-turn to the galleys of the *Secret History of the Mongols* which, hunched in one armchair, we go through with delight.

Time . . . is forever.

A wellness of being has come to Arthur; transforming, almost removing, him; setting him apart from the human norm – a state of exaltation that moves at times into one of ecstasy: so sudden, yet so sustained, as to make me at times

[1] Now renamed The Richmond Gate.

almost the looker-on. Yet it is I he snatches at, draws down, holds close, close, with: '*No*-one shall separate us now – nothing and no-one.'

We picnic in the long fern by the lake with Antonia,[1] with my small grandchildren, Justin and Matthew, both of whom since infancy have loved Arthur well. We visit my son's home, and know it as our own, book-lined even as my father's had been. And it is I who find myself encircled by Arthur's eyes' embrace as he says quietly: 'Alison and I will marry. We shall live at Highgate.'

And I, incredulous as John, yet hearing, even as others, the serene finality of the words – looking, even as others, on the radiance of that face – am dazed with joy. For us both, it seems, it is like a home-coming, an ineffable peace, after long journeying, hazardous and fearful. Each – but only with the other – has arrived.

And now, again, we are in Bloomsbury.

But – something has happened. Arthur is again at Gordon Square – a stone's throw only – yet he neither comes, nor rings nor writes. I encounter the maid in the little shopping street that is so like a village.

'Yes,' she answers, looking at me oddly, 'he's there. Dr Waley's there. He's quite well. He's very busy.'

Time passes. Days. At last I write a note – 'Darling, are you well? Is anything the matter?' – and slip it in at his door.

There is no answer.

Many days pass.

And, slowly, I come to know an apprehension which takes no form, but also a deep sadness with which I am indeed familiar.

And then, turning in to a back street, I see his figure approaching – a stooped and weary approach – his coat flapping open. But he is not aware of me, and I stand still, waiting – waiting until those eyes shall lift and the new glory that is certainty break from them.

[1] Antonia Gianetti, my son's wife.

Suddenly he stops. He has seen me.

The street is empty. But now, a moment staring, as at an apparition, he turns and runs – an exhausted, spiritless but determined run – back the way he has come and disappears round the corner.

My heart freezes.

'Nothing and no-one ...' I hear again his voice ... the words, ineffably tender, whispered low; 'Nothing and no-one ... shall separate us now.'

Yet – something and someone ...

I grope my way home – as he too, I now know, is groping his: in the old way, the old way, from time to time grasping at the cold iron railings. And for me too the lagging of nerveless feet, the sudden and deadly languor of loss, of near-despair.

'Au labyrinthe ...' I hear myself saying aloud, '*Au labyrinthe ...*' What return is this ... what return ... what intolerable pain must even yet be suffered?

Three weeks go by. Comes no word. No scrawled slip of paper, with its single Japanese character that says all, is pushed through my letter-box. Silence. And the darkness of the spirit: which I refuse: refuse.

I go alone again to Richmond. As one seeking a thing lost, I visit again our dearest haunts. Consciously, I evoke him. I entreat his return. And, as always, I wait.

And one day, he is on my stair. He enters the room, sits without a glance and, without preamble, says: 'I have taken some rooms. At 22 Great James Street. I shall live there. Perhaps you would like to help me move my books.'

His voice is flat, viewless. Detached. Remote. The voice of a robot. There is no word of marriage: of the tall house with its arched passage-way, with its wisteria-hung windows, with its garden: empty: waiting.

No. 22 Great James Street is, I see – as, indeed, is almost the whole street – unoccupied; with thunderous demolition going on next door; the flat, in a house of which he, as yet, will be the only occupant. The floors are raddled concrete. There is no view. There is no sun. How can he, of all men, *live* here: alone? No.[1]

I say, 'Darling – Richard Tawney has lately died, as you know, and I have been offered the first refusal of his flat – two floors of sun and balconies on to the trees of Mecklenburgh Square. Would you not prefer that? I would stay where I am, of course, in Handel Street – but we'd be near one another, with only the little St George's Garden between.'

He looks up. He says dully: 'It's . . . done now.'

In the days that follow there is much work; heavy and joyless: work without question – and certainly without answer. For us both it seems, eyes and arms and back and heart ache equally.

Nothing is said more of Highgate. I drive him to order what is needed for this place. Steel shelving for his library. Together we seek out a carpenter for cupboards. Together, we purchase a cooking-stove. Keys. Bolts. Padlocks. And chains.

The stage . . . is set.

---

[1] Japanese academics who visited Arthur here, set up a fund on their return home to finance better accommodation for him.

[2]

The Viper

Well: at 22 Great James Street things are going ahead. We have bought the steel shelving and all the books are up off the floor. Curtains now hang at the tall windows and across the eleven-foot division in the library. Odd mats are flung down on the painted concrete floor: but a single electric bar inserted in the wall is the only heating and a single central bulb from the ceiling the only light. A strip sliced off the front room now provides the amenities of a 'kitchen'. There are no power points. Here, opposite the harpsichord-cum-table, a tall curved window looks directly on a wall bearing a plaque with the legend – 'BEDFORD CHARITY BOUNDS! 1828'. From the narrow bed lodged into the corner opposite the door of the 'sitting-room' one sees high on the blind brick side of the house across the street the legend – 'GREAT JAMES STREET. 1721'.

I look at him.

Here. Where a corner pub and another in the street opposite fling drunks and rioters into the night: where every window is accessible. I look at him – who had always lived, who had so often said he *could* only live at the top of a house; above street noises and secure from such alarms.

There is of course no lift. A first-floor skylight that could drop a marauder into his library by a mere finger-lift of loose glass panels: where water enters – and has already entered – twice saturating the close-packed shelves.

In 1962, Great James Street is a down-graded, war-neglected

area where only the young and the adventurous go forth after dark. The once lovely Georgian houses – no longer residences of dignity, but semi-derelict offices of one kind and another – are fallen into disrepair and even decay. A few upper rooms house enigmatic, furtive characters. Adjacent streets, listed for demolition, are quite reduced to slums; the inhabitants employed in small local shops or rather more questionably, form a small compact world: an alien world indeed for him, in which it will surely be impossible to work; isolated; neighbourless. Scarcely a world – I am thinking, with a new sadness and apprehension – for a man travelling with ever-slowing gait towards his eighties and as psychologically and physically vulnerable as he.

Well: we know where we are. But – I think – not why. Arthur says: to justify the oddity: 'It's a nice street.'

'Beautiful. Architecturally.'

He says: 'There must be some sort of factory near by. From my kitchen window I can watch the workers coming up the street in their lunch-hour.'

'Yes.'

I think: 'Jot this down, posterity. Arthur Waley – scholar, poet, genius – aged seventy-five, ailing, living alone in an empty building – can, from his kitchen window, watch the workers coming up the street ...' The iron enters my soul: and I wonder if there is a harsh, rusty creaking in his own. Yet I know there is not. Just acceptance – and the bewilderment of exhaustion.

I think: 'This misery's got to stop.'

I say: 'Why, Darling?'

'Why?'

'Yes. Why? *Why* are you living here alone in this dark street? And I in another? What has *happened* to us?'

He is silent.

But I repeat gently: 'Why are you here?'

He says, with seeming irrelevance: 'Suppose I were to leave you my money ...'

I am appalled. Sick. But I say, as lightly as I can, 'Well.

[245]

That's easy. You're not to. Or better still, couldn't I sign some sort of legal document saying that, if in a mad moment you were to do so, I'd not touch a penny of it?'

No word comes from him.

But in the days that follow I do not leave it at that: it seems a possibility to me; and I go with it to the free legal advice group of the Mary Ward Settlement in Tavistock Place. There are four solicitors attending; one a woman, three men. Perhaps they are baffled by the predicament, but they consider it courteously. Arthur's name, of course, I refuse to divulge.

'Do you know this man's family?'

'No.'

'Do you know he has made a Will?'

'Yes.'

'Do you know his intention in the matter?'

'No.'

'Do you know if, in fact, he has money to leave?'

'Oh, yes. Some, anyhow. He has bought a house.'

They look at one another: they confer: at last: 'We suppose such a document as you describe *could* be drawn up. But do you know enough to suppose that this would ease the matter of the "pressures" put upon him?'

Ah – that I do *not* know. Nor would he – I *do* know well – in a thousand years confide them to me. No. Whatever they are, they are his business and his alone. And how would it be possible to keep my action from his knowledge? It would find its way there by reason of the very release which might ... or might not ... follow.

I can see that the four consider my proposal a bizarre one. And that their curiosity is already aroused. No. How could I have thought to humiliate him – my Darling – in this way? Better that things – whatever they prove to be – should run their course: be tackled one at a time.

In a fumbling sort of way I try to indicate this: thank my advisers, and retreat.

*   *   *

[246]

Here, at Great James Street – for all the shelves of books – we never read. Here, Arthur's left hand once only opened the harpsichord; with a finger touched a single note; quickly closed it. Too dispirited even to remove clothes we lie quiescent, side by side: persons, deeply sad, with no future; refugees, awaiting a signal whose meaning is disremembered; prisoners, with the vision of light but no more than the legend of freedom. As then, too sad for surmise, we speak seldom. And are careful to say nothing. At length Arthur would whisper: 'Dear, perhaps you should go now.'

And, 'Where?' I whisper back from the deep curve of his arm.

'Home.'

'I am home. This is my home. Not this dark unchosen place, but this armpit. I want no other. Oh, Hun, why weren't you born poor – a tramp! A hedge – a ditch – can be home enough for two who love as we do. Every time I leave you here in this ice-cold empty office building, my heart breaks. Tell me truly: do you like it when I'm gone? . . . Are you glad? . . . Can you work?'

'No! No! None of these things!' He wrenches me to him in a smother of kisses and his voice quivers to a whispered, 'It is so dreary . . . dreary . . .'

Again I think, 'This misery has got to stop.'

After a while I say: 'I've been to see our house.'

'Our . . . house.'

'Yes.'

I know the pain I am about to inflict: I suffer it too and it is important he should share.

'Yes. I crept down the arched alleyway to the garden gate in the lime avenue. It is dark with trees. Like a tunnel.' He does not interrupt. 'I climbed the hand-rail hidden in the leaves – so that I could look over.'

'What did you see?'

'Dogs. Hounds.'

'*Hounds.*'

This has jolted him to attention and I continue: 'Yes. They were burying great bones in the flower-beds. They were

[247]

worrying tennis shoes and tearing old trousers to shreds in the grass.'

'On the grass,' he repeats, dully; but his inner eye is now on the scene as acutely as my own.

'Well . . . actually . . . there isn't much grass left. It is hard earth. Like a football field. Like . . .' – cunningly I add the desolate image – '. . . like Gordon Square in the War.'

He looks again, and long, at this: the lawns, the garden-beds, flattened, destroyed. He says: 'Are they *allowed* to keep dogs?'

I am merciless. 'Why, yes. If you say so. It is your house.'

He flashes a reproachful eye at me: 'It is *your* house.'

'Mine? Ah, no. Never in a thousand years would *I* permit it.'

He accepts this. He says: 'The agent let it to friends of his. Who lives there? Did you see anyone?'

'Yes. While I watched, a woman with a little girl came out of the garden door and up the steps.'

'Did you notice anything more?'

'Oh, yes. There are no curtains. Except, that is, a grey army blanket looped across one of the first-floor windows. For privacy, I suppose. I'm going to make some tea.'

As I leave him he raises his eyes to me. They are curtained – I remember thinking – with a grey army blanket.

I return with the tray; and we drink in silence.

Suddenly I am in revolt. I jerk upright in my chair and say emphatically: 'It *won't do.*'

'What won't do?'

'Anything! Any of it! . . . Are we flesh and blood? Or are we wax? . . . Are we clay? It's not only wicked – it's *wrong*! Come out! Now!'

'Where?'

'Where? I don't know. It doesn't matter. We'll drive. We'll drive till we find the answer.'

And so it was that we came to the Viper Field: the field so high on Totteridge that the great arc of the sky is all its foreground – the turf so old and moss-cushioned, so untroubled by cattle or plough that we have come to think of it as ours; a gift from some former age.

In the late afternoon slant of sun, where the huge roots of an oak burst the rough green turf, I fling our rug and myself after it. The distance slopes down and away, a sea of green, and rises again to a far tree-fringed horizon. Stripping off our shirts we lie and let the warmth console our bodies, our minds a blank. Under my bare shoulder-blades a sharp root protrudes through a long-burned hole in the rug. I wriggle to escape it – and leap with a cry. Arthur, too, springs into a sitting posture.

'What is it? What is it?'

'A viper has bitten me!'

'A *viper*?'

'Yes, yes! There it goes ... black, scuttling ... across the rug ... slithering into the grass. But it doesn't *matter*. Listen. *I know what to do*. Now. Tomorrow. We turf the dog woman out and commence repairs. The house is literally flaking away, so it won't be considered surprising. You tell the agent you need it ... that you want to live in it yourself: that's reasonable ...

'Yes, yes, I know: you "live" at Great James Street. Right. Well, so you can; officially. Great James Street can go on being your library and your *pied-à-terre* in London ... the place to meet your friends ... and you keep it as your address. We'll even get cards printed. Meanwhile ...' – Where there were no words there are now a thousand, tumbling – '... meanwhile ... somebody has to direct the builders, the workmen, the renovations of the house at Highgate. And that's what *I* do. I, too, keep my official address at Handel Street but I camp up there among the workers ... to see that all is carried out well ... to supervise, you see. As room after room is repaired and decorated I move on, locking each as I go. Oh, Pit-pitten, *I* don't care if I sleep on a coil of rope! Yours – that topmost room with the view – shall be the first to be ready and then ... one night, then two, a week; and then always ... you live up there forever.'

His eyes are shining. He says; 'I shall be a recluse!'

'Yes! Me too! Me too! We'll be recluses. We'll barricade ourselves in – we'll keep boiling oil on the roof . . .'

'Boiling oil . . .' he purrs happily.

'It will be our redoubt. Our fortress.'

'But it's genius! Genius! Whatever made you think of it?'

'The viper. I mean, I didn't *have* to think. When the viper bit me I *knew*.'

'But you're stung? Oh my Darling, let me see. Yes, there are two little holes, like puncture marks . . . red and swollen . . . Did it hurt?'

'Of *course* it hurt. But not now: my arm's going numb . . .' I laugh, 'But who cares . . . who cares! We *know what to do!*'

And so we rock home in the little car, mad to get on with our plans.

Within a month my movable palliasse begins its journeyings from one room to another. The house at Highgate resounds with shouts and clatter and hammering. Transistors blare from floor to floor. Mr Baker, the electrician, leaps from stair to stair, his feet entangled in coils of flex. Ron, the plumber, comes and goes, broad face wreathed in smiles above a lavatory-pan. Bob, the painter, high on his sixty-foot ladder, lifts his magnificent voice in oratorio. Fred, the carpenter, an epileptic, barks like a dog . . .

While Arthur clambers about among the debris and retreats to his 'working-shed' at the bottom of the garden ... where rubble fires are burning constantly and potatoes roast in the embers. The place has become a camp. A din. And a delight.

It is more than three months before the hospital finds a correct antidote for my viper bite – or rather, they never find one and I live happily with my stiffness until the poison is absorbed into my system.

But by then its work is accomplished. We are no longer 'refugees'. We have uprooted the stake from our prison yard. Arthur's comings and goings are no more: or almost. For the first time in his life, he lives – and I with him – in a *house of his own*.

Standing at last at the tall top windows, with the workmen retreated somewhere into the bowels of the earth, we look out – not at a grey plaque but, beyond the garden, at the whole of a new London spread far as the eye can see . . . across the Thames . . . to the estuary . . .

'The City of the Plains . . .' I murmur.

'Sodome et Gomorrhe . . .' says Arthur.

I laugh. And then: 'Curious, Honey, that it should have to take a *viper* to inject common sense! D'you think the original serpent was one?'

[3]

Lovely as a Queen

It is our first Highgate winter. The first in a house of our own. The first alone together. Our village is ice-bound. A mountain village isolated from the world. The snows freeze. And, soon, the pipes of these English-built houses. For Arthur it has become, almost overnight, his beloved Switzerland. One wakes, as there, to the clatter and scrape of spades and shovels. One rubs a space on a steamed window – and is amused to see the parked cars trapped at rakish angles; their bowler-hatted owners, kitchen kettles held aloft, anointing recalcitrant wind-screen wipers while wives or children (Drakes before Elizabeth) fling coats before reluctant, out-raged wheels – until all is finally abandoned, the grinding ceases, gloved hands are thrust glumly back into deep pockets and the small unlikely procession augments, slipping and sliding, in the direction of the Tube.

Suddenly a wan sun: and the shout and colour of children dragging their sledges – to Kenwood; to the slopes of Parliament Hill Fields; to the lakes where skating is, as yet, forbidden.

But now, winter is indeed a problem. And Arthur, donning his ski-boots, balaclava and the Duke of Teck's overcoat,[1] takes a pail in either hand and moves off to join the queue in Pond Square where a Nubean princeling dispensing the indispensable has come into his own.

I am peeling apples. From the window of the first floor I

---

[1] An overcoat of ancient cut lent (given) to Arthur by the Duke of Teck when they were skiing together.

see Arthur returning. His pails are full and in his, as always, upwardflung glance to see if I await him, I note that his face is aglow. Entering this upstairs kitchen, he places the pails carefully inside the door, moves to his high-back wooden chair and bends to unlace his ski-boots. Dropping my knife I leap to do this for him, beating the snow on the floor where at once it melts into tiny streams. I kneel a moment, sitting back on my heels. As he draws off his gloves, unbuttons his coat, flings aside his balaclava – his eyes are on mine in a strange and shining look.

'Timeless' I think, as I rise again to my task and, in passing, switch on the radio. At once the room is transformed to the strains of a Strauss waltz: and, reaching the window, I turn again.

Arthur has risen and, the Duke of Teck's overcoat billowing out behind him, is approaching with arms outstretched. 'May I have the pleasure?'

He takes me in his arms – and, a length of apple-peel draped over one shoulder for royal insignia, we move sedately, languorously ... through the doors and over the parquet floors of the empty rooms into another age.

As we circle to the music's enchantment his eyes hold mine in a brown gaze: and never for one moment do I doubt what they say – I know I am lovely as a queen.

[4]

Miss Thackeray

From our high southern windows the world moves down and away in limitless whiteness: so foreign, so beautiful a world that I move a couch but lately purchased to make an 'encampment' before them – a room within a room.

'Look!' I say, as Arthur pushes it into place, 'There is some sort of small label on the back. Faded. Yellow with age.'

'Is anything written on it?' asks Arthur.

I crouch down to read the words on the fine strip pasted on the narrow wood that shows below the faded grey-green of the Regency velvet.

'Yes!' I cry; 'Something is written – it's so discoloured – in a fine spidery hand. It's a name. It's ... MISS THACKERAY.'

At once the ancient piece of furniture becomes 'Miss Thackeray's couch' – the alcove from which we have dragged it, 'Miss Thackeray's room'. In her quietly-rustling silks, she is as alive to us as was 'Miss Leverett' in her faded waterproof. As we seat ourselves again at either end, our small table set between us, her ringlets shake in gentle approval. Our house has a third occupant.

'What I'm rather worried about, Honey, is the water-tank in the roof. It must be frozen and it could burst. Don't you think I'd better climb into the loft to investigate?'

'Climb into the loft? Couldn't we get a man?'

'A man? You mean a plumber? At this moment of time, in this village, they're more precious than gold! And truly not necessary.'

At the foot of the ladder Arthur stands, holding it with

rigid hands, looking up into the blackness of the rafters where, a moment before, my feet have disappeared. Presently my head comes over the edge.

'Everything's all right. The tank's not solid: the pipes are, anyway, bound with thick felt. Hold on – I'm coming down.'

'Is anything up there?'

'Anything? No. Oh, but wait. Can you pass me a torch? There *is* something . . . over in the corner.'

I am crawling now on hands and knees under the grimed slope of roof tiles.

'It's a box.'

'Is anything in it?'

With difficulty I lift the lid a few inches, balancing the torch with my chin. 'Nothing. It's empty. No treasure.'

But the faint beam of my light falls on a small glimmer of whiteness. And twisting like a contortionist, I thrust my head inside. Then, closing the lid, I ease my way backwards to the trap-door: descend in silence; stand beside him.

'There was a name,' I say now, brushing the cobwebs of a hundred years from my hands and hair, 'on a label . . . in a sloping spidery hand . . .'

He looks at me quickly.

'It said . . .' – oddly, I feel I don't even need to tell him – 'It said . . . MISS THACKERAY.'

[5]

The Tenant

When we bought the house at Highgate I was still slender. Not the lithe, blade-like creature I had been at our first encounter in the magical spring of 1929, but still wire-strong, with instant reactions and deft, ballet-trained movement: attributes which were to be vitally needed and put to test.

Over the years I had let my black hair, which had, for wartime West End elegance, been cropped more or less to the shape of my head so that a comb or my fingers pushing it back off my brow was adequate coiffure, grow to below waist-length – straight silken ropes which were strange sub-conscious comfort to Arthur in the years when it often seemed he must drown in his sufferings. He would, in fact, in sleep coil his fingers in such tight grip – a grip which tightened even more at my slightest movement – that I was virtually a prisoner. On waking, I would loose the ropes of my hair with, 'So! You've pulled yourself ashore, sailor. Where would you be without your hawsers!' I never cropped my hair again.

These 'hawsers' were now grey as steel but, their life-rope function long since over, they were permitted to unwind and flow at will. In general, I looped the lot into a twist on the nape of my neck or swirled it on to the crown of my head. Still, however, at the end of a 'dressed-up' day, Arthur would stretch a hand to draw me down beside him, his fingers would deftly remove the pins – which had always to be five – so that it fell about my shoulders and he would lean and select a single silvered strand and lift it to his lips. It was a ritual.

Part III: Homecoming, 1962–6

'You should wear your hair down ... always.'

Curiously, though I confess to some dismay when the slight down began to appear on my upper lip at fifteen, I had suffered so little disadvantage that I had come to be completely unaware of its oddity. No man, to my knowledge, had ever found it a reason for recoil from me; many, indeed, all those I cared about, appeared to see it as an enhancement.

It was great happiness for me to realise that this was so also in Arthur's case. From the first, it was evident he held the silky hairs in tenderest affection. Later, he revealed to me that with Ainu women it was a veritable signature of beauty: if nature, indeed, had been so unkind as to omit it, the matter was quickly remedied with a deep tattoo. I discovered among Arthur's books a rare and remarkable one, undated, printed in Tokyo, by one John Batchelor, containing many illustrations of such women. There is a description of one, Yai-mah of the Hollows, lover of Kutri: '... and the tattoo round her mouth was of a glowing dark blue, well cut in and beautiful to behold'. The book is sub-titled, *Echoes of a Departing Race*. Amused, I held it up to Arthur. 'Am I that?' I asked him, 'An "echo of a departing race?"'

He smiled in that open, wonderful way. '*I* think you are,' he said.

I look again now at the features of great beauty, magnificent eyes, the straight brows of the Greeks, the glowing silken locks, the moustaches soft and thick enough to curl slightly at the ends. I feel again his finger-tips. I think of the beauties of the Russians: at the ball, for instance, in Dostoevsky's *The Idiot*: the Muscovite lady in Virginia Woolf's *Orlando*. There was, of course, I remind myself now, the added factor that I would have been prepared hilariously to have borne to the grave any disfigurement that delighted my Dear.

One day I asked: 'Do you think we should let part of this house, Darling? It's big for us, and we live almost entirely up here with the long view. It seems perhaps we should.'

[257]

'Wouldn't it be a great nuisance to you?'

'I don't think so. Below is so complete: its own kitchen: its own bathroom: everything ...' – I think of Beryl for whom our plans for it were so detailed, but do not speak her name – '... for somebody.'

He thought a moment; and I knew he was reluctant. But he said, 'Well ... if you like to do it.'

I didn't, of course, 'like' to do it: I was by now conditioned to the 'recluse' life we had designed, but I thought this need in no serious way be interfered with and, knowing nothing of Arthur's financial resources, felt it might prove some economy for him. I forthwith telephoned details of the accommodation to the American Club and, on a day when we had totally forgotten the whole project, our first 'tenant' arrived. She was youngish – who can tell with an American woman? – and instantly forthcoming. I led her into what would be her bedroom, its full-length windows dominating the length of the garden, and went to fetch Arthur for moral support. It was well I did.

We sat, triangularly, on three chairs: Arthur awkward and silent: and I thinking how bizarre a circumstance it was that presented him in the guise of a 'landlord'. Our American, however, was, as is usual, totally without inhibitions. With no reference, now, to the flat proffered, she bent on me an intent and kindly gaze.

'My *deer*,' she said to me across Arthur's frozen mask, 'your *features* are really verry, *verry* good.'

From sheer astonishment I made no movement and she leaned a little forward to view my face in better light.

'Yes ... *Yes* ...' – and, in rapid parenthesis to Arthur – 'I'm *verry* creative, you know.' She nodded her conviction of the fact and continued with rising enthusiasm: 'VERRY creative. *Now*. The eyes are fine. The nose is elegant. And the mouth is *reely* charming ... but,' – she paused and sighed her sympathy – 'BUT ... for those *sad ... unsightly* ... HAIRS.'

Still to our dumb amazement, she ran on ...

'NOW! ... I used to work for Helena Rubinstein ... AND

[258]

... if you would just let me tell you how to remove that little MOOstache you could look ... just *cute!*'

At this, Arthur jerked to his feet: his chair tipped sideways.

'NOT ... ONE ... HAIR!' he enunciated, in a voice I had seldom or never heard, as he showed the lady to the door.

With nothing spoken, we returned to the seclusion of our redoubt.

And it was some days later that I found a workman – 'under the gentleman's instruction' he told me – putting a heavy chain across the inside panelling.

[6]

A Social Occasion

For a week – for ten days now – we had both been ill: a virus contagion brought direct from Warsaw and completely baffling to the doctor. Dragging ourselves about the house, we nursed one another with what strength we could muster until at last the contest was won. Nevertheless, we were both worn with the battle, depleted and very weak, when one noon the telephone rang. It was X. I passed the receiver to Arthur but, since we were seated together, the words were audible to me: X would bring a friend for tea with Arthur at 22 Great James Street at 4 p.m. that day.

'You can't go, of course, darling. Say you can't.'

Arthur explained that he was far from well: indeed, that it was his first full morning on his feet; but he would be pleased to receive X and his friend at Highgate.

To my astonishment, the voice at the other end now took on a new quality: a startling one; demanding, harsh. No. He, himself, did not feel well enough to come out to Highgate – and his friend wished Arthur to sign some books for him.

'Very well; I will come,' said Arthur, replacing the receiver, turning to me, 'and you must come with me.'

But I was dumb with anger. 'Of *course* I'll come with you. But as for "very well" – there's nothing *well* about it! That wretched X. You've said more than once you disliked him. Why do you put up with such a friend?'

'He's not *my* friend. He was Beryl's,' he replied enigmatically.

On the tick of four a taxi drew up. There seemed a certain amount of confusion on the stair landing and when I went to open the door I was aware of suitcases. The two men stood among them and one of these X lifted inside the narrow passage. The anger that sprang into his sallow face at sight of me was comically ill-concealed as he led his friend to a still-reclining Arthur.

As a tea-party the occasion would scarcely be termed a success. X, seated with his small rather cruel hands clasped about one knee, was sullen, silent: and, I fancied, a little nervous. His lank companion, so seemingly superfluous – a lay figure – contributed nothing; and the room seemed to shrink with their presence. Arthur was abstracted with pain and fatigue; and, I imagine, boredom. I, of course, for I made no effort to conceal my coldness, was ignored. Yet, this permitted me some scrutiny and I had the disquieting impression that each waited upon the other's move – that *occasion* was in every gesture: the stage was set and the cast in their places; something, however, I thought, had gone wrong with the curtain mechanism.

Nothing of the slightest consequence was being said.

Nothing of the slightest consequence was said until the discomforted X, unable to wedge another syllable between the massive blocks of silence, announced that his friend had brought with him the books he wished signed: they were in the passage-way.

These, now, were brought; several at a time. Arthur tried to prop himself up with pillows and reached for his pen. I placed cushions under his left arm, and with the injured right one he worked slowly, laboriously – while X, moving restlessly back and forth, conferred in undertones with his friend beyond the door.

Presently he came with a request: might he show his friend Arthur's library? This of course was the back, and larger, room and lined from floor to ceiling with a lifetime's assembling of rare and precious books. A brief movement of the head was all the consent he received: but soon they were busily engrossed in their mutual traffic. A great deal appeared to be going on, with the opening and shutting of doors, but X was careful to appear regularly with yet another few volumes.

I had, of course, remained beside Arthur. We seemed to have got through some thirty or so sadly wild signatures when suddenly Arthur could do no more and I called the two creatures in to collect their spoils.

I was not, then, Arthur's wife. I could not, therefore, defend him. I could, however, utter my contempt: 'You must let us know what profit you receive in America on this evening's work. It should be ... interesting.'

X's face darkened with anger; his friend's features remained what appeared to be their normal blank as they departed, clattering their boxes down the stair.

'That ...' I said, turning to Arthur's now supine and silent form, 'was an abomination.'

It was perhaps a week later that Arthur asked me to drive him to Great James Street – he was doing some work on Ezra Pound, he said.

He was still far from well and again I made him lie on his bed.

'Which volume do you want? Stay there. Let me get it for you. I know exactly where they are – the fifth shelf up from the floor to the right inside the door.'

He smiled his pleasure at such exactitude but, 'No,' he said, 'I'm not certain which one I want. I'll get it,' and I went to make our tea.

From the kitchen, through the length of the narrow passage, I saw him standing still, just within the door of his library. I heard him say, 'Christ!' I went – and looked up – as he was looking – at an empty space.

I glanced quickly round the room, the once crowded shelves. The spaces ... were more than several.

[7]

Assault

18 May 1963.

At 9 a.m. the telephone rings. It is May-the-maid, who arrives each morning at Great James Street for an hour's dusting of the books. There has been a burglary – a 'break-in' – Dr Waley had better come down.

I had an appointment which I could not postpone.

'Leave me at Great James Street. I don't suppose it is anything of importance. May is greatly given to exaggeration.'

On this occasion, however, as events proved, May was thoroughly capable of classic understatement.

Since his *pied-à-terre* provided no storage space, Arthur had rented an extra small room in the basement and there deposited the entire contents – or so it seemed to me – of the similar small storeroom at No. 50 Gordon Square. Here, now, they were: from floor to ceiling, the familiar trunks, boxes, suitcases, containers of every sort; the larger locked and padlocked. I knew them well and almost individually, for over the years they had crowded the small room across the top landing from the library of his Gordon Square flat – but a matter of a few paces from his work-strewn desk and table. How often had I seen him rise from his chair beside the enormous couch with its load of open tomes to move rapidly to the smaller room, open a lid, remove or replace some document, some letter, some manuscript? Only brooms and brushes stood guard over this precious store – this hoard of a lifetime of scholarship and intimate association which he had succeeded in protecting from one address to another through two World Wars. I still have one of the familiar Greek-woven blue-and-white-striped dust covers that draped, in those far days, this mass of material.

The Great James Street room below was duly stacked one morning with the help only of May-the-maid: and that afternoon in High Holborn Arthur went with me to buy a padlock and chain which he fixed to the door. Since the floor was damp I suggested also a duck-board of the sort used on battleships and liners, and found a chandler where this might be obtained.

But whether or not the suggestion was acted upon I was never to know. For the room was ransacked, torn apart, padlock and chain wrenched away: even – it was said – the door panel smashed in.

And the records of a scholar's life, back to its first beginnings, back to earliest manhood, to childhood, to infancy itself, lay strewn, scattered, trampled: on floor, on stair, on hallway.

With what savagery, or haste, had such an exercise been carried out?

It was very early in the morning of that 18 May so the only other, and newly arrived, occupant of the house told me, that – hearing thunderous noise below – he had gone down in his pyjamas and 'stood aghast' to witness what was going on. It seemed the gang of about five had dropped over the area railings and smashed a window to get in. The rest of the story lay at his feet ... and *under* the feet of the thugs as they stood there, their 'foreman' grinning truculently. Later on that day I drove Arthur home in the little car. He was silent, dazed, in a state of shock. The smashed trunks, the broken boxes, the many thousand letters – themselves a unique chapter of literary history – the early notebooks; back to Cambridge, back to Rugby, back to the tentative writings of a small boy of ten looking out, not without apprehension, on the unexplored world – the family records, the albums, the cherished faded snapshots of wonderful occasions – and the pages of what the world calls manuscript. All these – a man's life – exposed, crumpled, smudged, torn, pressed deeply with the footprints of the intruders – all these had been roughly gathered together from floor and stair and hallway: hastily and temporarily bundled, flung, swept into the empty front room of the ground floor and the key turned.

When at length Arthur was physically able to consider the problem of removal, it was to discover that not one fragment of the previous hoard remained. When or how this second visitation was achieved I have never been able to ascertain: for, almost at once, a curtain of silence descended on the whole affair. Arthur, pleading for a clue, was told by the Police – so I was assured – that his property was in all probability on a certain 'dump' at the East End Docks. And again it was said, for he himself never confided it, that he found his way to the place described and, alone, in the half-dark of evening, climbed the mountain of city refuse in search of even so much as one of his manuscripts. And this scene haunts me forever.

Thereafter, Arthur asked me never to speak of the matter. And I recognised in the request a plea for mental survival. There followed inevitable months, indeed nearly the period of a year, of nightmares in which cries, groans, and even – though in deepest sleep – the thrusting over of furniture had their part. But yet – for so he was – the conscious mind acknowledged neither conflict nor affliction. Simply, to save his sanity, the thing that 'could not happen' had *not* happened.

[8]

Seaweed

1964.

We are at Highgate. I am pottering in the sun of the garden. Arthur, who has been hard at work writing in the low box-window of the small Victorian summerhouse, now emerges, flings himself full length on the cushioned sledge and watches with quiet pleasure. Soon I join him there and stretch out on the grass in the noonday blaze, part shaded and dapple-patterned by the apple tree. The murky pool holds jealously the wispy summer clouds.

We are silent, in the deep of content. His gaze moves slowly from the elegant arms of our flowering-cherry to the giant-high branches of the roses: travels up the wisteria-draped façade of the tall and lovely house, window by window, to rest at last in the blue infinity of sky.

Presently he says: 'It was your seaweed that saved me.'

'My seaweed?' I murmur, snatching at memory out of a ten-year silence: 'At Plaw Hatch? It reached you?'

'It . . . reached me.'

'No letters? Ever?'

'None.'

'Just . . . the seaweed.'

'Just the seaweed. From that moment I thought of you . . . constantly.'

And *my* thought, with a lift of joy – but I do not utter it – 'And so, you climbed into your best overcoat and went to see the Queen!' For – ultimately – the nightmare weeks behind him – there he had stood in my attic room, come in untidy haste from Buckingham Palace, holding out the Queen's Medal for Poetry and saying: 'It's real gold.'

He says now: 'What made you send it?'

I smile. 'Ah, what! You always ask that, don't you – "What made me?" "Why?" And I never know the answers. But I suppose ... of course it must have been the dream.'

'The dream? Tell me.'

'Oh well: when you went to Plaw Hatch it was a Friday. You had said you must work: *must*. That it was impossible at No. 50. That Gordon had cleverly found the perfect place for Beryl in the *New Statesman* – and that far from requiring persuasion, she herself was eager to go. That you would be away only for the weekend: just to see her settled there. That you would be back in town on the Monday.'

I paused, while my mind linked in – only now – the 'emissary' and the strange scene in St George's Garden. Could retaliations be so disproportionate, so dire? But I continued: 'Instead, it was many, many weeks. I began to be disturbed. I wrote – you always told me to – but there was never any reply: it was as though you had vanished off the face of the earth. Then I had to go to Brighton on a writing job. It was difficult, for my mind seemed never to belong to me but was yours, *with* you: and in some deep alarm. When I tried to penetrate this' – I turned to smile at him, 'with Bertie's tools of logic and reason – all was obscured. Then – on the last night – there was the dream.'

'Tell me,' he said again.

It was easy to evoke now: so vivid: so without pain. I continued: 'Cliffs rose: white cliffs, but shadowed: tall and sheer from a rocky base. While I watched, the tide turned: the sea that had lashed and torn began to recede, to slide back at tremendous speed, laying bare tier below tier – terrace below terrace – of flat grey rock. As I stood in wonder at this, you appeared from somewhere out of the black shadow. You were running, leaping, down towards the sea: pursuing it: urgently as though you must, *must* arrive: *must* reach those curving, snarling crests that drew everything with them. Even you, I thought: and sprang to follow. But you were already at some distance and swift. Across the flat you raced, leaping the four-foot drop and on across another, and another. But I too was swift; swifter, for I seemed to gain on you.

'But then I knew it was too late: you were already on the last of the terraces: the next leap must be that cunning and remorseless ocean: we were still far apart: there was no catching up. I stopped: I stood very still. I called to you: wordlessly. But with all my mind. At once your headlong rush was arrested. You did not speak or turn your head. We stood. Far apart. Motionless. Two small dark figures against the immensity of that scene – while the sea crashed out its crazy fury.

'But the storm in our two hearts had dropped to instant silence, to a heaven of stillness.

'I knew – and knew that we both knew – *that* fate would never claim you. Then. Or ever.

'I woke and, ignoring my packing, ran to the shore. From its scatter of coloured weed I took one small and silken strip – creamy, transparent, with smears of pink and green.'

'Yes,' Arthur murmured.

'I went to the Post Office: bought a strong stamped envelope: placed the damp, briney, lovely thing inside. Then, on an impulse, I asked the man at the counter to address it *for* me. To you. At Plaw Hatch.'

Our two minds wandered over that distant landscape.

After a while Arthur said, very low: 'Beryl thought you were hiding in every ditch.'

I considered this. 'Poor Beryl. Perhaps, in a way, she wasn't wrong? Not "hiding" – but *there*. In every ditch. In every tree. *With* you. Wherever *you* were. So long as you loved me, you see.

'And as for me – well, it's not a thing I can help. I don't even always *want* to be where you are – it's too frightening – but ... it's just *like* that.'

[9]

The Thing

One blue and shining day, Arthur desired above all things to seek out a certain small Kentish village.

Now he stood a moment at the church-yard's wicket-gate through which I had just passed, his hand laid lightly on the weathered wooden cross-bar. I turned, waiting. He said: 'The last time I passed through this gate I was seventeen.'

I squatted down on the roadside grass as he came towards me, and, flinging down his coat for the two of us, he did the same.

'Tell me,' I said.

'It was a family picnic,' he went on. 'We came by motor.'

'Not by brake,' I suggested, remembering the huge day-long picnics of my own youth.

'No: a Rolls actually, and chauffeured. The family wanted to go somewhere else – to the sea probably – but I very badly wanted to come here . . . and in the end my mother managed to persuade them.'

'I see,' I murmured, smiling, and mementarily identifying myself with his mother.

'I'd just read the history of this church and I wanted to take some rubbings.'

He paused.

'And the family were not very interested in rubbings?' I prompted.

'Not the least in the world,' he burst out, dismissing the other members, one and all, with sudden stress. 'Shall we follow the stream across the meadows? If we go far enough there are some splendid pools. I know the way.'

And crossing the road we climbed the wooden bars of a strong new fence and set out into the sun.

It took a good hour's leisured walking to find the right place. But soon, rucksack and clothes stowed under a bush, we had slithered naked down the sheer side of a clay cliff, dropped into the embrace of the dark-shadowed water and struck out for the willow-roofed pool.

I swam leisurely into the deep centre and, right arm held high, left hand holding my nose in the approved fashion, attempted without success to depth it.

Suddenly there was a sharp, thin hissing sound and the snapping of twigs, like pistol shots, above me. I looked up and, quivering not a yard from my face, was a pointed steel stem. It hung over my upturned eyes with the malevolence of a snake. But a fractional difference of timing and this perpendicular death from the upper airs would have pierced my skull, my chest – impaled me, held me fast – on the mud-floor at the bottom of the slow-moving, opaque water.

Or held . . . him?

I looked for Arthur. Grasping at roots, he had pulled himself up the slithering slope and, dripping, mud-streaked, now sat hunched on the crumbling edge of turf, his eyes fixed on the *thing*. A kind of horror showed in them. He sat rigid and silent. From below I could not see what he could see. What was it? I sprang up, seized a bough and, springing again, grasped the still-quivering shaft. Using both hands and all my weight I swung and wrenched at the slender gleaming metal.

Suddenly, with a tearing and collapse of upper branches, the thing came through, submerging me in a mesh of aluminium spars. Struggling free of these, I found myself roofed over by what appeared to be a vast silken open parachute; still caught and held aloft by the frail upturned fingers of the willow.

By now the weight of metal – spear and spars – had sunk out of my reach.

With an almost anthropomorphic fury against this unknown object's attack, I tore what I could of the great mass clear and, dragging it with difficulty through the water, clambered up the bank beside Arthur.

I was breathless as I looked up into the skies. His appalled gaze followed mine. They stretched clear on every side. We were tented over by nothing more awesome than the limitless blue of a summer day.

I flung myself on my back and, consciously to convince Arthur that nothing untoward was afoot, began to wring out the long rope of my hair. And, seeing me do this normal thing, he ranged himself alongside and lay in parallel with me in the direct blaze of the overhead sun.

'Funny,' I remarked casually, and added, 'funny-queer.'

His silence meant, I knew, that his alarm was still there; still active. I rolled over and plucked a wisp of grass. 'Target practice,' I grinned, 'with us for targets!'

I couldn't have said a more wrong thing: his eyes visibly dilated.

'Pitten,' I began again, making it up as I went along, 'they *have* to drop these things – John had to when he was training. They're sort of markers.'

He whispered, 'They could have killed you.'

'Nonsense, Honey! Not them! The whole thing ...' (what had he noticed – how much could I lie, I was thinking) '... was as light as matchwood.'

He looked at the still water, dark under the willow. 'It's not floating ...' he said, in denial of my words.

Now I was desperate: '*Because I trod it down, Silly.* Didn't you *see* me? And a devil of a lot of treading it needed too!'

'You mean ... it couldn't have hurt you?'

'Hurt me? Never! Shall we have our sandwiches now or after?'

As he turned to me I saw his eyes were clear. 'After,' he said.

When we woke it was to a deep hot breathing very close to our two heads. Arthur lay still. I rolled over and, lifting my chin, gazed into the wet nostrils and the huge astonished eyes of a young bull.

He was not alone. He was merely the leader. He had dared approach to sniff our very hair. His companions were half-circled a pace or two back – waiting upon his action – or, I thought quickly, his command.

I remained perfectly still, saying in a low voice to Arthur, 'Don't move. Keep very still ... In fact, pretend to go on sleeping. It's only a group of young steers overcome by curiosity. Our prone bodies, from across the field, must have looked rather unusual: after all, no-one ever comes here; we're miles out of bounds, you know.'

While my voice ran on, the leader took a half-pace back and, without removing his great, velvet eyes from mine, dipped his head and blew at the turf in front of my face.

'Not the most polite of gestures,' I muttered. 'What's the matter?' Slowly but deliberately I extended my arms along the ground towards him and opened my hands palms upward.

At once in response he bent and smelled them carefully – his wet, hot breath filling their cups and steaming in wreaths about my loose-curled fingers.

He did this several times, and presently his companions in telepathic accord drew near and did the same.

Arthur's curiosity, which would, as I'd often assured him, winkle him out of heaven or hell, had got the better of him. His eyes were open. He was watching, fascinated.

Beside us lay in its small heap the silken and still wet-gleaming parachute.

When the leader had finished with my hands he moved, very slowly, very cautiously, to this. Standing at neck-stretch, he thrust his great head forward and examined it. This time the group did not follow his example. They stood in semi-circle like a ballet chorus awaiting their cue.

Now the young bull straightened upright. Gently he withdrew first one foot and then the other, marking the grass with deep grooves as he did so and lowering his great shoulders in a sort of curtsey. It was a delightful movement.

'Darling,' I whispered now excitedly, 'Watch him! Watch! It's a sort of "bow of apology" for the intrusion. And look – the others are doing it too!'

And, sure enough, the whole chorus – but still with eyes fixed on us – was withdrawing in like manner. Never once did they turn their backs, but soon they were fanned out across the field. By the time we had sat up they were obliterated, 'in the wings', absorbed into the dark purple shadows of the far hedge.

Here, indeed, was the enchantment that, always, could end fear: Arthur's eyes were shining with pleasure.

'Ballet,' I smiled.

'Wonderful,' he murmured, and then, 'What did they want?'

'Why – to investigate two naked animals lying moveless beside a placenta.'

'A *placenta*?' he cried.

'Certainly,' I rejoined, 'Doesn't that wet gleaming thing – and especially from the far side of the meadow – look *exactly* like a placenta? It was obviously on the cards that either I or you had given birth to a calf. It was their *duty* to investigate.'

I reached for our rucksack: 'And I don't know about you but I'm mad-hungry.'

[10]

Venice

Moving without haste we are the last to leave the plane, the last to be handed down into the tiny motorcraft that skim the glassy way to the air-strip. Seated apart in the stern, from the flung curve of Arthur's arm I watch the low dunes slide by, their spear-like grasses reflected, their yellow sands slipping into the milky sea. All is sun-melted and serene. But for the tiny choke of the engine, all is silent. But for the odd half-clad figure of a youth fishing, solitary, at the end of a promontory, the world is uninhabited. Until suddenly, under its canopy of cloudless blue, lies the flawless pearl of Venice – so beautiful, snared in its centuries-old dream, one catches the breath.

'*Man* . . . has made it?' I breathe, incredulous.

We follow our porter, his diminutive frame all but concealed by our cases, on and on along the Schiavoni: over its little humped bridges, past the glittering Danielli until, weaving rapidly through the gay and fashionable crowds, he is soon lost to our sight. But, at last, no, there he is; distantly waiting.

Beside us now are balconied windows in a façade of crumbling magnificence. '*That* is where I would wish to be!' I exclaim. 'That is where I would wish to live forever!' But then I see that the doors are sealed; the windows, right to the highest of them, close-barred. I approach the great dead portal, read what is written and return to Arthur.

'A madhouse!' I laugh. 'Perhaps the *only* sanctuary!'

That night, storm breaks like a bombardment.

Without warning, the sky is ripped like a canvas roof of a marquee through which drop bolts of thunder. A thousand roof-tiles rocket to earth, a thousand shutters clatter like gunfire, a thousand potted shrubs hurtle from a thousand sills to crash and explode in yard-wide streets and paved courtyards.

We leap to the window.

But we do not fasten it. Instead we stand close: drenched in the rioting gale. Our naked heads lifted to meet its force, we offer ourselves to the sky's magnificence.

Rain dives in steely sheets to gouge the roof-tops and, scooping along ledges, send iron pots and earthen jars hurtling to the inner courtyard where, about its ghostly well, ecstatic oleanders dance a crazy welcome.

But now the deafened night is ripped anew by shriek upon human shriek.

From the high dim-lit cloisters that run two sides of the enclosed space comes a crescendo of animal terror. Jagged and shocking in its frenzy it rises to pierce the violence even of the storm.

As at a sign, now, behind the pillared arches, lights appear and flicker. A procession of white-robed nuns moves rapidly from left to right. Each carries high a tray and a candle. Each vanishes into the wings. A ballet lit by lightning shafts and curtained by a slant of spears.

'Sheer theatre!' I shout against the racketing storm.

'The Madhouse!' Arthur breathes, giving it its title, and with uncontrolled delight.

And then, almost on an instant, all fades. The animal cries fail, cease. Curtain fall. And the play is over. The storm – the entire company with its props and effects is up and away – rattling off to Padua.

And turning to one another in wonder, it is to confront now an army of half-clad maids who, bursting into our room with towels, pails, brooms and sponges, proceed with urgency – and wild hilarity – to mop up the swimming floor of the mad *Ingleses*.

As we move slowly through the gold Venetian days Arthur points out, dream-like, from time to time the canal-fronted mansions – this one and that where Beryl had lived: with this one and that. Some are illustrious names: but in general their lacquered days were arid, as hers, and are done.

Opposite one of these, we dine at a little table roofed by vines. He does not face the impressive entrance across the narrow water – finding, even now, more sufferable the clatter of life going on in the adjacent kitchens.

But I am poignantly aware that I have been brought here for a purpose: and I must bridge half a century. I – for him – must face again those portals; must enter them; must suffer with him what he suffered. Time ... is switched back. As he talks, I am conveyed by liveried gondoliers, by private gondola, emblazoned, richly cushioned. At the steps where now the water laps indifferently and a carelessly-thrown cigarette packet of modern 'American Blend' lifts and retreats, lifts and retreats, to join again the débris that idly floats ... To these steps, this pillared and elaborately bolted door, I am lead; my heart afire, each nerve aflicker to receive pain I know must come – indeed, is meant to come, is carefully designed. I must be received by Beryl's 'lover' of the time – a year perhaps, perhaps less. I must permit his boastings, his braggartry; I must accept, without quiver of pulse or eyelid, his shafts of sly derision ... must suffer again the soft-vowelled, murmured insult, so gently incised, and hear, my heart in torment, the high false laughter of the woman I had asked to be my wife.

'Love! Marriage, devotion, loyalty! How MORE than vulgar! And children? But these are for peasants, for animals of the field!'

I glance down at him here – the old man in the leaf-green light; his beret, his book beside him on the metal table; his eyes shrouded. I glance back at him there ... seeing – in other time – this checked cloth as silk, these common plates set out as golden: and him, the young Jew, who has nothing to offer but only these same denounced vulgarities – a virile body crazed to love, great beauty of feature, an inbred sensitivity, a spirit of white flame, the mind of genius. And the terrifying capacity to endure.

I excuse myself from the table, leave the garden and run to a hidden niche in the ancient wall: I beat my head against it while tears splash on to my clenched fists: tears of anger and pain – a fury of fury against those two, those many, whose boasted cult was cruelty; the 'civilised' cult; the 'Cannibals'; the cult of jungle beasts. And of pain? ... Ah, but pain is unquenchable and now is blent with my own.

I creep back to him. 'Where did you go?'

I open his hand on the table and lay my cheek upon it. He does not query its wetness. He has no need.

'I ... don't know.'

But something is exorcised: something has moved at last and forever into the past. No sting of bitterness is in my heart: neither – I find – bitterness nor blame. I look up. And in his ageless eyes is only ... the 'vulgarity' of love.

'I have given your order, my Darling ... I thought you would choose to have what I have.'

Yes. How else is love possible?

We are like cats in Venice. We never move far from our abode. We are not tourists. We have not come to see things. We are here only to *be* here: to fulfil a promise to ourselves – a promise made in time of hope, nearly twenty years ago – and perhaps to lay a ghost. But these things are unspoken. Both are painful, and if Arthur, as I – gives them conscious thought, he makes no sign.

Yet ... these *are* our sole reasons. And yes, he gives them conscious thought: for all the time here our thoughts pass backward and forward, the one to the other, as though our minds are fused. Sometimes a memory or a thought comes into mine, suddenly and forcefully, dodging my instant barriers, and I glance up and see the pain – my pain – in his eyes. Quickly I beat it back, turn it out, empty my mind of all but love ... and he turns on me a glowing gaze, almost of gratitude ... 'Thank you, my Darling, for not thinking that ... I couldn't have borne it.' (How many minds have we, that the one can control the other in this way?) And this happens constantly and so consistently, I wonder sometimes which of us – he or I – has thought the thought first; which way, as it were, the traffic runs? Sometimes one way, I think, sometimes another.

We sit in the sun ... wherever the sun is. On benches, on park seats, on steps, on copings, on bollards, on coils of rope, against sea walls – and just *are*: together.

But there are times – in this Venice – when his sadness encompasses me, closes down, folds over, so that I have to struggle free or faint of his pain. Then I get up, call a boat-man, demand refreshment, snatch up a book, open it any-where and read aloud – anything to penetrate the deeps of the spell which has descended: pain, from far-off in time – pain beyond my knowledge; though not my suffering of it.

Yet, if there is not happiness here – for that we fail to find – there is perhaps a thing that is more: and incomprehensible. We find it in the Giudecca. Content and ease that glows strangely. Warmed by our love and the spell of this time-deserted place of ghosts, it draws us back in experience and yet holds us together: so that, whatever the need is – fortitude, endurance, hope – we are as two-fold, doubly-strengthened, and can stand firm.

The Giudecca. I have not seen the Lido. I do not look inside San Marco. But I lower my bare feet into this flotsam and grime that taps lightly with the tide against the water-sculptured piles of the wharves – I run with the dark-eyed swarming children across the worn flagged spaces between decayed and ancient mansions; the strings of gay washing – banners in the sun – swung their entire width from window to window – reach out and slap smartly against my face as I run ... and I am *home*. I am home: with my Darling. *This* ... is why we have come to Venice.

I wander slowly back to him, squat on my heels before him where he waits on the low bridge coping, take his two hands, look up into the timeless beauty of his face, feel the tears move slowly down my own and ask him: 'Tell me – was I ever a Jew?'

'Perhaps.'

'Here? In this place?'

'Perhaps.'

'Is that why we have come?'

For answer, he leans to catch, and kiss, a silvered strand of my flying hair. And, my heart all but breaking with its load, I fall for release on the old re-iteration ... 'Oh, but I love you ... love you.'

On the Giudecca we are not happy. But we are clothed. So that I know 'happiness' for but a frail ornament.

From my early morning window the breadth of water is milk-white and opalescent in the horizontal sun. To the left, the Russian submarine is a hive of industry and already the broad quay is filling with hurrying figures, tables and chairs are being placed, awnings are descending. A full hour yet to breakfast but so lovely an hour indeed, we must use it ... and, picking up a banana and an apple, I make my way to Arthur. He is awake: dressed and packed.

'Oh, splendid!' I say. 'So am I. Don't let's waste one moment – we'll find a spot in the sun.'

All is stir below. Another 'groupa' is arriving: its leader, a very young man obviously new to the job, appears slightly demented. Our German *patron*, is as rarely, agitated. The maids, the porters, are scurrying, calling to one another in strident tones. We weave a way carefully between the stacked baggage of arrival and make for the calm and seclusion of our favourite bridge.

Seated, our backs to its stone, we watch, fascinated, the early morning activity of deliveries: arrival and departure of little boats with out-board motors or propelled by young boatmen who leap to the quayside for their unloading. One, at no distance, is laden with crates for the militia a street or two back. It takes some time to convey the daily cargo of beer and to return with the empties which, in turn, must be stacked securely.

Arthur has picked up his book.

Suddenly, there is an explosion at our feet. A beer bottle has been hurled directly at us. It falls short and shatters with

immense force, spraying us with its deadly scatter of glass. I
spring to my feet to see the arm still raised. A red flame of
anger shoots across my brain. My instant impulse is to dive
for the boat, board it, and strangle its two occupants. But
Arthur's terrified gaze holds me like a wand: *I* am their
target, it says. Yes, indeed it may be so ... another, more
accurately aimed ... but I plant myself to obscure him from
their vision.

'Savages!' I shout. 'Assassins! Vile brutes!' and, cursing the
restricted limits of my Italian, 'Foul morons!'

Gondoliers, fishermen, sailors, passers-by have leapt to the
edge of the water and lean from the arch of the bridge with
fists raised and more effective expletives – for the two row
wildly out on the silken surface and dodge behind the water-
traffic.

In all this Arthur has never moved ... and even now makes
no remark. What indeed is he thinking? This time I do not
know: my mind is frozen at the outrage. An old man seated
in the sun with a book. An old man seated on a paved
quayside, his back against a bridge.

I return to his side, pick up the jagged fragments and, from
around him, with my swinging towel, sweep the smaller into
the canal. He has got to his feet to shake himself, for glass
still gleams in collar-neck and in his scant hair ... while a
mumbled stream of angry comment continues from the assembled bystanders.

'*Death in Venice*' ... my mind throws up at me ... 'No. Not
a good thing,' and, for the first time, puts forward, 'Perhaps
... it is good we return.'

Venice ... is an international city.

It is the last morning ...

The 'groupas' have swarmed down on their warm rolls and
marmalade like pigeons in Trafalgar Square and, again with
shouts of directives from their leader, have departed. The
large breakfast-room is emptied but for ourselves, a serving-
table at which now the exhausted servitors eat, the distant
corner where the 'loving couple' sit silent crumbling bread –

this morning for once in no hurry to sally forth into the blaze of sun. Our few bags are strapped for our departure.

Arthur rises – 'I'll just go up to our rooms and see that we've left nothing. Don't you hurry: finish your meal in peace. Perhaps we might order more coffee?'

'Good. I shall. There's masses of time,' I reply, and he wends his way between the tables.

I am busying myself with my crusts when I am aware that I am not alone. Behind now and beside me the two are standing, the 'loving couple'. Slowly, then, the husband moves on: the wife stands motionless, close, her shadow cast on my chair. I glance down at her feet, and am amazed. They are unduly large. Now her hand is laid flat beside my very plate; its broad bangles, its curious inelegance. She is bending above me, and a man's voice hisses in my ear: '*How* did you *persuade* him to *marry* you!'

I think quickly, 'marry . . .?' – but, of course, it was Arthur who signed the book. Astonished, I glance up – to meet a coarse skin under its heavy make-up; a disturbing, and purely masculine, eye. 'It didn't *require* persuasion,' I answer clearly – and watch her rapid, clumsy (and, could it be, angry?) departure.

Whatever it is, Arthur returns to find me shaking with laughter.

'Darling, oh Darling,' I cry delightedly between gulps of steaming coffee . . . 'The woman's a man!'

His response is instant, and typical: 'Sssh!' he murmurs. 'We must be discreet.'

I think, 'Why, yes, it's Venice.' And rise to go.

[11]

The Valley

1966.

'Nothing the matter with our ignition.' I say with pride as, after many days of slow thaw and part burial in the icy street, our little car bursts into throbbing life. 'Lets go and see the "Wilderness", the hills behind Epping, shall we? Go through the forest the John Clare route, past the gates of the mad Judge Arabin, through the beeches, and eat our lunch up on the high ridge east of the forest.'

Against a leaden sky, on the private road that is our highest point, I stop the car and together we look out and down over the valley of the Lea. But today are no shining strips of water, no lit fields spotlighted as in a theatre by a sudden prying shaft from above so that the cattle are revealed near and detailed as toys from a Noah's Ark: no 'effects' make kaleidoscopic patterns of the tops of motionless trees; nor is there one square acre of snow to make for us a charcoal-etched Breughel world. All is in monochrome. Even where Highgate is, distance is colourless, misted perhaps in a light rain, unbeckoning, insecure.

'If we could cast our sight – as a fisherman does his line – or with the sure catapult-aim of David at his Goliath – could it, from here, arrive accurately, on the windows of our house?'

He lifts a quick glance across the valley. 'Not today.'

'Why not?'

'It would fall short.'

I say suddenly: 'Isn't sight curious. Everything of this valley here before us is in our eyes forever. In snow. In rain. In sun. And yet ... I'd be sad to feel that today's aspect, with none of these – nothing lit, nothing strangely delineated, nothing afloat or suddenly near – were the last we were to have of it, the last to take away.'

He is silent: and, wriggling lower, I tuck my head under his chin. Why does his heart, I think, my ear pressed close against its beating, go quickly . . . much quicker than mine? And then – for no reason, surely for no reason – my eyelids are stinging, the valley below us blurs over, a lump rises ridiculously in my throat. Why, too, do *these* things happen? Tears. For no reason. No answer comes. Unless it be the arm about me . . . tightening.

'The last we were to have . . . the last . . . to take away.'

I have never been back. No autumn now can call me. No spring. No summer. One does not go alone.

There exists still a small 1966 pocket diary which reads as its last item: 'February, Thursday 17: 11.00 S.O.S.'[1]

At 10.45 a.m. a powerful car, obscured by a furniture van in the middle lane which braked sharply, crashed the red lights at speed and lifted our small Morris into the air. The jolt was terrific. I was unhurt. Arthur, beside me, slumped. The doors were jammed. His legs were paralysed. His back was broken.

There is something divine in a man who, laid on the pavement in such plight, his spine shattered, seeks urgently between the forms of the kneeling policemen for one he loves; to hold the eyes an instant steadily, to say strongly . . . 'It was not your fault.'

The gentleman from Stafford was fined £15 – for 'careless driving'. Arthur Waley's life was over. He had five months yet before him: one in the private wing of London University Hospital, where it was discovered also that there was a cancer of the bone of the spine; and four months of spring and into summer, paralysed from the breast down, in his beautiful high room that overlooked a distant London – 'Sodome et Gomorrhe' – at the top of our house at Highgate.

[1] School of Oriental and African Studies.

[283]

[12]

'No ... Poets'

As the lift ascended from the operating threatre three nurses accompanied his stretcher and tried to rally him to consciousness. Apparently there was some concern, for one or another leaned to slap his face gently with the words, 'Wake up – wake up – Dr Waley – wake up now!' He remained unresponsive, deeply oblivious. But as the doors swung back and he was wheeled into the corridor, he uttered strange words. His voice clear and high and urgent, he cried, 'No Portuguese poets!'

The sister glanced at me and whispered, 'What does he mean?' But he had sunk again into his anaesthetized world.

When at length he was back in his bed and I had been entrusted with the all-important task of rallying him to consciousness, I felt I knew the way. I leaned low over him. 'Darling,' I said very distinctly, 'you must wake up now. I want you to wake because I have something important to say to you. I want you to hear me and to understand. Are you listening? *There will be no Portuguese poets,*' His eyes opened and his gaze met mine. '*No Portuguese poets,*' I repeated, smiling and bending to kiss the ice-cold cheek,' No Portuguese poets, my Darling, – ever again.' His gaze continued to hold. 'I promise you,' I said; and the eyes fluttered and closed.

The young nurses entered, bustling with hot-water bags. 'Is he out of the anaesthetic? Has he come round?'

'Yes,' I said, 'he has come round.'

'What was all that about "Portuguese" ...' asked one.

'Oh, that was just a sort of joke,' I cut her short. 'But I've made him a promise which is not a joke. And he knows I shall keep it.'

[13]

Neither Rocking nor Weeping

The hospital permits me, in this private ward, to remain with him. The police have returned the little car to me, so that now I bring a mattress from my attic flat; and my son to carry it up for me. Across the dim room, against the bright corridor, Arthur sees him stand a moment, tall – and hesitant. His voice rises loud and clear: 'Hullo, John. I have cancer of the spine.'

Over his shoulder, John whispers to me: 'Has he?'

And I breathe back the one word: 'Yes.'

John enters the room, soundlessly places the mattress on the floor beside the bed, straightens his long young back, takes Arthur's hand in his: 'Hullo, Arthur.'

I see again the first encounter of these two: the ten-month child, naked on a bed, one foot clutched in his hand, his solemn eyes lifted to the stranger who gazes, but one moment, wordlessly down.

I have entreated the sister in charge to give us the newly-vacated corner room with its two tall windows: the one offering the great height of the Post Office Tower against the sunset sky; the other a façade of a famous furniture store.

'And look,' she says brightly, 'look, Dr Waley – you can see *Maples*!'

He raises his eyes to her with a gentle smile: 'See Maples – and die?'

She hastens from the room.

But here I can load the place with flowers. Here I can bring his own familiar treasures. His four-cornered Chinese shaving-bowl. His books. Here, lying together in sunlight, we read the life of Dylan Thomas. And here I say: 'Hun, there's a letter from the hotel in Rome about our rooms at the foot of the Spanish Steps. (I hear again his happy, 'We'll visit all the galleries. The gardens. We'll swim in the Tiber!') We booked for April. Would you like me to cancel them?'

'Wait a little. They may still be useful.'

And indeed he seems so much better that I spend the odd night at the attic flat – in the middle of the wide bed beside the wide-flung window, the evening's pigeons cooing softly in the Tree of Heaven.

One morning I arrive at the hospital in the dawn-light, creep to my mattress and lie silent. But he is awake and waiting; for now he lowers his hand over the side of the bed to feel for mine. Our fingers entwine. He says softly: 'Darling ... You may telephone one morning and be told I died in the night. Everything of mine is yours. But I have written you a cheque for a thousand pounds. Things take rather long, sometimes, to arrange.'

I cannot speak. If I shed tears they are in my heart: for he must not see them. I kneel up, wordless. Our faces are level; our eyes linked; our gaze, as threaded on a single thread. Suddenly his smile is radiant: 'Oh – but *isn't* it wonderful that you are *not* one who sits at the foot of a bed, rocking and weeping!'

Rocking and weeping. And was not – somewhere – somehow – my whole world doing just that? But yet there is a grief more deep than these could assuage.

I open the palm of his hand, kiss it, fold the fingers over the kiss. 'I love you.'

[14]

Home

The ambulance men carried him, wrapped in the red ambulance blanket, up our two flights of stairs. Slowly and with, it
seemed to me, a wonderful tenderness they laid him on the
open bed and left us. I waited until I heard the slam of the
street door; slipped off my clothes and lay down beside him,
pulling the covers over us. Beyond our eastern windows the
highest clouds were receiving the first faint burnished reflec-
tion of a setting sun.

Presently he said: 'We are home. You have performed
another miracle.'

'Are you in pain?'

'I have no pain.'

'Are you ... quite comfortable?'

'I have never been so comfortable in my life.'

It was then, like a slow-washing tide, that the truth flowed
over me. I lay still, moveless as he, while its waters seeped in
through crack and crevice, filling quietly the pools of my
mind. In them, the future lay submerged. That bright pebble,
hope, would never shine again. Yet ... and perhaps it is so in
any finality ... I felt, in the quiet of acceptance, a kind of
peace. I felt it in him too; beyond this heaven of painlessness,
more than a respite; a release from journeying.

I must be alone.

I slipped from his bed, thrust aside the dividing curtains,
went to my own room and lay down, rigid, contemplating
this new knowledge.

I said it at last – this truth – over and over in my mind: his back is broken ... his back is broken ... his back is broken ... until – for such is mercy – it had no meaning. And what did *he* know? I rose and returned to him, slid again beneath the sheet, curled into his armpit. He knew – I had no doubt of it – what I knew: exact. 'I love you,' I said. There seemed no other words.

'And I love you. More than anything in the world.'

The world? What was the world? It was as though we both lay looking out, unawed, at an eternity of worlds.

I turned my head on his pillow. 'Goodnight, Pitten.'

'Goodnight, my Darling.'

[15]

The Hourglass

We are at the high window; his bed wheeled close, I drifting somewhere at his side. We read. We talk. Absorbed completely by the Here and Now of being alone; together; unthreatened. We watch the first red strip of sun lift into gold over the Lea Valley. We see the tall new city blocks, spotlighted by their western setting, sail like white-winged Phoenician galleons into the grape-dark harbour that is Finsbury Park. The evening star rises, jagged with light, and lifts high. All is great with beauty. But then, quite suddenly – by tacit but unspoken agreement – we know we are watching an hourglass.

One evening it comes to his lips: 'Time . . . is running out.'

I cannot bear the pain. So I say, almost savagely: 'Don't grumble at time. We know nothing about it. And perhaps *it* knows perfectly well where it's running. After all, it ran us here.'

Nevertheless, I know the moment is too much for us. I leap to my feet, dash to the bathroom, fill up the hand-basin and plunge my face into the cool water. I come back carrying a wet sponge and small linen hand-towel which I put down carelessly on his lap while I lean far out to view the flowers of the wisteria. 'There never was such a Maytime . . .' I murmur.

I draw up a little stool and lean my arms along the sill. I say, 'Would I have liked you, at Cambridge?'

It succeeds.

'Oh, not in the least, I expect. Or, certainly, you'd have liked Rupert better.'

'Why?'

[289]

'Oh, because everybody did. He was beautiful and so gay. And he'd have liked you.'

'Three very good reasons why ...'

'Yes?'

'Oh, nothing. I was a perverse child. I expect, at the very first gesture, I'd have dropped instantly back into the shadows with you. All the same, I did cry when he died.'

'You *cried* ... when Rupert *died*!'

'Oh yes. Half the world did. It wasn't for Rupert, of course. It was for youth. One "suffered" his poems, however bad – because one was young. Because one hadn't lived. All the same, with me it was a teeny bit more personal than that because my half-brother[1] had known him in Tahiti. Perhaps what he told me was my first chink of ... Cambridge. He got the strangest impression: of a creature "in flight". *From* something. I was in flight too. *From* something. And George, my half-brother, was: always. In flight. We never spoke of it but we both knew. We just kept running. George and Rupert, of course, chose death. And both chose Gallipoli. I chose ... life. And here. At this window.'

A distant plane appears, moves vertically up the sky a little and is folded back into the blue.

'There goes St Exupéry ...' I murmur.

He nods, and I think, 'What shall I do? What shall I do? To whom else shall I ever speak who will understand? But I say: 'It was of course one of my father's "places". So, when I was a child, I had a burning ambition to go to Cambridge.'

'Oh, how lucky for me that you didn't achieve it!'

'And for me?'

'Well – that's harder to answer.'

'I'd have been very clever.'

'Yes, indeed.'

'Would I have become a woman don?'

'Ah – if you would ... we *have* the answer.'

'Would you rather I were a mariner's moll?'

'Much.'

[1] George Muir Grant, Lieutenant Adjutant with the New Zealand Forces.

I grin – gyrate about the room – launch into one of our favourite 'love ditties', low, seductive and tender . . .

> 'Soldier gave me
> Just one shilling.
> Sailor gave me
> Shilling more.
> Sailor called me,
> "Dusky Darling".
> Soldier called me,
> "Bloody . . ."'

'Darling . . . Darling!' The reproof in his tone makes me involuntarily glance towards the door and evokes (for me to see as clearly as I know he himself is seeing her) Rachel, his mother: so that I murmur, 'Sorry, Sweetheart.' And hear myself add, 'Would *she* have loved me?'

'Yes.'

'I love *her*. Forever.'

'Why?'

Now I sit back on my heels and laugh. 'Oh, great Christ, am I to answer that one too! Because she *bore* you, of course. The fruit of the world.'

He is silent. Then – his eyes again on the thing called 'Time': 'Whose world?'

'Oh, well – mine, anyway. And that's the best anyone can say. Worlds are individual . . . as well as myriad.'

But we are back in this one. He says: 'You . . . might have achieved anything.'

'I? What *do* you mean? Socially? You know what a contempt I have for scrabbling of that sort.'

'I've wasted your life.'

'*No-one* can waste another's life! We choose what we use our lives for. You chose. I chose.'

'You could have done anything you chose.'

'But I did, I did, I *did*!' – I am triumphant – 'I *made* my choice. I'm *doing* it. Now this minute.'

His voice drops to a whisper: 'Loving me?'

'Loving you. What more could *any* woman choose . . .' I am

on my knees, my head in his lap, 'or hope for ... this side of heaven? When I was small, one of my duties was to accompany my grandfather to the cathedral on Sunday mornings. My legs couldn't touch the floor. I sat on my hands to ease the ache in them. High above my head in the dark of the rafters was a great blackened beam on which was written in Gothic letters of gold: GOD IS LOVE. I gazed at it, playing with the words. "Then ... LOVE IS GOD," I whispered; adding, "QED."

'My grandfather understood. But later when I repeated my discovery to my mother she was very angry with me. She didn't know it was true.'

And so – with a nod of acknowledgement – he lets me chatter on ... while time runs ... but for a moment pauses.

The light in the castellated sky moves from gold to rose, from rose to blue of evening.

He is sorting out the strands of my hair: searching for the pins and dropping them silently on the floor for me to grope for in the morning.

[16]

The Lake

There were evenings that were quite wonderful: hours etched forever: the firelight, the quiet; the love of one another; the drawing, almost of the same breath. At such times – alone together – it seemed as though nothing had happened, nothing of real importance, to either of us; as though Time could scarcely be richer; or content.

I had planned a hammock or sling, of tough drugget, to be worn like a halter about the shoulders of 'the bearers', John, my son, and Richard, the young artist from the studio at the foot of our garden: a simple thing in which Arthur could lie at ease, be lifted, be carried, with almost no movement. It, later, made even the three flights of stairs possible, his incredulous viewing of his books . . . ranged at last, and in their former careful order, safe from marauders, under his own roof: 'You can meet your friends again . . . here, in this room . . . David will come, and Sachie . . .' and his delighted, 'But . . . they are just as they were! I can put out my hand and touch them!' It made the garden once more (but once only) accessible. The visit to the lake. Our marriage. The sling had to be carefully planned; one hundred per cent strong, expertly tested for ease and safety. It took many evenings, and now it neared completion: the pieces cut, folded, sewn; the little hand-machine set up, that had been with me four times in my flights across the world. At such working times this large high room, shut so serenely from all outer and troublous things, we called our ghetto.

On one such evening, then, when I had wheeled the bed to the centre of the room and facing the fire – where, propped high on his pillows, Arthur could watch me at work as he so loved to do – I glanced up quickly and saw on his face a look of radiance that made my heart stop with wonder.

I got up and went to him. 'Do you know . . . tonight, you're so more than wonderful . . . and you look . . . almost happy.'

'*Almost* happy? I'm *completely* happy. With that lovely Haydn concert, and then my Darling reading to me so perfectly and now – this Here and Now – how could I be happier?'

Tears stung my eyes. I kissed his hands, quickly, lest they should fall on them. I dared not speak. Who says, I thought blindly, man is not something more than man – that can transcend all the evils of the world, disaster, pain and the certain knowledge of departure? . . . and, for that instant perhaps, we both – far, far beyond our two selves – were worshipping . . . what? Presently I moved back to my sewing-stool: the joy, the inexplicable thing, persisting.

'Tomorrow,' I say, 'we will see the lake.'

'The lake?' Arthur repeats after me, snatching up the word . . . his mind darting, yet not daring.

'Yes. The lake. At Kenwood.'

He says, the words scarcely audible, 'We will go to Kenwood?'

'Of course.'

'How?'

Lying paralysed from the breast down, a crumbled spine, plus a gangrenous, deep unhealing wound, at the top of two flights of stairs, it is indeed a reasonable question. His eyes lift, shining, to mine and I see that they hold no shadow of doubt – nor would have, had I said, 'Tomorrow we go to Covent Garden Ballet' – but only a curiosity in regard to technicalities. I come across to his bed and, casually, I fix the pillows: 'How?' I repeat. 'Well; in the sling I've made you. Why, do you suppose, have I been sewing at it all these days? I've shown it to the doctor and he's passed it as secure. In fact, he says there's nothing a tenth as simple or effective in any hospital that he knows . . .'

I chatter on . . . But Arthur's eyes are fixed upon a miracle.
Tomorrow . . . he . . . *he* . . . will see again the lake at Kenwood.

How wonderful, always, is the dawn from our high window.
Soon we lie and drowse in shafts of horizontal sun. But as
eight o'clock approaches Arthur becomes disturbed. Under
my ear, his heart is galloping. Will the nurse – whose business
is the body – put a stop to this wonder of wonders . . . that is
the business of the mind and of the spirit?

'John and Richard will be here at ten,' I murmur, 'to carry
you down to the little car. I've rehearsed them in the way
they wear the sling – the broad loops over the head and about
the shoulders, like a yoke . . . they look like Swiss milkmaids.
And young Anna[1] wants to come . . . and Jane will have to
accompany us, but only for the car part . . .'

So . . . it is true. It is true. It was no dream. Under my ear
I hear the heart-beat slacken to a norm and the arm that
holds me perceptibly releases its tension.

The door opens; the nurse stands there. Jane . . . with
starched disapproving bosom, from which she now slowly
draws the thermometer. And Arthur's gaze is riveted. It
might be, indeed, Cleopatra's adder . . . as deadly. There is so
much that bosom disapproves.

Miracles, especially, are not to be encouraged.

I look up. 'Good morning, Jane,' I say, and add – rather
as an afterthought – 'We are going to see the lake at
Kenwood.'

She is silent. Her grey eyes are opaque as stones. Then,
'Have I your permission to use the telephone?'

'By all means.'

She is going to ring the doctor.

But the thing is fixed. Officially. I have seen to that.

In a sitting position of absolute normality, in his hammock-
sling of Victorian drugget, Arthur is descending the stairs
between his tall 'bearers'. In his Arab-striped dressing-gown,

---

[1] A young distant cousin of my own who arrived from New Zealand in time to give
Arthur much delight.

he looks like some Eastern potentate setting out on an official call of no great consequence.

Gently now the strong arms lift him into the passenger-seat of the little open car. Over his shoulders and the back of the seat I slip a broad girdle of doubled drugget that holds him rigidly secure. His hands are free and folded loosely in his lap. As I start the engine I glance at him happily. The sun beats down on the brown vivid face and as we move off a light breeze lifts his hair. He draws a long breath of the intoxicating spring air and smiles back at me. In the driving-mirror I see the boys load into their following car cushions and rugs, with Jane the nurse and the delectable Anna.

Was ever such a picnic – or such a moment, I am thinking, in time?

And now before us the lawns of Kenwood drop sharply, slope away. On them, distant figures move in lengthening perspectives: couples, enrapt; children, speeding like arrows and pursued by small crazed dogs; figures, limned on a screen of green – vivid, diminutive, and eternal. In its setting, against the dark woods, hedged by reeds, embroidered with water-lilies, agleam like a jewel, the lake – wholly lovely – lies below.

We lift his chair on to the shallow stone plinth, into his favourite corner against the pillared windows of the orangery. At his side I spread the enormous fur rug. The boys strip off to the waist and stretch out their strong browned bodies to the sun which shines hot upon us from a clear noon sky. Anna lies with eyes closed, arms spread wide. Her bright-shining pigtails in which she has fastened flowers fling out from her slender neck in the delicate, moving carelessness of youth.

People pass and re-pass. We – all, it seems – are abstracted: unaware of them: a serenity, in a silence none cares to break, a very joy of being, has descended upon us like a benediction. Arthur makes no gesture, but calls me wordlessly and I curl myself up, as always, close against his knees. His hand, slipping down to his side, secretly, but with a passion of urgency,

seeks out my own. Our eyes meet. And in that moment I
know that human love – even the love of two creatures, the
one for the other – can be as near divine as may be: beside
which, all other considerations, death, parting ... fall away
... are trivia.

We sleep. Or dream. Perhaps an hour passes ... and it is
Arthur who at length recalls us to this world. He says: 'Aren't
we all getting hungry? Couldn't the boys go and get us some
sandwiches?'

Their eyes open: they spring up.

At the end of the terrace at Kenwood one descends steps
to the old coach house, a shallow crescent of building with its
central clock in the classic manner, where now refreshments
are served. Soon they return, with ham and tongue, glasses
of bitter lemon and straws.

So, we picnic: and chatter – with no care in the world.

Unaware, and hungry, Arthur eats my sandwich as well as
his own. I watch him happily. He says, between mouthfuls:
'You finished yours very quickly, didn't you?'

'I gobbled,' I say, laughing.

Now we move back to the car. Jane-the-nurse is waiting
with a pill which she insists Arthur must take before the
journey back. Time and again I am amazed at the rigidity of
nursing behaviour – 'We are not required to do that,' – 'That
does not come within our duties.' ... 'Ah, then it must come
within mine,' I answer and proceed to do what must be done.
But now, though she is obviously astonished, puzzled, at
Arthur's appearance of well-being, even radiance, the boys
are dispatched for water. They take with them a plastic cup,
but no garden tap can be found.

'I need very little,' says Arthur. 'Perhaps we could get it
from the windscreen wiper.'

But this Jane considers quite improper and John and
Richard offer to return to the refreshment counter, remarking
however that they know that we had the last of the bitter
lemon.

'I'll take my pill in Coca-cola,' announces Arthur defiantly.

And this – raising the cup in salute to Jane's unsmiling face – he presently does. His eyes, as he holds her gaze, are putting a question – but it is as clear as any spoken word: 'What can this pill do more for me ... since I have quaffed the lake?'

[17]

The Unthinkable

As the doctor shuts Arthur's door quietly behind him he stands a moment, thoughtful, on the top landing before making his usual headlong plunge down the stair. He says quietly: 'I have had some very strange letters from the family.'

He begins to move down the stair, I following. I say: 'From the family . . . his brother?'

He gathers speed, but before he reaches the bottom steps he turns to me. 'Yes. You know what it is, of course: they want him back in hospital.'

This is unthinkable. I am bewildered. 'It would kill him . . . But wait. Legally they are his next of kin. Could you prevent them?'

'Legally? No. They could go against my recommendations. They could demand it.'

He looks at me; a look I shall not forget; a look of anger, of impotence, and . . . yes . . . compassion.

'You . . . *are* his life,' he says; and adds, 'You . . . wouldn't have a leg to stand on.'

He is gone. I close the door. I dare not mount the stair again; I dare not be with Arthur, with that X-ray mind that plucks thoughts from my own as from a mirror: I dare not bend over that trusting, imploring face. I hear again his strange words: 'You and I . . . are our only hope.' I am numb with grief and fear.

[18]

Age

He is seated in his chair in the glow of the fire – in the ringed pool of light from the tall lamp: an old man, with broken spine. An old man ... paralysed from the breast down. An old man ... looking backwards over his shoulder at the rich-laden years slipping rapidly into distance. Images swing into sudden focus – blur out – sink again, submerged, in the stream of time.

'You ... should never have left me,' he says.

I do not answer.

'Why did you?'

I consider, silent. I say quietly: 'I think ... I thought you were a ... philanderer.'

His eyes flicker and fall. The sadness that comes now into his face, I know, will always stab me to remember. Too much, to explain. Too much, to reveal. Too ... late ... now.

I creep to him, sink down between his knees, take his two hands and make them cup my face. 'Darling ... Look at me. I don't think it now, I know – now – you were not. So nothing matters. Does it?'

His mouth quivers for an instant. His eyes, in which tears stand, burn into mine. Can I endure the radiance? 'No,' he says slowly, 'nothing matters.'

And love (as love can) holds us in one embrace.

'You must not love her. You must not think of her. You must cut her out of your mind – out of your heart. You *must not love* her.'

And his despairing ... 'I have *tried*. I have *tried* not to love her. I have failed.'

[300]

[19]

Certainty

I stood before him but at some little distance from his bed, my hands folded, my head drooped; broken with fatigue, with love; and with defeat. I dared not lift my eyes to his. I felt their watching, their gaze burning through my lids; and I knew my own loaded with misery. I said: 'They . . . want me back in Handel Street,' and, desperate, at the end of my strength, I added, 'And I want to go.'

There was a silence heavy as all the ages. It hung between us, tangible, with its load of years.

And then I heard Arthur's voice, strangely strong – strong in perception and in resolve – saying that strange thing. It said: 'You and I are our only hope.'

It said, with great earnestness: 'Will you marry me?'

It said, with – could it be joy, a bubble of delight? And that wonder of poignant humour: 'I'm not much of a catch . . . but . . . please marry me.'

I still stood silent. For some reason I was seeing vividly a strange scene. Tahiti. I was primitive. I was Gauguin's native girl. What rags are the trappings of this world. I went to Arthur's bedside and, kneeling, covered my face with my hands. But I felt the hot tears trickling between the fingers. Then his hand on my head. I felt my heart must burst open its turmoil. Its pain. Its joy. I lifted my face. His was shining. At that moment I felt – I saw – time stretching, back into the ages, into the 'Egypt' of my dream; and further; further.

Perhaps we both did. For I kicked off my shoes and slid into the bed beside him, clothed as I was. Curled up and all but crouched in the embrace of that strong right arm, we seemed to gaze together, wordless, down an infinity of ages.

Myself, I stared with awe and unbelief, back along the staggering years of endurance, of bewilderment, of uncertainty – at a single certainty.

'We have always been married,' I said. And felt the arm tighten.

Our Own Devices

It is the morning of Monday, 23 May, 1966. As usual, we have wakened with the first rays of the sun. As usual, I have brewed our coffee on the little spirit-stove that stands always on the round brass tray. I have wheeled the bed beside the up-flung window. The day is already almost hot and we lie with the covers tossed aside. We drowse and talk; we talk ... and drowse again. From five o'clock until eight o'clock: these are our 'precious hours'.

At last the nurse has removed the sponges, the towels, the trays of sterile dressings and put fresh covers on the pillows. The smell of bacon drifts up the stairs, and she is more than ready for her breakfast. But she stands a moment in the doorway, looking back at us: 'Well,' she says, 'I'll leave you two to your own devices.'

Bared to the waist, browned by the sun; no-one could think him paralysed from the breast down.
Suddenly he says: 'How does one get married?'
'Two,' I say.
'Two,' he smiles.
'Do you mean, in a hurry?'
'Yes.'
'When?'
'Tomorrow.'
'Tomorrow? I just don't know.'
'Telephone the police.'
'The police? Why?'

A Half of Two Lives

'Ask them.'

I sit up and, reaching for the telephone, do so. Highgate Police Station. I turn to him: 'They say we must have a special licence. They've given me a number to ring.'

'Well? Ring it.'

I do so. He is listening attentively. But my end of the conversation is mostly no's ... 'Oh, no ...' and ends with 'I see.'

'Well?'

'Not much luck.'

'What did they say?'

'I rang the wrong shop.'

'The *wrong shop*!'

'They say I'm not a Roman Catholic.'

'Quite right.'

'They've given me another number. It's the Archbishop of Canterbury.'

'Well, ring it.'

I do so. This time the conversation is longer, but at last I put up the receiver and turn again to him: 'Worse,' I say.

'Worse?'

'They say I'm not an Anglican.'

'Quite right.'

'They say I've never been confirmed.'

'Quite right.'

'They say I'm not even a Christian.'

'Quite right.'

'They say I'm a divorced woman.'

'Quite right.'

'They say ... you're a Jew.'

'Quite right!'

'Well, so ... it's no go. They make virtue very difficult don't they. It's no wonder half their congregations "live in sin".'

'Ring a registry office.'

'Which one?'

'*I* don't know. Does it have to be the right one?'

'I expect so, Honey.'

'Ring the police again.'

I do so.

'They say Wood Green.'

'Well, ring them.'

Again, I pick up the receiver and dial.

Again he is listening attentively.

But again my conversation ends with, 'I see.'

'Well?'

'No go.'

'Why?'

'They say they can't send a man out.'

'A "*man out*"! We don't need a plumber! Out where?'

'Well, here. To marry us. To marry anybody. Anywhere!'

'Why not?'

'The law won't allow it.'

'Why?'

'They say ... this room's not "Hallowed".'

We look at one another. Lost in the strangeness of the world, we look at one another.

He says, quietly: 'Not hallowed ... This room. Oh my Darling ...' and I am in his arms.

After a while he says, 'Ring them again.'

'What shall I say?'

'Ask them how soon we can be married ... in their ... "hallowed" room.'

I look at him. But I do so.

'They say, Thursday: at eleven.'

'Say yes. Tell them we'll be there.'

Oh, but *now* I look at him. My hand is over the mouthpiece.

'Well? What are you waiting for? If I'm well enough to be taken to see the lake at Kenwood I'm well enough to go to my own wedding!'

For a moment my hand remains over the mouthpiece. I cannot speak. I am thinking, Oh my Lord God, how I love this man ...

'Well?'

I uncover the receiver. I say: 'Yes. Yes, I'm still here. Yes. Thank you. Thursday at eleven. We'll be there. The name is Waley.'

[305]

The name . . . is . . . Waley.

Suddenly a lump mounts in my throat. Tears sting my eyes. Darling, Darling . . . Oh, Darling. I plunge my face into his pillow and lie still. Presently he lifts a strand of my hair and kisses it. I wriggle on to my back. Upon our bared shoulders the morning sun streams in from the clear May sky . . . And each knows the other is back at the same point in time. A metal table under an awning. Antoine's. Charlotte Street. And yes . . . *May, 1929.*

'Well,' he whispers, dragging his gaze from contemplation of that other day, 'well, that's fixed.'

I nod. With difficulty. For my nose is under his chin and I have flung my right arm across his chest. I murmur: 'Do you remember the tiny lost church we found in Somerset when we went to find where Coleridge lived? The old discoloured book?'

'Yes.'

'You wrote our names in it.'

'Yes.'

'I left you among the gravestones and went back to see what you'd written.'

'And what did you find?'

'"Arthur and Alison Waley".'

Under my hand I feel his heart-beat quicken and his right arm tighten about me.

'Quite right,' he says.

And – almost at once – we are asleep.

[21]

Frenzy

'They're going to get married!'

Downstairs all is frenzy. Hushed but vibrant. The stairs. The landings. Behind closed doors. The air is electric. 'They're going to get married ... They're going to get *married* ...!'

For May-the-maid had come up with our coffee.

I am lifting Arthur's shoulders, propping the pillows. He turns his head and says simply: 'Good morning, May. I am going to get married.'

She puts down the tray slowly and with care. Now for a moment she stands silent ... while a most surprising change comes over her features. They harden: they seem almost to shrink. The mouth closes in a tight, unpleasant line. There is anger. And there is ... alarm.

Now she has brought her hand down flat on the table. She is almost out of control. She bursts out, loud and strident: '*Sir!* You said you would *never marry!*'

Had he? This interests me. How long ago? Three years? Thirty?

He lifts his eyes to her face. His voice carries a calm, a serenity – and a finality – which silences her.

'Well, May – I've changed my mind.'

[22]

Marriage

It is our wedding day. A May day of glittering sun. John and Richard have carried Arthur in the hammock down the stairs to the little waiting car, its shabby hood thrown back as on its many jaunts; and this but one more. Arthur, browned by the many weeks at the window, is seated beside me in his Arab-striped dressing gown; the wide sash of holland slipped over his shoulders and the seat-back to keep him rigid.

As we move off alone – the rest of the small party following in other cars – a breeze lifts Arthur's hair, his quick glance is a lover's glance and he takes my left hand from the wheel and folds it in his own.

'Dear Darling,' I whisper, 'I love you madly – but I need that hand to deal with the gears,' and, grinning ruefully, he relinquishes it.

'It's all wrong, of course,' I laugh, 'I should be holding a bouquet! And you should be nervous, not just happy. The trouble is we've been married too long. Like the miners of the west coast of New Zealand who, strangely seized with conventional whimsy, piled their great-grandchildren into coaches-and-six and set out over the impassable passes of the Southern Alps to be married "right-and-proper" in Canterbury Cathedral. Shall we go by Alexandra Palace? It's the only alp we have handy.'

From its morning height the clouds move in their vast sky and below in the valley of the Lea shine the sheets and strips of water that are the reservoirs, like the glitter of shields and swords.

At the door standing waiting in the sun is young Anna. She

is in a straight brief dress of oleander cotton ending in a childish frill and her slim legs, her sandalled feet, are bare. Over her shoulders her hair hangs in two burnished plaits in which, in place of ribbons, she has woven small blossoms.

'Oh, *look* at Anna, how very lovely! A child out of the *Kilvert Diary*. Oh, promise me you won't marry her instead!'

'It's very tempting,' he replies low.

Arthur is seated in his light canvas chair and wheeled to the 'hallowed room' of Wood Green Registry Office.

'Will you take this woman?' . . . 'Will you take this man?' . . . We have answered firmly and Arthur has slid on to my finger in token the narrow octagonal band of Victorian silver. We are married.

A long, strange journeying indeed.

It is Thursday, 26 May 1966.

Sir Stanley's[1] spare figure is standing tall at our bedside; his long lean fingers are extended to touch lightly the crisp whiteness of the sheets; his face is shining with pleasure. 'You two!' he is saying, 'have made my day!'

Arthur glances quickly up, shy as a boy: 'We seem to have made many people happy as well as ourselves,' he replies modestly.

Sir Osbert's champagne is drunk and we are again alone.

Arthur is silent: for indeed there is much to think about. When he speaks it is with a bewildering lightness of touch.

'We can tell our friends we are going to the Lakes[2] for our honeymoon. And you must arrange with Pulmans to have some cards printed – to send to our friends abroad. It would be *too* tiresome a task for you to write to them all.'

'A good idea. And, Hun, there is another thing: I must tell Hugh.'

'Yes, I've been thinking about that.'

'I shall ring him now.'

When I ring I take the telephone and place it between us

[1] Sir Stanley Unwin, the publisher of Arthur's work over many years.
[2] Our name for the Highgate Ponds.

on the high-packed pillows. I am relieved that Hugh himself answers. At the sound of my voice, even over years, his own comes back with the familiar 'Was ist?' left over from a long-ago au pair.

'Oh Hugh, I'm glad it is you. There's something I wish to tell you. Yesterday . . . I married Arthur Waley.'

There is a brief silence . . . then Hugh's voice, soft and weighted with feeling: 'I'm glad you did that. Make him very, very happy . . .'

'Thank you, Hugh. Goodbye.'

But Arthur has turned away – his face strangely moved. 'Oh, oh,' he is saying, '*how* generous! *What* generosity!

'Pitten, do you realize . . . you are a "husband"?'

'Yes.' His arm tightens about me.

'And I'm . . . that dreadful word . . . "wife"?'

'The best word in the world.'

'AND that we've committed that most disgusting of crimes . . . marriage?' And now I glance sideways at him as I quote, in his own high-pitched tones of once-upon-a-time – his 'Bloomsbury Voice' – '*None* of my friends believe in it – *none* of my friends!'

But at this he snatches me down with strong arms and stops my mouth with kisses.

[23]

The Brothers

We had been expecting Hubert, so that when he rang I went down myself to welcome him, following on his heels as he ascended to the top of the house. I had left Arthur prepared and happy to receive him, reclining at ease against his mountain of pillows. I looked quickly from the one to the other. Both faces showed only the youthful, amused smoothness of two who share a far-stretching landscape of intimacies ... and I went quietly from the room – how well, indeed, they knew one another – to leave them alone.

As I descended the stairs once more I could hear the voice of May-the-maid, strident, in the kitchen. She is at her histrionics again, I thought – but she fell to sudden silence as I entered. Jane, too – she was seated at the end of the table in her crisp white nursing uniform, her strong, bare arms stretched out before her – was silent. I glanced at them both, took the tray which had been prepared but to which I added a few touches and a gale-blown rose, still lovely in its dishevilled crimson, which I had snatched from the garden, and returned to the brothers.

Rain dashed against our high windows, while long and strong tentacles of wisteria flung themselves at the panes as though for frenzied entry. A sudden darkness had appeared in the sky, as of storm. But I saw that the light in which Arthur and Hubert moved was of another time, a time afar off and undisturbed by freaks of weather – it was as though they, visibly, sauntered in its rays – and soon I again hastened to leave them alone together.

When, hearing preparations for departure, I returned, both

looked refreshed as from some health-giving expedition to another clime. A region known only to themselves, I thought, as I turned towards Hubert, who was peering bewilderedly about the room.

'You won't find it here,' I laughed, 'I gave your coat to May to hang. It's in the kitchen. I'll not say my farewells here either; I'll follow you down in a moment; you know the way.'

When, presently, I descended Hubert had seated himself just inside the kitchen door and was scribbling on a slip of paper. May came now from the sink, drying her hands and flinging back her head with a certain assertive familiarity of manner which I had, it occurred to me, not observed in her before. 'Well – goodbye, Sir,' she was saying.

'Goodbye, May.'

With a quick gesture he slipped the scrap of paper into her hand and, as quick, she thrust it into the pocket of her apron.

I followed Hubert to the door. It opened on a gust of spray from the long arm of a rose tree which had broken loose from its staples.

'Well,' I remarked, 'you've not far to go if you're staying with Daniel.'

'We are staying at an hotel in Knightsbridge,' he answered, climbing into his coat.

'Knightsbridge! But that's across London!' I cried. 'Hubert, wait! Jane is on duty. Let me just dash up and explain to Arthur and I'll drive you there in the car.'

He had already struggled past me into the rain and now I followed, touching his arm to detain him. With a roughness I could not have guessed was his, he shook himself free and, bending double against the storm, flung back over his shoulder; '*You! You* drive me! You're the worst driver in London!'

He was gone. And with the charge, so unexpected, leaving me bewildered, I remounted the stair slowly to Arthur's room.

I felt there was much, indeed, I did not understand. I said: 'Hubert . . . would not let me drive him.'

Arthur uttered the one monosyllable: 'No.'

It sounded informed.

I walked about the room, a little aimlessly. At length I said, staring down into the drenched and swaying garden: 'He believes I . . . did this thing to you.'

Again a monosyllable: 'Yes.'

There was a flat finality about it that, as it were, held me gently below the surface.

I look down at the swaying garden . . . but it is not the garden that I see. I see Arthur, laid on the pavement, his spine broken, his body from the breast down nerveless. I hear the man from Stafford saying, 'I'm sorry,' – and without turning I hear my own voice answer with a question: 'Can you *undo* what you have done?'

The ambulance already is beside us. The police stand aside. The ambulance men bend over Arthur's prone figure. I am kneeling on the ground – and their legs are a forest of trees dividing us . . . whom nothing can divide. And now Arthur with strong arms is thrusting them back, so that our eyes may meet. In his gaze is the simple statement – 'My life is over. My feet are on the foothills of death . . . a long and lonely climb.' And in mine – 'You will never be alone.'

A voice is saying; 'Do you feel any pain, Sir?'

But Arthur and I are listening only to unspoken words; and the voice receives no answer. Instead, Arthur is stretching a hand to touch me. His eyes, also, hold me. Then his voice comes – firm, almost admonitory. 'Remember . . .' it is saying, slow and clear, 'remember . . . *it was not your fault.*'

And it is in this moment that I know what is meant by the thing called the 'divinity of man'.

At length I struggled free. I turned my face to him; where, against his pillows, he was waiting for my words. I said quietly: 'The evidence – the Police Report: they brought their own charge against the driver who crashed us – the witnesses . . . Hubert *knows* it is not so.'

There was a pause. Then Arthur said, as quietly: 'Nothing

[313]

and no-one could make Hubert believe other than that which he wishes to believe.'

I turned and sank into the low chair and, like Jane, stretching long bare arms, let my head sink down on them. An exhaustion more than physical seemed to claim me, and soon I felt the tears, sliding hot and sideways across my face.

Arthur's hand touched my hair.

I said, without moving: 'Oh, poor Hubert.'

' "*Poor* Hubert"?'

'Oh, yes. Yes. How terrible for him. How can he endure to share the air I breathe? If it were the other way round ... if I were he ... I would want to kill me.' My head was still buried between my arms. I whispered now – desperate with pain: 'I want ... I want ... if I could die for you.'

Arthur groped for my fingers and twined them silently in his own. 'Live for me,' he said. 'It will be more difficult.'

I had forgotten – indeed I had no curiosity about – the note in May's pocket; but when I found myself again in the kitchen she drew it forth and brandished it. With a new, disturbing truculence she demanded: 'Read *that* for me, Miss Alison.'

It was the title she seemed now, since my marriage, so curiously to find adequate. She showed no embarrassment, and I was to remember later that she was illiterate. Jane, who until now had been a lay figure, lifted her head and was watching. I uncrumpled the scrap and read aloud: 'We observe that you already are having difficulties. This is our address in the country ...' and it followed.

'Difficulties, May? *Are* you in difficulties?' – how many times had I helped her over a stile of one kind or another – 'Is it anything I can help with?'

Glancing up, I was surprised to see her face set in a firm grimace, her mouth a tight line, as one exasperated. She shot out a hand and all but snatched back the paper which I still held lightly between my fingers. 'I want that,' she muttered, inexplicably. 'My Tommy'll want to see that.' Bending jerkily, she thrust the note into the pocket of the black waterproof bag which stood always on the floor beside her as she worked, and with an unduly jaunty, 'Well – I'll be going. I've got things to do . . .' she marched stiffly towards the door, pausing less than an instant as she passed Jane to stare fixedly into her face.

Jane's head dropped. But, when May had gone, it lifted and she turned her face to me. To my surprise her heavy cheeks were suffused with a deep flush, which, as our eyes held, extended over the strong neck and disappeared into her uniform.

I laughed lightly: 'Dear Jane – you'll think you've struck a house of mysteries!'

But she did not return my smile.

Instead, she opened her mouth to speak – closed it again with a snap – rose and walked from the room.

I had moved from where I stood and now, too, I remained motionless.

Soon I heard her door click shut, and the key, unaccustomedly and curiously, turned in the lock.

[24]

A Scholar and his Books

Arthur, now, never mentioned his books. Almost, I felt, and for this very reason, they – their possible fate – was constantly in his mind.

On a Friday, little Anna rang up with an idea, of greatest urgency. She and some friends would transport Arthur's library, steel shelving and all, to be with him at Highgate. Of course! Of course! Why, indeed, had it not been done long since!

By dusk on that Saturday the shelves were secure in their places at their new home, the books, carefully packaged and numbered according to their shelves, stood about, many rows already filled. One room at least was completed! There, from floor to ceiling – and in their order – Arthur's beloved books were home with him.

The sun of Sunday dawned bright as a golden guinea. I had Arthur carried down into the garden. Facing the wisteria-tangled balconies of the house he loved, he lay in a hammock-seat and, all unknowing that it was a celebration, drank Osbert's champagne.

But he was sad to quietness that day.

I knelt on the grass beside him. The yellow sunlight filtered through the hanging branches of our cherry tree. The nurse was banished with a book.

'Which do you choose – that I should do the garden or stay here close beside you?'

'Stay with me,' he whispered. 'Don't leave me.'

But a joy – a perfect and isolated joy – was to come. His

'bearers' arrived and, carrying him indoors, paused by previous instruction as though for breath at the foot of the stair.

'Rest in here,' I said, throwing open the door of the high-
ceilinged room whose windows looked back over the garden
we had just left. 'Why not rest here?'

It was long since Arthur had received his party guests,
sitting among their coats and wraps, exchanging happy fragments of esoteric conversation while the whole house filled
and flowed with gaiety, in that room.

Now it was empty but for a second hammock-couch, light
and movable, and, from floor to ceiling, row above row of
rare books.

Arthur's eyes lifted and roamed, lifted and roamed, in
unbelief. We laid him gently down and waited. The radiance
of his face was wonderful to see: we fell to silence.

He lay, lifting both arms to the crowded shelves, incredulous. 'But ... they are all *just as I put them*. I can stretch out
my hand and *touch* them ...'

The surgeon arrived. He went straight upstairs to confer with
the nurse. I was still standing in the hall when he descended.

'Mrs Waley, I would like a word with you privately. I have
spoken with the nurse and I must absolutely forbid that Dr
Waley should be brought downstairs again. Do you understand?'

'But ... his books. It is life to him to be with them – to
touch them – even to see them.'

'Well, he's seen them. I must ask you to give me your word.
Have I your word?'

I saw again Arthur's face: that upsurge of joy. Tears welled
into my eyes. I could not speak. I made no answer.

The surgeon stood in the open doorway, his hat in his hand.
And then he said a thing loaded with doom, so that my heart
seemed to die in me. He said, staring the while into my
shocked face: 'What ... will the *coroner* say?' – and stepped
into the street.

[25]

The Days to Dying

I wake. One eye is still buried deep in his neck. I open the other and, without moving, strain to see his face. His face is serene. His eyes are open wide.

'Hullo, Pitten.'

'Hullo.'

'You all right?'

'Very.'

With my free right hand I trace with the tip of my finger the silhouette so close to my sight – the outline – of brow, nose, lips (he snatches a kiss as I pass over lips), chin, throat. With my open palm I rub at the hairs of his chest, the hairs that curl like bracken, and, like bracken, are multi-coloured in the slant of the morning's sunlight.

'I wish I had hairs on my chest . . .' I say, in idiot joy.

He is silent.

Presently he says: 'Was I a trouble to you last night?'

'A trouble? You've been a trouble to me ever since I first set eyes on you.'

He gropes for my hand, draws it down under the bed-clothes and grips it hard.

We are both shy of talking of deep matters.

'Tell me what you think,' he says.

'Oh, Pitt. What *I* think? Well, if you mean what I *think* . . . I think it's rather conceited to try.'

There is a pause. He is listening. He is waiting for me to go on.

'I think . . . human beings are human beings – and – limited.

We hate to acknowledge this. But if we weren't limited we'd be gods. Ants don't *really* know all that much about their ant-hill, do they? And if you asked a grub what a butterfly was, I doubt if he'd have the answer – even if he were a Bertie-Russell-grub. Being me is wonderful. Being you is even a thousand times *more* wonderful. WHY we are US doesn't worry me. Does it worry you?'

'No.'

'There's one thing, though. I just don't believe it's all for nothing ... the pain, the beauty, the wonder, the horror ... and all the events that seemed so catastrophic ... yet brought us to this place – this Here and Now. We'd never have chosen them. We couldn't have done without them. Not one of them. Not the smallest part. Not the littlest detail. Why – it's life ... an organised genius. How *can* one believe in chaos! And now it's *your* turn. What do *you* think?'

He holds me very close.

He whispers, 'I think as you do.'

[26]

Time

With the first soft silken rustlings of birds in the wisteria – the first faint murmurings, sleepy and tentative, that, like soft fingers, fumble for the dawn – I slipped from my bed and stood at Arthur's side.

I was surprised to see that he was already awake. He lay motionless, his eyes focused straight ahead, at nothing in my sight, and I stood a moment, silent, before I said: 'Hello, Postman.'[1]

His gaze still fixed and unwavering, he yet responded instantly: 'Hello, Lady Five.'

Even so ... I stood beside his bed and waited until he should make return, for I could see he had journeyed beyond where I could well follow and the birds had sunk again to their second brief sleep and the light of day had broadened perceptibly before he said: 'Time. Do you know about time?'

Turning his head on the pillow, looking up at me, he opened his mouth to speak again; but faltered; and no words came. His eyes – fixed on mine – said them for him ... 'It's running out,' they said.

I slid into bed beside him and put my cheek where he loved so to have it, in the now sadly deep hollow of his shoulder. Then I lay very still. 'Yes,' I said, 'I know about time. There's our Here and Now ... that is but a moment of it. There's our two lives ... they, too, but a moment of it. It's taken all of both of them – every agony, every terror, every tear, every despair, every certainty ... and much, much joy – to make

[1]'The Two Lunatics' from *The Real Tripitaka* translated by Arthur, (Allen & Unwin, 1952).

this Here and Now ... this place where we are.' I lifted my head a moment and smiled at him: 'It's a good place. Isn't it?'

'Oh, so good.'

'Shall I go on?'

'Go on.'

'Our Here and Now ... I think we'd have to go back over it all to our beginnings – yours and mine – to know what it's made of. And the job didn't even begin there ... it couldn't have. So how can we suppose it ends here?'

He held my eyes. He was looking for tears – for one sign of disbelief in me of my own words. But I could feel no doubt of them, and instead I smiled.

'D'you know what, Pitten? ... I think we've just about reached the beginning. *Now* do you understand what I think about time?'

He put up his hand and I took it in mine.

'*Maintenant. Main tenant* ...' I whispered, using one of our private plays on words. Then I slid from under the covers and went to stand by the window, but still where he could see me in profile against the moving sky. I could feel that he was still examining my face.

I said: 'Don't you *know* I shall never leave you? Don't you know I *can't*? You're me. As I am you. We both know it. We can't be parted now. It ... "wouldn't make sense".' A favourite phrase of his always.

I came back to his bedside and knelt so that our faces lay level on the pillows. 'And, oh my Darling ... there's been such ... sense!' Our eyes held until our two gazes seemed to enter, the one into the other. 'And nonsense!' I laughed, rising. 'And now I'm going to get our coffee.'

At the door I paused and looked back at him. The morning sunlight striking now horizontally to his pillows was making his face a glory.

And I knew only one thing. One strange thing.

Arthur is going to die. He is going to die. He knows it. And I know it. Yet ... God! ... what have we done to deserve to be so happy!

[321]

[27]

Morning

Across the room the first rays of the sun strike parallel and touch the closed lids of my eyes with June warmth.

For a long moment I lie still.

Then I open them. A great serenity is everywhere. The first bird-chorus in the wisteria, thick-leafed now and clambering in at the window, is dropping again to silence with a few sleepy twitterings.

The long branch of fifty red roses which I had torn from the garden in the gale of the night – childishly, I had counted them for him – spreads across the far wall awaiting the swing of the sun.

Is he awake?

The bed-head hides him from my view. Soon, as always, I shall move all to the open window and we shall lie together drenched in dawn light and the deep of content.

Suddenly I see his right hand lift. It lifts high above the bed-head, the full length of his arm. The head comes into view – and now the shoulder. My heart stops. How is it possible? My mind, my reason, beats out the words, *But he is paralysed . . . but he is paralysed . . .* My eyes cannot leave him. Another arm comes into view: the other shoulder. *He is sitting up*. Reason, hope, belief, unbelief tumble together like the chips of coloured glass in a kaleidoscope. My mind is chaos: broken.

I leap from my bed. I am at his side. I am saying: 'Darling! Darling! What are you doing?'

He turns his eyes on me. He says, surprised: 'I am getting up, of course,' . . . surprised – at the stupidity of my question. Surprised – at the bewilderment in my voice.

And surprised . . . at last . . . that his lower limbs do not obey his intention.

The look of 'all is well' fades from his face: slowly he lowers himself among his pillows.

But – and for us both – the bounds of reason have been shattered. Mind . . . has been routed.

Bewilderment breaks in an agony behind my eyes and I sink to my knees beside the bed, my head on my arms turned from him that he might not see despairing pity, despairing grief, that stops my very breath.

But again – as always – all is known between us – and as tears roll silently sideways across my cheeks and between my fingers I feel the light touch of his own – *groping now, and feeble* – on my head. I turn and face him: I say strongly, 'Where you go, I shall go. I shall *never* leave you.'

And, as strongly, he answers, 'I *know* you won't.'

And so, dry-eyed once more, I push the bed into the gale of sun and wind at the wide-flung window, strip back the single blanket and climb in under the sheet beside him.

Now I stretch a hand for books. As always, favourites are lifted from their shelves and strewn or piled on table, chair and floor. My hand alights on Donne and it falls open. I read: 'Where, like a pillow on a bed . . .' but at once I know where we are. Gordon Square. Spring. 1929. The daffodils thick about us. My voice hesitates . . . I force it on:

> 'A Pregnant banke swell'd up, to rest
>   The violet's reclining head,
>   Sat we two, one another's best.
> Our hands were firmely cemented
>   With a fast balme, which thence did spring,
> Our eye-beames twisted, and did thread
>   Our eyes, upon one double string;
> So to'entergraft our hands, as yet
>   Was all the meanes to make us one,
> And pictures in our eyes to get
>   Was all our propagation . . .'

Arthur's eyes are closed. The lashes are wet, as mine are. I fling down Donne. What is there? ... What is there that is free of pain? ... and more than pain ... of what is unendurable?

I take up *The Way and its Power*[1] – the Mencius passage in the Introduction:

> 'The Bull Mountain was once covered with lovely trees. But it is near the capital of a great state. People came with their axes and choppers: they cut the woods down, and the mountain has lost its beauty. Yet even so, the day air and the night air came to it, rain and dew moistened it. Here and there fresh sprouts began to grow. But soon cattle and sheep came along and broused on them, and in the end the mountain became gaunt and bare, as it is now. And seeing it thus gaunt and bare, people imagined that it was woodless from the start ...'

I put it down. Nothing is said. I pick up *Kilvert's Diary*. Dear Kilvert. I search out picture after picture, moving with him, in tenderest detail, through the muted landscape of his days.

Still Arthur lies quiet, he makes no sign. I pick up the newly published paperback of *Chinese Poems*[2] and it falls open at the brief 'Love Poem' by Fêng Mêng-lung. I read:

> 'Don't set sail!
> The wind is rising and the weather none too good.
> Far better come back to my house.
> If there is anything you want, just tell me.
> If you are cold, my body is warm.
> Let us be happy together this one night.
> Tomorrow the wind will have dropped:
> Then you can go, and I shan't worry about you.'

At the end there is silence. But suddenly the eyes open in a smile.

'I made Sir Stanley add that, in the new edition. They

[1] Translated by Arthur and published by Allen & Unwin in 1934.
[2] Allen & Unwin, 1966.

weren't pleased. It meant changing all the numbers. It's for you.'

As suddenly, they close again. The breath comes calm, evenly. All is well.

I lower my head gently to its resting-place in the hollow shoulder. We sleep.

An hour later I wake and look at my watch.

Yes, as I thought, it is near eight. The day – the two nurses, the two maids; the hubbub, the business, of the day – will be upon us. Arthur has not moved. I extricate myself gently from his side, my hand from his hand, and slide to the floor. I stand up and go to the window. I push up the bottom sash.

At once I am aware of the silence – the gale no longer twisting the branches of the trees; the garden standing motionless below in its scatter of petals.

I fling up my arms and call over my shoulder: 'Darling! the wind has dropped!'

Arthur's eyes, I see, are open now and watching me. Our gaze holds. He says, quietly, in clearest accents: 'Then I may go . . . and you shan't worry about me.'

For the second time my heart stops.

I return to his side, and – our heads pillowed close – we lie wordless.

But there are deeper . . . far, far deeper . . . means of communion than speech can ever know.

Almost happily, I slip down and settle my head back in its familiar resting-place and fling my right arm across the brown width of his chest. For an instant I open my eyes: beside me, the gold hairs clustered inside his ears – 'the fledgelings' – are gleaming in the sun: my eyes close again.

The nurses are here.

And now the doctor leaning, with face of compassion.

My son, too, stands looking down at us with a strange look: surely an infinity of love.

Arthur's gaze is fixed on the brightly-moving sky: but

returns slowly; lifts to the wide sweep of the roses; loiters on John's still-shadowed face; moves again to mine.

It is scarcely even a whisper ... 'Wonderful ...' he says.

The doctor, the nurses, stand silent.

And still our cheeks are pressed close.

It is the twenty-seventh of June. We have been married a month and a day.